ENCYCLOPEDIA OF
ROCKS,
MINERALS, AND
GEMSTONES

Laura,

Happy Xmas, 2007,

Love Andrew

x o x

ISBN 1 84044 086 4

Produced by **Brown Partworks Ltd**
8 Chapel Place, Rivington Street, London EC2A 3DQ, UK
www.brownpartworks.co.uk

Project editor: Jane Lanigan
Editor: Sally McFall
Editorial director: Anne O'Daly
Design: Seth Grimbly, Iain Stewart
Picture manager: Susannah Jayes
Production manager: Matt Weyland

PICTURE CREDITS

Geological sample images courtesy of Chris Pellant

Additional images courtesy of:
Cobra and Bellamy, London p13 middle bottom; Rolls Royce p16 top right; NGK p17 bottom; Nick Oldnall
http://www.xray2000.co.uk p40 bottom; Saab P42; Angus FIre Armour Limited, Oxfordshire p46 middle right;
Pilkington Plc p51 middle left; The Mythical Image Studio/James H W Campbell, Surrey p66 bottom; Art
Explosion p72 bottom; ICI/Dulux, Paint from the Instore Mixing System p74 bottom; Art Explosion p76 middle
right; NASA p79 bottom left; Art Explosion p83 bottom left; David Ashton Jewellery, London p107 middle right;
Art Explosion p112 middle right; David Ashton Jewellery, London p115 middle; Panasonic UK/Product PR p127
bottom; Art Explosion p128 bottom; Art Windows/www.artwindows.com p129 bottom; Art Explosion p132 middle
left; David Ashton Jewellery, London p136 bottom; Daler-Rowney Ltd p140 middle right; Art Explosion p142 middle left; M Abram Ltd, London p159 middle left; Potterycrafts Ltd, Stoke on Trent p164 middle right; Potterycrafts
Ltd, Stoke on Trent p 180 middle right; Le Creuset/Grayling Public Relations, London p181 bottom right; Art
Explosion p184 bottom right; Colbri Waldorf/Burton McCall, Leicester p195 middle right; M Abram Ltd, London
p207 middle right; Dani Jewellery, London p209 middle right; Alan Shaw Communications, Suffolk p210 middle
right; Hess Pumice Products Inc/www.hesspumice.com p222 middle right; The Scotts Company (UK) Ltd, Surrey
p226 bottom middle; Philips p229 middle right; Potterycrafts Ltd, Stoke on Trent p230 middle right; Majestic mar-
ble/www.majesticmarble.com p239 middle right; Dani Jewellery, London p240 middle right; NASA p241 middle
right; M Abram Ltd, London p249 middle right; The Delabole Slate Company Ltd, Cornwall p252 top right;
Gillette Group UK Limited/Duracell p255 bottom; M Abram Ltd, London p279 middle right; M Abram Ltd,
London p284 bottom left

Printed and bound in Hong Kong
1 2 3 4 5   01 02 03 04 05

ENCYCLOPEDIA OF
ROCKS,
MINERALS, AND
GEMSTONES

Brown
PARTWORKS

INTRODUCTION

AN encyclopedia of this kind cannot avoid repeated use of technical terms. Many of these are explained in detail at least once in the most appropriate entry and then summarized in the glossary at the end of the book. Other terms need to be understood from the outset.

Minerals, rocks, and gemstones

The entries in this book are described variously as "minerals," "rocks," or "gemstones." A mineral is narrowly defined: all specimens must have the same chemical formula and crystal symmetry (*see* below).

Rocks, on the other hand, usually contain a combination of several different minerals. However, some rocks may be composed of only one mineral, in which case they are described as monomineralic. There are three main types of rock: igneous, metamorphic, and sedimentary. An igneous rock is formed from molten material, known as magma if it is underground, and lava if it erupts onto the surface of the Earth. Metamorphic rocks are rocks that have been altered by heat and/or pressure. Sedimentary rocks are formed by the accumulation and consolidation of layers of loose sediment or by the accumulation of chemicals that precipitate out of water.

A gemstone is any naturally occurring material that happens to be regarded as valuable. Few generalizations can be made about gemstones because each specimen is judged and priced on its own merits. As a result, not even all diamonds are precious—those that lack clarity and sparkle are used as abrasives and cutting tools in industry. Some minerals have gem varieties. Corundum, for example, is not a gemstone but may take the form of precious ruby or sapphire. Other gemstones, though naturally occurring, are not strictly minerals because their composition is variable.

Each entry is color banded so that whether it is a rock, mineral, gemstone, or metal can be seen at a glance. Rocks are color coded purple, minerals green, gemstones orange, and metals blue. Where the name of a rock, mineral, or gemstone is shown in bold in the text, this means that there is an entry on this material elsewhere in the book.

The Mohs Scale of Hardness

Hardness (the resistance offered by a mineral to abrasion or scratching) depends on the strength of the bonds that hold the atoms together in a crystal structure. Some minerals, such as talc, are so soft that rubbing them between the fingers will break the bond. At the other extreme is diamond, which is so strongly bonded that the only naturally occurring substances that can scratch it are other diamonds.

The hardness of any mineral is determined by the ease of scratching one of its smooth surfaces with the sharp edge of a mineral of known hardness. In 1812, Austrian mineralogist Friedrich Mohs proposed that 10 relatively common minerals be used as a scale. These minerals are, in increasing order of relative hardness: talc, 1; gypsum, 2; calcite, 3; fluorite, 4; apatite, 5; orthoclase, 6; quartz, 7; topaz, 8; corundum, 9; and diamond, 10. Each mineral can scratch those with the same or a lower rating, but cannot scratch higher numbered minerals.

Crystal symmetry

One of the most important distinguishing features of minerals is their internal structure—in some cases it is the only distinguishing feature.

Cubic system   Tetragonal system   Monoclinic system   Triclinic system   Hexagonal and trigonal systems   Orthorhombic system

In mineralogy, there are seven systems of crystal symmetry (or crystal systems): cubic, hexagonal, monoclinic, orthorhombic, tetragonal, triclinic, and trigonal (*see* box, above). Nearly all minerals conform to one of these systems although a few, such as wurtzite, conform to two, depending on the conditions in which they were formed. Many scientists believe that even geological materials such as amber, which appear to be amorphous (without any definite shape), will one day be shown to have some kind of symmetry.

If a solid body is turned through 360° in any direction and the same shape may be seen more than once during the rotation, the body is said to display symmetry. Some mineral crystals repeat themselves twice during such a revolution, others three, four, or six times (no crystal shows five-fold symmetry).

The most symmetrical crystals are those that conform to the cubic system of symmetry. Their basic shape resembles that of a gaming die, with three pairs of sides that are the same length, breadth, and height, and intersect at angles of 90°. Such formations often appear in multiples—eight- or 12-sided variations on this basic theme are common. Halite is one of the best known minerals that crystallizes in this system.

The basic shape of any crystal in the tetragonal system is like that of a box that has had its top and bottom removed. It is an "open" shape that needs to combine with some other shape or shapes to make a complete crystal. Cassiterite crystallizes in the tetragonal system of symmetry.

In the monoclinic system, no pair of crystal faces has the same length, breadth, or height as any other. Any crystal of this type has a twofold axis—in other words, when it is revolved through a complete circle it will show the same shape twice. Examples of monoclinic crystal symmetry include gypsum.

Crystals in the triclinic system have no face with the same dimensions as any other and none of the faces are at right angles to any of the others. It is the least symmetrical of all the systems. The faces are often of equal sizes, but the essence of symmetry is not the faces themselves but the angles between them. Axinite is one of the minerals that conforms to the triclinic system of symmetry.

Every crystal that conforms to the hexagonal system of symmetry has a six-fold vertical axis. Three of these axes are equal in length and arranged in a horizontal plane, while a fourth is at right angles (perpendicular) and unequal to them in length. The other two axes may be anywhere. Beryl is a famous example of this type.

The trigonal system has only recently been shown to be distinct from the hexagonal. It is not always clear which is which and the two are represented by the same diagram, above. The simplest trigonal crystal consists of a solid shape with three equal axes that are equally inclined and not at right angles to each other. Dioptase conforms to this system.

Orthorhombic crystals have three faces that are unequal in length, breadth, and height but are all at right angles to each other. Examples include barite.

It is hoped that the above is all the information that a beginner needs before undertaking a more detailed study of mineralogy. Other questions are answered as they arise.

ACANTHITE

Although most silver comes from argentite, this mineral first has to be turned into acanthite before the silver can be removed.

*Acanthite forms in hydrothermal mineral veins in association with **pyrargyrite**, **proustite**, native **silver**, and other sulfides, such as **galena**. It also occurs as a weathering product of primary silver sulfides.*

Main Sources: ◆ *Czech Republic* ◆ *Germany* ◆ *Mexico* ◆ *Colorado and Nevada, United States*

Acanthite is very similar to argentite. The two minerals contain exactly the same elements in identical proportions—every molecule of both is composed of two atoms of silver and one atom of sulfur. Their chemical formula is Ag_2S. The most important difference between the two is their internal structure: crystals of acanthite are monoclinic, while those of argentite conform to the cubic system of symmetry. Externally, many acanthite crystals have a rather spiky appearance. It is from this that geologists have taken the mineral's name, which is derived from *akantha*, the Greek word for "thorn."

Acanthite and argentite are found in close association with each other in the Earth's crust, but they are formed at different temperatures. Argentite solidifies at 350 to 354° F (177 to 179° C), whereas acanthite crystallizes only when the hydrothermals (hot liquids) from which both minerals originate have cooled below these temperatures. As a result it is possible to turn acanthite back into argentite artificially by heating. Acanthite is also much more plentiful and widely distributed than argentite, because most silver sulfide is deposited at low temperatures.

Argentite may contain up to 87 percent by weight of **silver,** but in order to remove the silver, the mineral has to be heated above the temperature at which it will turn back into acanthite. So, although argentite is held to be the world's principal source of silver, it has to be made into acanthite before the metal can be extracted. Thus both minerals are equally important as ores.

Left: Acanthite is gray when freshly removed from the Earth but may darken to black on exposure to the atmosphere.

ACTINOLITE

Actinolite and the gemstone nephrite contain the same elements. However, because actinolite is less attractive and more difficult to cut and polish, it is far less valuable.

*Actinolite usually occurs in **schists** resulting from the metamorphism of **basalt** and **diabase** or detrital sedimentary rocks. It is also found in some igneous rocks.*

Main Sources: ◆ *British Columbia, Canada* ◆ *New Zealand* ◆ *Russia* ◆ *Alaska, California, Pennsylvania, and Virginia, United States*

Above: Long, fibrous (acicular) crystals of actinolite.

Green, black, or a combination of both, the exact color of actinolite depends on three factors—the amount of iron the specimen contains, the direction of the light that illuminates it, and the angle from which it is viewed. This color-changing effect is known as pleochroism.

Actinolite has the same chemical formula as the gemstone nephrite—$Ca_2(Mg,Fe^{2+})_5Si_8O_{22}(OH)_2$. However, it is not precious because its crystals are less tightly compressed. They are therefore less attractive to look at and more difficult to cut and polish.

ACTINOLITE-TREMOLITE SERIES

The amount of magnesium and iron in actinolite may vary from specimen to specimen because it is subject to continuous atomic substitution. When the amount of iron increases beyond a certain point, the mineral ceases to be actinolite and becomes tremolite. Thus, actinolite and tremolite form a solid solution series.

Actinolite is also an amphibole mineral, one of an important group of rock-forming hydrous silicates widely distributed in igneous and metamorphic rocks. Hydrous minerals are defined as those that contain the elements of water (hydrogen and oxygen) even though they do not carry the liquid itself. By contrast, minerals that have fully formed molecules of water of crystallization attached are said to be hydrated. Examples include **apophyllite** and **gypsum**.

Most minerals have a type locality, a particular place that has provided a classic specimen against which subsequent finds may be tested for authenticity. The type locality of actinolite is Sobotin, Czech Republic.

NEPHRITE

Nephrite is one of the two main sources of **jade**; the other is jadeite. The name is derived from the Greek *nephros* (kidney) because during the Middle Ages this precious gemstone was worn to stave off renal disorders.

ADAMITE

Although of no industrial use, adamite may be collected for its attractive crystals and bright colors.

Adamite is found in metallic, ore-bearing veins that have been altered by oxygen. It often occurs in association with azurite, calcite, limonite, olivenite, and smithsonite.

Main Sources: ◆ *Chile* ◆ *France* ◆ *Greece* ◆ *Mexico* ◆ *Namibia* ◆ *California, United States*

A damite is a rare mineral named after French mineralogist Gilbert-Joseph Adam (1795–1881), who discovered it at Chañarcillo, Chile. It was confirmed as a distinct species in 1866. The mineral is made up of zinc, arsenic, oxygen, and hydrogen. It is classified as a member of the olivenite group, one of several hydrous arsenates of various metals.

Although it has no industrial uses, adamite is of interest and sometimes value to rock and mineral collectors because of its beautiful crystals. These conform to the orthorhombic system of symmetry and usually appear as bright

yellow or green spheroids. This coloration is caused by traces of copper, although some specimens may be pink or violet, a variation caused by cobalt.

IMPURITIES

Both the copper and the cobalt in adamite are actually impurities. In other words, they are present in the mineral but do not form essential parts of its makeup. Hence, neither is mentioned in the chemical formula for adamite, which is $Zn_2AsO_4(OH)$.

In addition to the bright-colored crystals some adamite specimens may give off a light of their own when placed under an ultraviolet lamp. This fluorescence is bright yellow in color.

ALTERATION PRODUCT

Adamite is a secondary mineral—one that is formed from a preexistent, primary mineral or minerals. Primary minerals, by contrast, crystallize straight from molten material or fluids in or on the Earth. Adamite is closely related to paradamite, which was first identified at the Ojuela Mine in Mapimi, Durango, Mexico, and confirmed as a species in 1956. This pale yellow mineral has the same chemical formula as adamite but crystallizes in the triclinic system of symmetry.

Left: Spheroidal mass of adamite.

AEGIRINE

Aegirine belongs to a group of about 20 silicate minerals known as pyroxenes but differs from others in the group in that it has long, needlelike crystals.

*Pyroxenes such as aegirine may be found as both major and minor components of a wide variety of igneous and metamorphic rocks. They are also common in Moon rocks and in stony meteorites. Most aegirine is found in sodium-rich igneous rocks, such as **granite** and **syenite**.*

Main Sources: ◆ *Canada* ◆ *Greenland* ◆ *Kenya* ◆ *Nigeria* ◆ *Norway* ◆ *Russia* ◆ *Scotland* ◆ *Arkansas and Montana, United States*

Usually green in color, aegirine was first discovered in Norway and named after Aegir, the Scandinavian god of the sea. It is a pyroxene, one of a group of about 20 silicate minerals all with similar physical, optical, and chemical properties. Among the most important pyroxenes are **augite**, **diopside**, **jadeite**, and **spodumene**.

ROCK-FORMING MINERALS

Many pyroxenes meld into one another as one or more of their component metals is gradually replaced by others within a single deposit. They nearly all have about the same hardness, scoring either 6 or 6½ on the Mohs Scale, and their specific gravity is usually between 3.1 and 3.9. One of the most distinctive properties of pyroxenes is their cleavage (the way they break up along planes). All pyroxenes cleave along two intersecting lines that run at 87° and 93° from their crystal faces.

As with all other pyroxenes, the darker the aegirine, the more iron it contains. Thus the color varies from dark green to brown or nearly black.

Above: Aegirine typically forms in prismatic crystals or in fibrous aggregates.

The most important way in which aegirine may be distinguished from the other members of the group is in the external shape of its crystals. Most pyroxene crystals are prismatic with square cross-sections and occur as irregular grains. The prisms of aegirine, on the other hand, often appear as long, acicular (needlelike) crystals and occur as discrete grains or radiating aggregates. Many crystals of aegirine are also twinned. This means that they share a face or faces with one or more of their neighbors.

ALLOPHANE

Allophane is known as a mixture because its chemical compounds are not chemically linked but are bound together in a gel.

Allophane is found principally in cavities and fissures in metal-bearing ore veins and also in some coal deposits.

Main Sources: ◆ *Brazil* ◆ *England* ◆ *Germany* ◆ *Italy* ◆ *Arizona, California, Colorado, Massachusetts, Nevada, New Mexico, Pennsylvania, and Utah, United States*

Not strictly a mineral, allophane is what is known as a mixture (*see* box, below). It is generally composed of about 35 percent by weight of the compound alumina (aluminum oxide) and 22 to 28 percent of another compound, silica (silicon and oxygen). There is no chemical link between these two—they are bound together only physically in a gel that appears to have no particular structure. Hence, allophane could be described as amorphous. However, some scientists suspect that it may eventually be shown to conform to one of the seven crystal systems, so its symmetry is best described as undetermined.

Authorities disagree about the etymology of the English word allophane, which comes from the Greek meaning "other appearance." Some say that the name

Above: The composition of allophane is highly variable, so it may appear in many different shapes and colors.

refers to the way the substance changes its appearance after having been heated under a blowpipe. Others believe that allophane is so named because of its occasional resemblance to the blue copper carbonate mineral **azurite**.

Some allophane contains five times more alumina than silica together with significant amounts of the minerals halloysite and **variscite**. These mixtures are known as schrötterite. By contrast, allophane that features more than 28 percent silica is known as torniellite, after Torniella, Italy, where it was first discovered.

COMPOUNDS AND MIXTURES

Mixtures differ from compounds in that:
1 They are not held together by a chemical force
2 Their components can be in any proportions, whereas those of a compound are fixed
3 They can be separated by physical means, whereas compounds can be broken only with difficulty, usually by heating
4 Two substances may be mixed but they are still the same two substances; when two substances are joined chemically in a compound, they make a new material.

ALUMINITE

Aluminite crystallizes as white or gray nodular masses meaning that the crystals themselves are indistinct to the naked eye.

*In the Earth, aluminite is found in clay-filled chalk pipes and potholes, where it is commonly associated with **calcite** and selenite, the transparent variety of **gypsum**.*

Main Sources: ◆ *Czech Republic* ◆ *England* ◆ *France* ◆ *Germany* ◆ *Hungary* ◆ *India* ◆ *Italy* ◆ *Russia* ◆ *Spain* ◆ *Colorado, Missouri, and Utah, United States*

Also known as hallite or websterite, aluminite is an aluminum sulfate. Its crystals have a monoclinic structure, but these fundamental shapes are seldom apparent to the naked eye and may be seen only under a hand lens or microscope with at least a 10-times magnification. This is because most deposits of this mineral are massive aggregates that appear as indeterminately shaped white nodules.

HYDROUS MINERAL

Aluminite is represented by the chemical formula $Al_2SO_4(OH)_4.7H_2O$. The presence of the OH (hydroxyl) radical means that aluminite is said to be a hydrous mineral. In addition, it is hydrated by H_2O—this being water of crystallization. In other words, the water is attached to the main body of the mineral, rather than being an integral part of it, and so may be expelled by heat.

Aluminite is closely related to meta-aluminite, a mineral with a similar chemical formula but only five (as opposed to seven) molecules of water of crystallization. The two species also look alike and are almost impossible to tell apart without detailed analysis.

RUSTY COATING

The surface of aluminite often features, and is sometimes covered by, a patina (thin coating) of limonite. This is a form of rust that is deposited by the earthy rocks in which aluminite typically forms. If a specimen is found that is discolored in this way, or if it is simply covered with mud, it may be cleaned quite easily by dabbing the surface with a cloth or cotton bud soaked in distilled water. Tap water should not be used for this operation because it is likely to contain impurities that may react with the aluminite and damage it.

Below: This is what aluminite aggregates look like when all surface impurities have been removed.

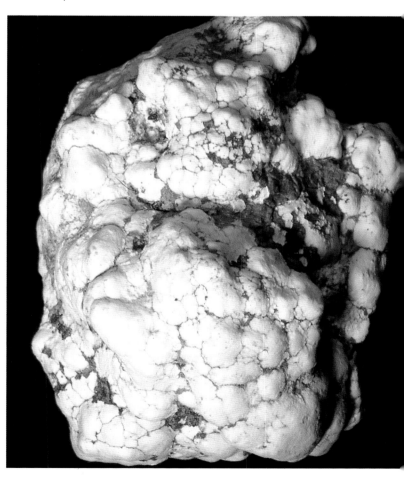

ALUNITE

Alunite has a range of industrial applications including its use in the manufacture of styptic pencils and as a white pigment in paint.

Alunite is a secondary mineral formed mainly by the alteration of **pyrite** *in sulfate-rich waters. It is also found in fumaroles (volcanic steam vents). Some deposits contain appreciable traces of sodium and phosphorus.*

Main Sources: ◆ *Australia* ◆ *Italy* ◆ *Spain* ◆ *Ukraine* ◆ *Colorado, Nevada, and Utah, United States*

Alunite—which is also known as alum stone—is a hydrous sulfate of potassium and aluminum. Although it was identified as a distinct mineral only as recently as 1824, it has been mined extensively since the 15th century.

Below: Although this specimen of the mineral alunite appears to have little shape, microscopic examination reveals numerous crystals.

Alunite has a wide range of industrial uses. It is an important source of potash alum, which is used as a mordant (dye-fixer), especially in the treatment of leather. It is also the main component of styptic pencils, which are used to stem the flow of blood from cuts caused by shaving.

ADDITIONAL USES

Alunite may be used as a sealant or filler for certain grades of paper, and in fertilizers. The mineral is basically white, so it is used as a white pigment by painters. Although it may sometimes appear brown, gray, red, or yellow in color, these are actually discolorations caused by the presence of various impurities.

Another potential use of alunite is as a source of aluminum. However, at present there is no need to extract the metal from this mineral because there are still abundant and readily accessible reserves of **bauxite**, the world's main source of aluminum.

TESTS

Alunite has a very high melting point and therefore does not liquefy when heated in a closed test tube. It will, however, give off its water of crystallization if this operation is carried out. Another test for this mineral is that it decrepitates (makes a crackling sound) when heated in an open flame. During this process, the flame itself will be turned red by the potassium the alunite contains.

WHAT IT ISN'T

Some of the materials used in fireproofing and the treatment of sewage are known as alum. However, they are not made from alunite—rather they are sulfates of aluminum alone, with no potassium.

AMBER

Well known for the jewelry that can be made from it, amber is also famed for preserving the fossil remains of insects and small animals.

Amber is formed from the resin secreted by pine trees. Over millions of years this gummy substance was compacted by the pressure of later deposits of gravel, sand, and other sedimentary materials that settled on top of it. It was turned into solid lumps, which were eventually dislodged and transported by geological activity to alluvial deposits on river banks and seashores.

Main Sources: ◆ *Denmark* ◆ *Dominican Republic* ◆ *England* ◆ *France* ◆ *Germany* ◆ *Italy* ◆ *Mexico* ◆ *Myanmar (Burma)* ◆ *Norway* ◆ *Romania* ◆ *Russia*

Above: Some of the most valuable amber contains insects perfectly preserved for thousands of years.

A precious gemstone, amber is used to make earrings, bracelets, necklaces, and many other types of jewelry and ornamental objects. Some amber contains the perfectly preserved remains of frogs, insects, or lizards that became stuck while the amber was still liquid. These fossils provide valuable information about life on Earth millions of years before the rise of human beings.

Amber is only slightly denser than water and will therefore sometimes float. This helps to explain how the gemstone often comes to be distributed far away from the coniferous forests in which it first formed.

WORN FOR PROTECTION

Amber has been known for thousands of years. Its English name is derived from *anbar*, the Arabic word for ambergris. This waxy, yellow fluid, secreted by sperm whales, was once thought to be the source of the mineral. Another theory of ancient times was that amber was formed from lynx urine. Ancient Romans believed that amber would encourage those who wore it, so it was given to gladiators before they entered the ring to fight. Other ancient people believed that amber would protect unborn babies and ward off fire.

ELECTRICAL CHARGE

When it is rubbed, amber develops a charge of electricity, and this can be seen in the way that it attracts particles of dust. The English word electricity is derived from the Greek *elektron*, meaning amber.

Although it has long been thought to be an amorphous mineral, X-ray analysis has recently suggested that amber may, after all, have some previously unrecognized crystal structure. If this structure can be positively identified, it will make the mineral easier to manufacture synthetically.

AMBLYGONITE

Although classified as a gemstone, amblygonite crystals are usually only cut for collectors, being too soft to be used as jewelry.

Above: A translucent mass of amblygonite. Most pure specimens are white, but some are colored by impurities.

*Amblygonite is a rare mineral that forms in coarse-grained, granitic igneous rocks. Such rocks include **pegmatites** and other lithium minerals, for example **tourmaline** and **spodumene**. It also occurs with albite, which it resembles in appearance.*

Main Sources: ◆ *Brazil* ◆ *France* ◆ *Germany* ◆ *Myanmar (Burma)* ◆ *Maine, United States*

The name of this mineral is taken from the Greek *ambly*, meaning blunt, and *gonios*, meaning angle. This is because when amblygonite is hit with a hammer or subjected to pressure, specimens break up at an obtuse cleavage angle to the crystal face.

Although many minerals form next to completely different species, some are surrounded only by closely related types. In a line of such similar materials it may from time to time be possible to detect a very gradual alteration in the chemical composition of adjacent crystals. Such a change continues by almost imperceptible steps until the original mineral has transformed into another species.

GRADUAL TRANSFORMATION

Amblygonite is the end member of one of these lines, which are known as solid solution series. The composition of a typical deposit of this mineral will change slightly from one crystal to the next. Amblygonite is a phosphate of aluminum, lithium, and sodium. It also contains fluorine and a hydroxyl radical (one atom of oxygen and one of hydrogen). Moving along the line of crystals, the amounts of fluorine and sodium are gradually reduced until the series reaches its other end member, montebrasite. This mineral is a phosphate of aluminum and lithium and always contains less fluorine than amblygonite (*see* box, below).

Many crystals of the amblygonite–montebrasite series of minerals share a face or number of faces with one or more of their neighbors. This phenomenon—known as twinning—is typical of, but not exclusive to, solid solution series.

Both minerals were first located at Montebras in France. Amblygonite was confirmed as a distinct species in 1817, while montebrasite was identified as distinct in 1871. Their exact relationship, however, was not positively established until 1969.

CHEMICAL FORMULAE
Amblygonite: $(Li,Na)Al(PO_4)(F,OH)$
Montebrasite: $LiAlPO_4(F,OH)$

ANALCIME

Analcime is a zeolite, a group of hydrous alumino-silicates. These minerals are characterized by the ease with which they lose and take up water.

Analcime is found mainly with other zeolites (see box below). It usually forms as icositetrahedral crystals or in massive, compact habits and occurs as a secondary mineral in cavities in basaltic igneous and sedimentary rocks.

Main Sources: ◆ *Greenland* ◆ *Iceland* ◆ *Italy* ◆ *Northern Ireland* ◆ *Norway* ◆ *Scotland* ◆ *Washington, United States*

Some of the largest crystals of this attractive mineral are as big as an adult male's fist. Its name is derived from the Greek *analkis*, meaning "without strength." This is a reference to the fact that, although it normally has no electric charge, analcime may develop a weak charge when heated or rubbed.

Analcime was first identified on islands off Sicily, Italy. It was confirmed as a distinct mineral in 1797 by René-Just Haüy (1743–1822), the French mineralogist sometimes described as "the father of crystallography."

FORMED IN TWO WAYS

A hydrated silicate of sodium and aluminum, analcime is formed in two ways—as a primary product from molten material or as a secondary mineral through the alteration of **nepheline** or **sodalite**. Analcime is related to leucite, a silicate of potassium and aluminum. The two minerals are often found together and are difficult to tell apart without chemical analysis to determine which crystals contain sodium and water of crystallization and which do not.

Analcime is a member of the zeolite group, one of about 20 minerals that, when heated, give off their

Above: This specimen of analcime shows clearly the glassy sheen (vitreous luster) for which the mineral is noted.

attached water of crystallization in a single action. This characteristic distinguishes the group from normal hydrated minerals, which emit their water gradually, in small amounts at different temperatures.

Once the water has been expelled, the resulting gaps in the zeolites' atomic structure may be filled easily by more water or other materials. This gives these minerals a wide range of industrial uses, particularly as chemical sieves. For example, the small packets that are placed in camera cases to prevent the equipment from being damaged by atmospheric moisture are commonly known as silica gel, but this is a misnomer. The packets are in fact zeolites.

ZEOLITES

The other zeolites featured in this book are **apophyllite**, **harmotome**, **heulandite**, **mesolite**, **natrolite**, **scolecite**, and **stilbite**.

ANATASE

Anatase is one of the most important sources of titanium, a strong, lightweight metal with a variety of industrial uses.

*Anatase forms in metamorphic rocks, particularly **schist** and **gneiss**. It also occurs as an accessory mineral in some igneous rocks, for example **diorite** and **granite**.*

Main Sources: ◆ *Brazil* ◆ *France* ◆ *Norway* ◆ *Russia* ◆ *Switzerland* ◆ *Colorado and Massachusetts, United States*

Above: The titanium extracted from anatase is an important component of the alloys used to make jet engines.

Anatase is one of three closely related minerals that together provide the most important sources of titanium. Anatase itself is a form of titanium oxide. The other two titanium minerals, both with exactly the same chemical makeup as anatase, are **brookite** and **rutile**. Despite the similarity in composition, there are important differences between the trio—each has its own specific gravity and each deflects light differently from the other two. Minerals such as these, which are superficially similar but have profound underlying differences, are known scientifically as polymorphs.

TITANIUM AND ITS USES

Titanium is a silvery gray metal that is as strong as steel but only half the weight. First identified in 1791, it was not isolated until 1910.

MOON METAL

Titanium is the world's ninth most abundant element, comprising about 0.63 percent by weight of the Earth's crust. Analysis of rock samples from the Moon has shown that the metal is even more abundant there, with some rocks consisting of up to 12 percent titanium.

Since 1946, when scientists first developed an economical purification process, titanium has had a wide range of industrial uses. For example, it is used for the rotors, fins, and compressor parts of jet engines, especially those used to power aircraft such as Concorde, which must be as light as possible in order to attain supersonic speeds. The metal is also alloyed with tin and aluminum to make steel that is extremely strong at high temperatures. When combined with aluminum, molybdenum, and vanadium, titanium also provides strength in extreme cold.

Another important product of this metal is titanium tetrachloride, a colorless liquid that gives off fumes in moist air. Titanium tetrachloride is used in the manufacture of artificial pearls and iridescent glass and to create smokescreens. There is also titanium dioxide, a derivative now used almost universally in white paint in place of lead, which has been found to be highly poisonous.

ANDALUSITE

First discovered in Andalusia, Spain, this silicate of aluminum is both an industrial mineral and a gemstone with unusual optical properties.

*Andalusite is found mainly in metamorphic rocks. It is associated with **cordierite**, **corundum**, **kyanite**, and **sillimanite** and is said to be trimorphous with the last two named. This means that the three minerals have the same chemical formula (Al_2SiO_5) and often appear almost identical, although there are nevertheless important physical and chemical differences between them.*

Main Sources: *◆ Brazil ◆ Madagascar ◆ Russia ◆ Sri Lanka ◆ Spain ◆ California and Massachusetts, United States ◆ Zimbabwe*

Above: Prismatic andalusite crystals. When cut and viewed in cross-section, some may show the shape of a cross.

Named for the region of Spain where it was first discovered, andalusite has many industrial uses. It is highly resistant not only to heat but also to corrosion by acids. It is thus an important component of sparking plugs (*see* photo, below) and synthetic mullite, which is used in the manufacture of ovenproof ceramics.

CHANGING COLORS

The finest quality andalusite crystals occur as pebbles that have been smoothed by water. These can be polished and cut into jewels. The appearance of the gemstone may be greatly enhanced by a optical phenomenon known as pleochroism. This refers to the stone's capacity to appear in different colors when viewed in different lights and from different angles. As a result, a specimen of andalusite may appear to be either greenish, reddish brown, blue, pink, white, or gray in color, all depending on how it is viewed.

ANDALUSITE–KANONAITE SERIES

In some deposits, the aluminum in andalusite may gradually be replaced by manganese. In other words, one crystal may be pure andalusite, its immediate neighbor may contain one atom of manganese in place of aluminum, the next may have a few manganese atoms, the third may contain dozens, and so on. When this continuous atomic substitution is complete and all the aluminum has gone, the resulting manganese silicate is known as kanonaite. The two minerals thus form a solid solution series.

THE SHAPE OF THE CROSS

The most precious form of andalusite is chiastolite. The impurities this variety contains cause it to reveal a cruciform (crosslike) shape when sliced. Some people believe that this gives the stone mystical properties, and it is therefore used as an amulet to ward off evil.

ANDESITE

Common in areas of mountain building, andesite is formed from a variety of lava that causes particularly violent volcanic eruptions.

Andesite is an igneous rock that is found in most areas of the world where there has been volcanic activity. It may contain a wide range of accessory minerals (minerals that occur in the rock in very small amounts). These include **chalcopyrite**, **ilmenite**, *and* **magnetite**. *Andesite may also feature large quantities of natural glass.*

Main Sources: *This rock is widely distributed throughout the world. Among the most notable of the many deposits in the United States are the mountain ranges that extend along the Pacific seaboard through Alaska, California, and Oregon.*

Andesite is named after the Andes, the great chain of mountains that forms the backbone of South America. However, it occurs in many other parts of the world as well.

ANDESITE AND BASALT

Andesite is similar to the most widely distributed rock on Earth, **basalt**. The main differences between the two rocks are the quantity and types of **feldspar** that they contain. Basalt, which is formed from magma (molten rock) at high temperatures, contains more than 50 percent by weight of calcium-bearing plagioclase feldspars. By contrast andesite, which is formed in less extreme temperatures, always features less than 50 percent of these minerals. Thus andesite can generally be distinguished from basalt by its lighter color.

EXPLOSIVE ROCK

Usually a brownish or gray-colored volcanic rock, andesite may also feature shades of purple or green. It is formed from a type of lava that causes very violent eruptions. This is because the liquid is rather viscous (sticky) and tends to clog up volcanic vents until the pressure builds up to such an extent that it causes an explosion. Lava flows from andesite volcanoes are more abundant than flows of any other variety except basalt.

Andesite's geological occurrence is closely related to plate tectonics. Where ocean plates are sinking below the continental crust, andesite lava is created at great depth and volcanoes are formed on the surface. This process—known as subduction—is particularly evident along the western seaboard of South America.

Left: Andesite is fine-grained, but some deposits may be interspersed with larger crystals (phenocrysts).

ANGLESITE

Anglesite is an attractive mineral, distinctive for its beautiful crystals. Classified as a gemstone, it is fragile and faceted for collectors only.

*A secondary mineral of lead, anglesite normally forms in the oxidized zones of lead veins. Masses may also be found around a core of **galena**.*

Main Sources: ◆ *Australia* ◆ *England* ◆ *Mexico* ◆ *Morocco* ◆ *Namibia* ◆ *Scotland* ◆ *Idaho, New Mexico, and Pennsylvania, United States* ◆ *Wales*

This rare sulfate mineral forms in beautiful prismatic or tabular crystals that may give off a yellow fluorescence when placed in ultraviolet light. It is normally white or grayish in color, but may have a pale blue, green or yellow tinge.

Anglesite gets its name from the Isle of Anglesey in Wales, where it was first identified. It was confirmed as a distinct mineral in 1832.

Anglesite is a minor source of lead, although it is almost never mined on its own account but generally unearthed by chance during the commercial extraction of galena, the main ore of this metal.

Above: Although massive aggregates of anglesite are opaque, crystalline formations may be transparent.

ASSOCIATION WITH GALENA

It is no coincidence that these two minerals should be found together—anglesite is a secondary, or alteration, product formed by the weathering of galena and often forms an earthy concentric coating around the primary mineral. Both anglesite and galena are also commonly found in association with **cerussite**, a carbonate of lead.

HIGH SPECIFIC GRAVITY

Like all lead-bearing minerals, anglesite is heavy—it has a specific gravity of 6.2 to 6.4. This means that it weighs 6.2 to 6.4 times more than the equivalent volume of water at room temperature. Each molecule of anglesite contains about 68 percent by weight of lead, a very high concentration.

WEATHERING

Weathering is the breakdown and decomposition of materials on or near the surface of the Earth. It involves both physical and chemical reactions and is dependent on climate, topography, vegetation, time, and the composition and texture of the parent rock. Temperature and rainfall are also significant factors—rocks decay fastest in warm, humid climates. One of the most important chemical reactions that take place in weathering is oxidation. This process involves the addition of oxygen, from water or the air, to the atomic structure of the affected mineral.

ANHYDRITE

A useful mineral, anhydrite is closely related to gypsum and may form as a result of this other substance losing water.

*Anhydrite is found mainly in evaporite deposits, where it is left behind when seawater dries up in hot sunshine at temperatures in excess of 107° F (42° C). It is also found in **dolostones** and **limestones** and in some ore veins, where it is a gangue—an unwanted substance that is discarded after having been extracted from the Earth during the search for something else.*

Main Sources: ◆ *Austria* ◆ *Canada* ◆ *England* ◆ *Germany* ◆ *Poland* ◆ *Russia* ◆ *Switzerland* ◆ *Florida, Louisiana, New Mexico, South Dakota, Texas, and Utah, United States*

Anhydrite is a form of calcium sulfate with the chemical formula $CaSO_4$. Its closest relative is **gypsum**—the hydrated form of the same compound, with the chemical formula $CaSO_4.2H_2O$. This explains the name of the mineral, which comes from the Greek *anhydros*, meaning "without water."

INTERCHANGEABILITY

The two minerals, anhydrite and gypsum, are easily interchangeable. In damp, humid conditions, for example, anhydrite may acquire water and become gypsum. Similarly in an arid climate, gypsum may dehydrate and transform into anhydrite. Apart from

Above: Anhydrite with visible cleavage planes—the lines along which the mineral will break up under pressure.

the water of crystallization, the main differences between anhydrite and gypsum are specific gravity and crystal shape. Anhydrite weighs almost exactly three times more than the equivalent volume of water at room temperature, while gypsum has a specific gravity of only 2.3. In terms of crystal shape, gypsum is monoclinic, while anhydrite conforms to the orthorhombic system of symmetry.

Anhydrite has a number of industrial applications, being used in the manufacture of cement and plaster, as a fertilizer, and as a drying agent in paints and varnishes. Rock formations composed mainly or exclusively of this mineral may also be cut and polished for use as ornamental stones.

ANHYDRITE ROCK

The name anhydrite is also given to sedimentary rock formations that contain large quantities of the mineral. Rocks composed exclusively of anhydrite or any other single species are termed monomineralic deposits. Heterogeneous anhydrite rocks, on the other hand, may also contain gypsum, **halite**, and limestone.

ANKERITE

Ankerite, part of the same group as dolomite, is a secondary mineral that may contain varying amounts of iron.

*Ankerite is often a gangue mineral (an unwanted substance) that forms in mineral veins, for example with iron ores, **gold**, or sulfides. It also occurs in seams of **coal**.*

Main Sources: ◆ *Austria* ◆ *England* ◆ *Italy* ◆ *Pennsylvania and South Dakota, United States*

A carbonate of calcium that also contains iron, magnesium and manganese, ankerite's chemical formula is $Ca(Fe,Mg,Mn)(CO_3)_2$. It was first identified in Styria, Austria and was confirmed as a distinct species in 1825. It is named after Austrian mineralogist Mathias Joseph Anker (1771–1843).

This mineral forms a solid solution series with **dolomite** and **kutnohorite**. Imagine a line of crystals. At one end is kutnohorite, a mineral with the same chemical formula as ankerite but with two and a half times as much manganese as magnesium. A little further along the line comes ankerite. This mineral always contains at least 10 percent iron, and the balance between manganese and magnesium is much

DIFFICULT QUESTION

Part of the definition of any mineral is that all specimens must contain exactly the same components in exactly the same proportions. How, then, can ankerite contain varying amounts of iron? The answer is that each of its molecules has three spaces within its structure that should theoretically always contain one atom of iron, one atom of magnesium, and one atom of manganese. But 10 such molecules have room for 30 atoms of metal. If four of these spaces contain iron, and the other 26 are divided equally between magnesium and manganese, then the specimen as a whole is clearly ankerite. Even though the molecules that contain no iron are not strictly ankerite, in practice it is impossible to isolate such small fragments—minerals are normally defined by the composition of their crystals, not by the contents of each individual molecule.

more even. At the other end of the line is dolomite, a carbonate of calcium and magnesium that contains no iron or manganese at all because these two metals have been substituted within the series by others.

Ankerite is a secondary mineral formed through the action of magnesium-bearing liquids on pre-existent limestone deposits. In general, the darker the ankerite crystals, the more iron it contains.

The type locality of ankerite is the Wheatley Mine near Phoenixville, Pennsylvania—a specimen from here is used as the standard against which other possible finds are measured for authenticity.

Left: Ankerite is a translucent mineral with a vitreous to pearly luster.

ANNABERGITE

A pale or apple green mineral, annabergite is normally found as a crusty or earthy coating on rock surfaces.

Annabergite is a rare secondary mineral that forms in the oxidation zones of ore deposits and is found as a powdery coating on the surface of valuable nickel-bearing minerals such as chloanthite and **nickeline***.*

Main Sources: ◆ *Canada* ◆ *France* ◆ *Germany* ◆ *Greece* ◆ *Italy* ◆ *Spain* ◆ *California and Nevada, United States*

Annabergite is sometimes known as nickel bloom—the term bloom is used because it resembles the dusty coating of the same name that is sometimes found on fresh fruit. It has the same structure as **erythrite**, which forms in a similar way, but has a different chemical makeup. The two minerals are thus said to be isostructural.

Annabergite is a hydrated arsenate of nickel with the chemical formula $Ni_3(AsO_4)_2.8H_2O$. When a sample of annabergite heated in a closed test tube, its water of crystallization is driven off and forms a pool on the inside of the glass.

The mineral belongs to the vivanite group, the other members of which include erythrite—with which it forms a solid solution series—and **vivianite** itself. It is thought the group may have a fourth member, cabrerite. However, scientists have not yet established whether cabrerite is a distinct mineral or merely a magnesium-rich variety of annabergite. The chemical formula of cabrerite is tentatively believed to be $(Ni,Mg)_3(AsO_4)_2.8H_2O$.

LARGE, GREEN CRYSTALS

Although annabergite generally occurs in crusts or powdery masses on the surfaces of other minerals, fairly large crystals may sometimes be found. These are of great interest to mineralogists because of both their rarity and their beautiful green or yellow-green coloration. However, such crystals are not easy to keep in collections because they are very soft and may be scratched easily with a fingernail. They are also easily damaged by the impurities in tap water, so should only be cleaned using distilled water.

Annabergite gets its name from the town where it was first identified, Annaberg in Saxony, Germany. It was confirmed as a distinct species in 1852.

Below: Annabergite often forms in crusty green coatings on the surface of nickel-bearing rocks.

ANTIGORITE

Found in many parts of the world, antigorite is an attractive, iron-bearing mineral with numerous ornamental uses.

*A secondary mineral, antigorite is formed when hydrogen, oxygen, and iron are added to the primary (preexistent) minerals **enstatite** and **olivine**. The principal agent of this chemical reaction is water, although air may sometimes also play a part. Antigorite is found in the igneous rock **serpentinite**.*

Main Sources: ◆ *Australia* ◆ *Brazil* ◆ *Canada* ◆ *China* ◆ *England* ◆ *Finland* ◆ *Germany* ◆ *Italy* ◆ *New Zealand* ◆ *Norway* ◆ *Poland* ◆ *Russia* ◆ *South Africa* ◆ *Switzerland* ◆ *Arizona, California, Colorado, Massachusetts, New Jersey, Pennsylvania, South Dakota, Utah, and Wyoming, United States* ◆ *Venezuela* ◆ *Zimbabwe*

Its attractive green or yellowish-green coloration, along with its resilient structure, make antigorite suitable for being carved and polished into decorative slabs and ornamental eggs. The finest pieces are also sometimes sold as cheap substitutions for **jade**. Such specimens are marketed under the trade name bowenite. The green surface veins in some forms of **marble** are sometimes made of antigorite.

FLAKY AND FIBROUS

Antigorite is a hydrous silicate of magnesium and iron and belongs to the kaolinite-serpentine group of minerals. The minerals of this group are mainly fibrous and flaky. Alternatively they may form in lamellae (sheets or thin layers). They have tiny, intergrown monoclinic crystals. Among other well-known examples of the group are a reddish-brown to green variety known as lizardite and an iron-free variety, **chrysotile**. In the Earth, antigorite may be associated with chrysotile along with stichtite, a hydrated carbonate of magnesium and chromium.

Above: When viewed under a hand lens, crystals of antigorite typically appear in thin, flaky strips.

The name antigorite is taken from that of the locality in which it was discovered, the Valle di Antigorio, about 20 miles (32 km) northwest of Lake Maggiore in northern Italy. However, it has since been found in large quantities in several other parts of the world.

ANTIMONY

Although of limited use on its own, antimony has a wide range of industrial applications when alloyed with other metals.

*A metal, antimony forms in hydrothermal veins that have been altered by the action of hot water. It is often found in association with the minerals **galena**, **pyrite**, **sphalerite**, and **stibnite**, as well as with the native elements **arsenic** and **silver**.*

Main Sources: ◆ *Bolivia* ◆ *Borneo* ◆ *Canada* ◆ *Chile* ◆ *China* ◆ *Czech Republic* ◆ *Germany* ◆ *Italy* ◆ *Mexico* ◆ *Portugal* ◆ *Russia* ◆ *Sarawak* ◆ *South Africa* ◆ *Sweden* ◆ *California, United States*

Antimony is a metal that makes up about 0.0001 percent of the weight of the Earth's crust. Its chemical symbol, Sb, is an abbreviation of *stibium*, the Latin word for this metal.

USEFUL ALLOYS

Antimony is of little use on its own because it breaks very easily. However, it may be combined with various other metals—including solder and some forms of cast iron—to make alloys. In particular, antimony is alloyed with tin to make pewter and with lead to make plates for storage batteries. Non-alloyed antimony may be used as an important component of bullets and to provide coverings for telephone cables.

Antimony oxide is added to textiles and plastics to prevent them from catching fire. It is also used in paints, ceramics, and in fireworks and as an enamel coating for plastics, metal, and glass.

TYPE METAL

Type metal is an alloy of antimony, tin, lead, and sometimes copper. It is melted and poured into molds or castings then left to cool, expand, and solidify into sharp reproductions of the outline shapes.

Antimony is distinctive for its high resistance to the passage of electricity through its body. This characteristic makes it useful as a component of semiconductors (devices that permit variations in the supply of power to electrical appliances).

Antimony melts at 1,168° F (631° C) and boils at 2,975° F (1,635° C). It has a specific gravity of between 6.6 and 6.9, meaning that it weighs 6.6 to 6.9 times more than the equivalent volume of water at room temperature.

Left: Distinct crystals of antimony are rare—the metal forms mainly in massive, lamellar, granular, or acicular aggregates.

APATITE

Apatites are actually a closely related group of minerals, the gem varieties of which may be mistaken for other minerals.

The apatite group of minerals is widely distributed in metamorphic and sedimentary rocks, but the finest specimens are found in **pegmatite,** *an igneous formation. Apatites are also the main components of human teeth.*

Main Sources: ◆ *Brazil* ◆ *Canada* ◆ *Germany* ◆ *Kenya* ◆ *Madagascar* ◆ *Mexico* ◆ *Myanmar (Burma)* ◆ *Norway* ◆ *Portugal* ◆ *Russia* ◆ *Spain* ◆ *Sri Lanka* ◆ *Sweden* ◆ *South Dakota, United States*

Above: A prismatic crystal of apatite. Note the surface sheen, which is described as vitreous or subresinous.

Apatite is the name of a group of fluorophosphate minerals. The most important member is fluorapatite, a fluorophosphate of calcium with the chemical formula $Ca_5(PO_4)_3F$. The name fluorapatite is often, confusingly, shortened to apatite.

FLUORAPATITE

Fluorapatite may look very similar to beryl, olivine, quartz, or tourmaline. In fact the ease with which it may be mistaken for one of these species has given rise to its name, and the name of the group as a whole—the English word apatite is derived from the Greek *apate,* meaning "deceit."

Despite fluorapatite's great beauty and its strong resemblance to various gemstones, it is not usually precious in itself. This is because it has a rating of only 5 on the Mohs Scale of Hardness and is therefore too soft to withstand the wear and tear to which it would be subjected if it were worn as jewelry. However, some of the most attractive specimens of this mineral are faceted in order to bring out their best colors and are displayed in mineral collections.

Apatite crystals are usually prismatic or tabular, although habits may also be granular or massive. Some fluorapatite crystals are very large—one specimen in the Smithsonian Institution in Washington, D.C. weighs 500 carats (3½ oz.).

INDUSTRIAL USES

The main use of apatites is as a source of phosphorus, a nonmetallic element of the nitrogen family. It is extracted by heating the minerals with coke and silicon dioxide at temperatures of 302° F (150° C). Phosphorus is used in alloys, pesticides, and matches.

CHATOYANCY

Some fluorapatite may have tiny fibrous impurities lodged inside its atomic structure. This is particularly true of specimens from Myanmar (Burma). When crystals with these inclusions are cut and polished *en cabochon* (into dome shapes) they show a beautiful optical effect known as cat's eye or chatoyancy.

APOPHYLLITE

Originally believed to be a single mineral, apophyllite was recently found to be two distinct species that form a solid solution series.

*Apophyllite occurs in **basalt**, **gneiss**, or **limestone**, and may also be formed at low temperatures in sulfide ores. It is commonly found in association with **calcite**, **prehnite**, **quartz**, **scolecite**, and with zeolite minerals such as **analcime** and **natrolite**.*

Main Sources: ◆ *Brazil* ◆ *Germany* ◆ *India* ◆ *Mexico* ◆ *Northern Ireland* ◆ *Scotland* ◆ *Michigan, New Jersey, and North Carolina, United States*

Originally classified in 1806 as a single mineral, apophyllite is now known to be not one but two naturally occurring hydrated silicates of potassium and calcium. The name comes from the Greek *apo*, meaning "to get," and *phyllazein*, meaning "leaf." This is a reference to the way in which the two white, gray, or colorless minerals exfoliate (flake or separate into layers) when heated with a blowpipe.

SUBSTITUTION

The minerals in the group form a solid solution series. One end member is hydroxyapophyllite—chemical formula $KCa_4Si_8O_{20}(OH).8H_2O$—the other is fluorapophyllite—$KCa_4Si_8O_{20}F.8H_2O$. As can be seen from the formulae, between these two extremes the hydroxyl radical (OH) is substituted by a single atom of fluorine (F) as one mineral gradually transforms into the other. Both minerals were confirmed as distinct species in 1978. Prior to this they had been included in the blanket term apophyllite.

TOO SOFT

The finest apophyllite crystals are sometimes faceted to bring out their best lights, but specimens are too soft to be used in jewelry. Instead they are confined mainly to mineral collections, where they are protected from damage in glass or plastic cases.

Above: Apophyllite minerals form typically in cracks in volcanic rocks.

NATROAPOPHYLLITE

Natroapophyllite—a similar mineral with the formula $NaCa_4Si_8O_{20}F.8H_2O$—was first discovered in a mine at Okayama, Japan, and authenticated in 1981. It is the sodium (Na) analog of fluorapophyllite with crystals that conform to the orthorhombic system of symmetry. Crystals of the other apophyllite minerals are tetragonal.

ARAGONITE

Sometimes used as a gemstone, stalactitic forms of aragonite may be cut and polished to form ornamental slabs or beads.

*Aragonite may occur in metamorphic rocks but the most extensive deposits are found in sedimentary formations close to the surface of the Earth, notably in limestone caves, as an evaporite in hot-spring deposits, and in beds with **gypsum**. The mineral forms in crystals that are glassy-white, slender, and tapering, as well as in columnar masses, stalactites, and crusts.*

Main Sources: ◆ *Austria* ◆ *Czech Republic* ◆ *England* ◆ *Italy* ◆ *Namibia* ◆ *Spain* ◆ *New Mexico and South Dakota, United States*

A ragonite, which is usually colorless, gray, white, or yellowish, was confirmed as a distinct mineral species in 1797. It is named after Aragon, the region of northeastern Spain where it was first identified.

It has the same chemical formula as two other minerals—**calcite** and vaterite ($CaCO_3$)—but occurs in different crystal shapes to these. The crystal systems of both calcite and vaterite are hexagonal, while aragonite conforms to the orthorhombic system of symmetry. Minerals such as this trio, which have great similarities but at least equally important differences, are said to be polymorphous.

TWINNING IS COMMON

Crystals of aragonite usually share a face or faces with one or more of their neighbors. Aragonite crystals that are not twinned in this way are actually quite rare. This effect may make the crystals appear six-sided but, since this is not a true reflection of their internal shape, they are said to be pseudohexagonal, rather than hexagonal.

Aragonite is less stable than calcite. In other words, it is more likely to be altered into some other mineral or minerals and is therefore rarer. Another distinguishing characteristic is that, when it is placed under ultraviolet light, some specimens may give off a blue, pink, or yellow light. This phenomenon is known as fluorescence.

FORMS IN SEASHELLS

Interestingly, this mineral also occurs as a secretion in the shells of various marine organisms. So, for example, aragonite is the main chemical component of **pearl** and mother-of-pearl. Many fossil shells are made of calcite, but it is likely that these were originally composed of aragonite that altered to its polymorph over time.

Below: Typical crystals of aragonite showing distinctly six-sided shapes.

ARFVEDSONITE

Black or greenish black in color, arfvedsonite is one of the common amphibole group of minerals.

Since its original discovery in Greenland, arfvedsonite has been located in several other parts of the world. It occurs mainly in igneous rocks, especially **syenite**, *but may also be found in regional metamorphic formations such as* **schist**.

Main Sources: ◆ *Canada* ◆ *Czech Republic* ◆ *Finland* ◆ *Greenland* ◆ *Norway* ◆ *Russia* ◆ *Ukraine* ◆ *Colorado and New Hampshire, United States*

Above: Arfvedsonite is a hydrous silicate of sodium and iron that is particularly associated with Greenland.

First located near Ilímaussaq, Greenland, arfvedsonite was named after Swedish chemist Johan Arfvedson (1792–1841). It is an amphibole mineral, meaning that it is one of a large group of silicates with either monoclinic or orthorhombic crystals. The crystals of arfvedsonite are monoclinic and it is thus related to **actinolite**, **glaucophane**, **hornblende**, **riebeckite**, and **tremolite**.

Most arfvedsonite takes the form of aggregates with no particular external shape. However, clearly defined crystals do sometimes occur, these being mainly prismatic, rodlike, or tabular in form. Crystals of arfvedsonite are commonly twinned (share one or more faces with neighbors). This effect reflects the mineral's internal structure, which comprises long chains or ribbons joined together by two shared atoms of oxygen. Minerals that display this characteristic are classified as inosilicates.

SPOT THE DIFFERENCE

Arfvedsonite: $Na_3Fe^{2+}_4Fe^{3+}Si_8O_{22}(OH)_2$
Magnesio-arfvedsonite:
$$Na_3(Mg,Fe^{2+})_4Fe^{3+}Si_8O_{22}(OH)_2$$

Iron can form two different types of bond with other chemical elements. In scientific terms, then, it is said to have two valencies. This is reflected in the chemical notation—ferrous iron (Fe^{2+}) has two links, while ferric iron (Fe^{3+}) has three. Where a chemical formula refers simply to Fe, it is understood to mean ferrous iron.

ATOMIC SUBSTITUTION

Another characteristic of arfvedsonite is that some of its iron may gradually be replaced by magnesium. When this atomic substitution is complete, the result is a new mineral called magnesio-arfvedsonite. Arfvedsonite and magnesio-arfvedsonite are end members of a solid solution series.

When arfvedsonite is heated in an open flame, it melts quite easily and forms a black glass that has a high iron content and is therefore magnetic.

ARKOSE

A dark red or brownish sedimentary rock, arkose forms from feldspar-rich sediment deposited in water or on land.

*A variety of **sandstone**, arkose is a widespread rock found in deposits of all geological ages. It is usually formed through the disintegration and weathering of **granite** and **gneiss**.*

Main Sources: *In the United States, arkose is particularly abundant in the coastal mountains and Sierra Nevada of California.*

Arkose is a red, pink, or gray sedimentary rock that is abundant in many parts of the world. Once granite and gneiss, both crystalline rocks, have been worn down by natural forces such as wind and flowing water, their fragments may be transported over fairly short distances and redeposited as sediment in lakes, rivers, or shallow seas. The sediment is subsequently cemented together by clay minerals, for example **kaolinite** or dickite, and by various iron oxides such as **goethite** and **limonite**, and arkose is the end product.

Individual particles of arkose measure over $\frac{1}{20}$ in. (1.3 mm) in diameter—it is thus classified as a medium- to coarse-grained rock.

Arkose always contains between 25 and 50 percent by volume of **feldspar**. The remainder of the rock is made up of biotite, muscovite, and **quartz**, together with some virtually unaltered leftovers of the older rocks from which it was formed. Arkose is said to be a fairly immature rock formation because of the large percentage of feldspar it contains.

Although arkose often looks very much like granite, close comparison will reveal that while granite is crystalline and tightly interlocked, grains of arkose are typically less shapely and are arranged in a less orderly fashion. They also show signs of weathering.

PLACE VALUE

In some parts of the world, arkose is found in sufficient quantity to be used locally as stone for building. However, it is never taken far from the quarries in which it was unearthed. This is because of its low value—the cost of transporting it by road or rail would be greater than the profit that could be made from selling it at its destination.

Below: The shiny, white grains in this arkose are quartz; larger pinkish crystals are feldspar.

ARSENIC

Probably best known for its poisonous nature, arsenic is a rare element that may actually be used in some medicines.

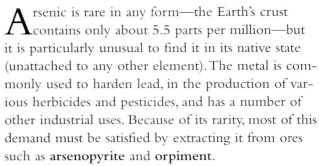

*Arsenic is a metal that occurs in isolation only in minute quantities. It forms in hydrothermal veins, where it is associated with even smaller amounts of **antimony**, **bismuth**, **gold**, **silver**, or iron, and may be accompanied by various ores of nickel and cobalt.*

Main Sources: ◆ *Australia* ◆ *Canada* ◆ *Chile* ◆ *Czech Republic* ◆ *England* ◆ *France* ◆ *Germany* ◆ *Italy* ◆ *Japan* ◆ *New Zealand* ◆ *Romania* ◆ *Russia* ◆ *Arizona, California, Louisiana, Nevada, and South Dakota, United States*

Below: This cluster of arsenic is typically rounded—in scientific terms, it is said to have a botryoidal habit.

Arsenic is rare in any form—the Earth's crust contains only about 5.5 parts per million—but it is particularly unusual to find it in its native state (unattached to any other element). The metal is commonly used to harden lead, in the production of various herbicides and pesticides, and has a number of other industrial uses. Because of its rarity, most of this demand must be satisfied by extracting it from ores such as **arsenopyrite** and **orpiment**.

The English name of this element is derived from *arsenicon*, the Greek for yellow orpiment.

HEAVY METAL

Arsenic is pale gray when freshly extracted from the Earth, but darkens quickly on exposure to the air. This tarnish cannot be removed. The metal is fairly heavy, weighing 5.7 times more than the equivalent volume of water at room temperature.

When heated, arsenic gives off fumes that smell of garlic. At temperatures of over 752° F (400° C), the metal burns with a bluish flame and forms arsenic trioxide, also known as white arsenic, which is used as a rat poison. At about 1140° F (615° C), it turns directly from a solid into a gas, missing out the normal intervening liquid stage. This unusual effect is known as sublimation.

HIGHLY POISONOUS

Arsenic is well known for being highly poisonous to humans and even brief exposure to this metal will cause diarrhea and cramps. Chronic poisoning, meanwhile, leads to anemia, paralysis, and malignant skin tumors. Nonetheless, some arsenic-based medicines are used to treat certain infections. The most widely used of these is Salvarsan, an antisyphilis drug.

ARSENOPYRITE

This silvery, metallic-looking mineral tarnishes easily, so may appear brownish or pink in color. It is the most important source of arsenic.

Arsenopyrite is found mainly in high-temperature hydrothermal veins where it is often the first mineral to form. The ore also occurs in metamorphic rocks and basic igneous rocks and is most commonly associated with chalcopyrite, galena, gold, pyrite, quartz, silver, sphalerite, and tin ores such as cassiterite.

Main Sources: ◆ *Canada* ◆ *England* ◆ *Germany* ◆ *Italy* ◆ *Portugal* ◆ *Sweden* ◆ *Switzerland* ◆ *New Hampshire and New Jersey, United States*

The most widespread and abundant ore of the metal **arsenic**, arsenopyrite also contains iron and sulfur, the two elements of **pyrite**. Its chemical formula is FeAsS. This mineral is also sometimes known in English by its German name, *Mispickel*.

Crystals of this silvery white mineral are monoclinic. However, they are often twinned and as a result may misleadingly appear to conform to the orthorhombic system of symmetry.

Arsenopyrite might look something like silver, but it is more brittle than this valuable element and gives off a garliclike smell when heated or struck.

DANAITE

In its pure form, arsenopyrite is composed of 34.3 percent iron, 46 percent arsenic, and 19.7 percent sulfur. In certain deposits, however, some of the iron may be replaced by up to 12 percent by weight of cobalt. This variant form is known as danaite, and fine specimens of it can be found at Fanconia in New Hampshire.

Danaite has not yet been confirmed as a distinct mineral species. This is because scientists are still testing it to ascertain whether the cobalt it contains is an integral part of the mineral's atomic structure. It may

Above: If arsenopyrite is struck with a hard object, it will give off a garliclike smell characteristic of arsenic.

be that this metal is merely an impurity—in other words, an extraneous element that just happens to be there. Although danaite may eventually turn out to be a distinct species, scientists work slowly and circumspectly on such analyses. This is with good reason—the other metals that have so far been found in arsenopyrite (**antimony**, **bismuth**, gold, and silver) have all turned out to be impurities.

ARTINITE

Artinite is formed when certain fluids permeate preexistent igneous rocks in a process known as serpentinization.

*This mineral is formed at very low temperatures in **serpentinite** and other ultrabasic igneous rocks that have been oxidized by exposure to hydrothermal liquid at a late stage in their development. Magnesium silicate minerals in the rocks react with water, and the carbon dioxide water contains, to produce magnesium carbonate, the two main mineral forms of which are artinite and **magnesite**.*

Main Sources: ◆ *Austria* ◆ *Italy* ◆ *California, Nevada, New Jersey, New York, and Pennsylvania, United States*

Confirmed as a distinct species in 1903, artinite was named after Ettore Artinini (1866–1928), professor of mineralogy at the University of Milan, Italy. It is both a hydrous and a hydrated mineral—in other words, it contains both hydroxyl radicals (chemical formula OH) and also has attached water of crystallization. The chemical formula of artinite is $Mg_2CO_3(OH)_2.3H_2O$.

Among the other magnesium-bearing minerals with which artinite is commonly associated are **brucite** and hydromagnesite.

SPRAY OF NEEDLE SHAPES

Crystals of artinite conform to the monoclinic system of symmetry. Although they commonly occur as massive aggregates of no particular beauty, some appear in sprays of acicular (needle-shaped) growths that are highly sought after by mineral collectors.

When freshly extracted from the Earth, the surface of artinite is often covered with dirt. The mineral should not be cleaned with water, which may damage the crystals, but instead should be briefly immersed in alcohol to remove any soil.

This white mineral, sometimes with transparent crystals, often appears similar to, and thus may be

Above: Tiny, needle-shaped crystals of artinite with a distinctly silky luster.

confused with, hydromagnesite and magnesite. One way of telling specimens apart is to heat a sample of each in an open flame. Artinite is the only one of the three that does not fuse (melt) during this test, but instead emits water and carbon dioxide gas, leaving a dark residue of magnesium oxide.

ASTROPHYLLITE

Named for the bladed, leaflike appearance of its crystals, astrophyllite is a complex mineral that may contain up to five different metals.

*Astrophyllite forms in cavities and fissures in **syenite** and other igneous rocks. It is commonly associated with **aegirine**, **feldspar**, **mica**, pyroxenes such as **pyroxenite**, **quartz**, **riebeckite**, and **zircon**.*

Main Sources: ◆ *Canada* ◆ *Greenland* ◆ *Norway* ◆ *Russia* ◆ *Colorado, United States*

Crystals of this mineral are often shiny and appear in lamellae (thin sheets) with pointed, ends that resemble foliage. This gives astrophyllite its name, which is derived from the Greek words *astron*, meaning "star," and *phyllon*, meaning "a leaf." The finest formations are star-shaped clusters that may be brownish, bronze, or yellow in color.

COMPLEX CHEMISTRY

Astrophyllite has a complicated chemical makeup. It is a hydrous silicate of potassium, sodium, and titanium, but may also feature iron or manganese, or both. Very few minerals contain more than two metals, while this one has up to five. In addition, astrophyllite forms a solid solution series in which the atoms of titanium are gradually replaced by yet another metal, niobium. When this substitution is complete, a new mineral, kupletskite, is formed.

This mineral was named after Boris Kupletski and his wife Elsa Bonshtedt-Kupletskaya, both of whom carried out research on its properties in the Kola Peninsula of northern Russia in the 1950s. Unusually for minerals related in this way, the two have different crystal shapes—those of kupletskite are monoclinic, while astrophyllite crystallizes in the triclinic system of symmetry.

Another close relative is caesium kupletskite. As its name suggests, this mineral contains caesium, together with lithium and all the elements of kupletskite. It was confirmed as a distinct species in 1971, 15 years after kupletskite and 117 years after astrophyllite itself. Crystals of caesium kupletskite conform to the triclinic system of symmetry.

The type locality of astrophyllite is at Brevig in Norway. It is against specimens from here that all subsequent possible finds are tested for authenticity.

Below: Astrophyllite with radiating star-shaped crystals—formations like these are known as stellate aggregates.

ATACAMITE

A secondary mineral, atacamite is sometimes mistaken for one of its associated minerals, malachite, because of its green coloration.

*Atacamite is a halide, one of a group of minerals that contain one of the halogen elements astatine, bromine, chlorine, fluorine, or iodine. Halides are formed during the evaporation of saltwater from salt lakes and seas. The best known and most comercially valuable halides are **fluorite** and **halite**.*

Main Sources: ◆ *Australia* ◆ *Austria* ◆ *Bolivia*
◆ *Chile* ◆ *England* ◆ *Italy* ◆ *Kazakhstan* ◆ *Mexico*
◆ *Namibia* ◆ *Peru* ◆ *Russia* ◆ *Arizona, United States*

Atacamite takes its name from the Atacama Desert in Chile. It contains copper and, although it is not as important an ore of this metal as **chalcopyrite**, it may nevertheless be mined industrially when it occurs in sufficiently large quantities. Each molecule of this very dark green or bright green mineral is composed of two atoms of copper, one atom of chlorine, and three hydroxyl radicals. Its chemical formula is $Cu_2Cl(OH)_3$.

CLOSE RELATIVES

Atacamite's closest relatives are paratacamite and botallackite. Paratacamite is made up of exactly the same elements in exactly the same proportions, but the elements are arranged differently within the atomic structure of the mineral. This is reflected both in its different crystal shapes, which are monoclinic as opposed to atacamite's orthorhombic form, and in the chemical formula of paratacamite, which is written $Cu_2(OH)_3Cl$.

Botallackite has exactly the same formula as atacamite, but this mineral crystallizes in the monoclinic system of symmetry. Because of their close chemical and physical resemblance, these three minerals are said to be polymorphous.

UNUSUAL FORMATION

All three minerals are secondary minerals, or products, and nearly all deposits have been formed through the oxidation of primary (preexistent) copper deposits. The exceptions to this process are the atacamite deposits found on the slopes of Mount Vesuvius in Italy. These deposits formed after gaseous substances were ejected from the volcano during an eruption. When the gases cooled, they passed directly from vapors to solids, without first becoming liquids—a process known as sublimation.

In addition to the above close relatives, atacamite may also be associated with **cuprite** and **malachite**. Atacamite is found almost exclusively in very dry and arid areas. This is because it will dissolve on contact with water.

Above: Atacamite forms in thin, prismatic or tabular crystals that are often striated and twinned.

AUGITE

The commonest pyroxene, augite is a dark green, brown, or black mineral found in most parts of the world and on the Moon.

A widespread mineral, augite is found in basic and ultrabasic igneous rocks (see box, right), for example **pyroxenite** *and* **basalt**, *and in some metamorphic rocks.*

Main Sources: ◆ *Czech Republic* ◆ *England* ◆ *Finland* ◆ *France* ◆ *Germany* ◆ *India* ◆ *Italy* ◆ *Japan* ◆ *Norway* ◆ *Scotland* ◆ *California and Montana, United States* ◆ *the Moon*

BASIC AND ULTRABASIC

Igneous rocks are classified according to the amount of silica (silicon and oxygen) they contain. Hence basic igneous rocks contain between 45 and 55 percent total silica, while ultrabasic igneous rocks contain less than 45 percent silica and virtually no quartz.

A mineral with a distinctive glassy sheen, augite derives its name from the Greek word *auge*, meaning "luster." It is a silicate of calcium, magnesium, and iron, although some atoms of these three metals may be replaced by aluminum. Its crystals are often twinned, sharing a face or faces with one or more of their neighbors.

PYROXENE GROUP

It is an important member of the pyroxene group of minerals—all of which are silicates that may contain aluminum, calcium, iron, lithium, magnesium, manganese, sodium, or titanium. Pyroxenes are also all inosilicates, meaning they are silicates that form in chains or ribbons that may stretch out over considerable distances. There are two types of pyroxenes—orthopyroxenes, which all have orthorhombic crystals, and clinopyroxenes, which crystallize in the monoclinic system. Augite is a clinopyroxene, as are **aegirine**, **diopside**, and **hedenbergite**. The most important orthopyroxene is **enstatite**.

VARIANT FORMS

Fassaite has the same chemical components as augite plus calcium and extra oxygen, while titanaugite is augite with titanium. Although some authorities classify these two varieties as distinct minerals,

it remains possible that the additional elements are merely impurities that do not form an essential part of the atomic structure. In the absence of conclusive evidence either way, it is advisable to classify fassaite and titanaugite as variant forms of augite, rather than as separate species.

Below: Dark, prismatic crystals of augite. Note the characteristic vitreous luster (glassy sheen).

AURICHALCITE

Sky-blue or greenish blue in color, aurichalcite may form as attractive, needle-shaped crystals. Such specimens are highly collectable.

Aurichalcite is a secondary mineral found in numerous parts of the Earth where preexistent ores of copper and zinc have been transformed by waters containing carbon dioxide. It is commonly found on a groundmass of **limonite**. *The mineral is also often associated with* **azurite** *and* **malachite**.

Main Sources: ◆ *Democratic Republic of the Congo (formerly Zaire)* ◆ *England* ◆ *France* ◆ *Greece* ◆ *Italy* ◆ *Mexico* ◆ *Namibia* ◆ *Russia* ◆ *Scotland* ◆ *Arizona, New Mexico, South Dakota, and Utah, United States*

A hydrous carbonate of copper and zinc, aurichal-cite takes its name from *aurichalcum*, the Latin for "yellow copper ore." However, this is not a reference to the color of the mineral itself, which is most commonly sky blue but may sometimes be green, but rather to that of the metal.

Aurichalcite has been known to humans for thousands of years but was not confirmed as a distinct mineral species until 1839.

ACCIDENTALLY UNEARTHED

Although aurichalcite may be unearthed during the industrial excavation of great ore masses, this is purely by chance. The mineral is not mined on its own account because it occurs only in small quantities and because it would be economically impractical to extract the metals it contains. Any specimens that do come to the surface as a result of mining or excavation are either discarded on spoil tips or sold on to collectors.

Aurichalcite crystals conform to the orthorhombic system of symmetry but generally appear in tufted aggregates and encrustations on the surfaces of other minerals and rocks, most commonly **limonite**. The most collectible specimens resemble laths or tiny needles—such habits (the characteristic appearance of a mineral) are said to be acicular. These are rare and are highly sought after by mineralogists.

TEST

When heated over a bunsen burner, aurichalcite does not melt. It will, however, color the flame green, the characteristic reaction of copper-bearing minerals.

Below: Greenish blue aurichalcite on a groundmass of brownish red limonite.

AUTUNITE

An important source of uranium, autunite is a radioactive mineral.
It must be stored carefully to prevent harmful radiation leaks.

*A secondary mineral, autunite forms as a result of the alteration of uranium minerals in **pegmatite** or **granite**.*

Main Sources: ◆ *Australia* ◆ *Canada* ◆ *England* ◆ *France* ◆ *Germany* ◆ *Italy* ◆ *South Africa* ◆ *California, New Mexico, Utah, and Washington, United States*

This hydrated phosphate mineral is an ore of uranium, the radioactive metal used in atomic energy generators and nuclear weapons.

Autunite is named after the city of Autun, France, where it was first discovered. It was confirmed as a distinct mineral in 1852. It is a fluorescent mineral. This means that, when placed under an ultraviolet lamp, it may emit a bright yellowish-green light of its own. Some of the finest crystals of autunite come from the Daybreak Mine in Spokane, Washington.

OTHER URANIUM ORES

Most uranium is obtained from **uraninite**, but the element is very rare. Even though it appears in about 150 different minerals, uranium still comprises only about three or four parts per million of the Earth's crust. For that reason, almost any accessible source is used whenever possible. In addition to autunite, the other main ores of uranium are **carnotite** and **torbernite**. Since all four secondary uranium minerals commonly form in close association with each other, they can be mined together.

DEHYDRATES EASILY

When autunite is freshly extracted from the Earth, it has a bright yellow or yellowish-green color. However, if it is left in dry air, its water of crystallization will evaporate. This causes the mineral to alter into dehydrated meta-autunite, which is colorless.

Above: An aggregate of bright yellow, tabular, twinned crystals of autunite.

To prevent this reaction, a small open phial of water should be placed next to any specimen of autunite. Even more importantly, the mineral must be displayed only for short periods and must spend most of the time in a case covered in a sheet of lead to prevent leakages of harmful radiation.

RARE METALS
Despite its rarity, uranium is nonetheless more plentiful in the Earth's crust than mercury, **antimony**, or **silver**, none of which occurs in more than 0.5 parts per million.

AXINITE

The finest specimens of this mineral are of gem quality, but only Californian axinite is good enough to facet.

Axinite forms in granite cavities and in metamorphic rocks that are rich in calcium-based minerals and quartz. It may be associated with **tourmaline**.

Main Sources: ◆ *Brazil* ◆ *France* ◆ *Germany* ◆ *Italy* ◆ *Mexico* ◆ *Switzerland* ◆ *Tanzania* ◆ *California and New Jersey, United States*

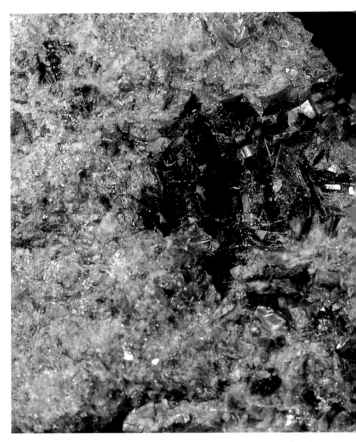

Above: The distinctively shaped crystals of axinite make this mineral a collector's favorite.

Axinite gets its name from the sharp-headed, ax-shaped crystals that are the most valuable forms of this rare gemstone. It is usually brown in color, but some specimens from Tanzania are blue, and it is also strongly pleochroic. In other words, the color of a particular stone may appear to change, depending on the direction of the light that illuminates it and the angle from which it is viewed. For many years, axinite was mistakenly believed to be a brown form of a similar mineral, tourmaline. It was first positively identified as a separate species by French mineralogist René-Just Haüy (1743–1822).

LIMITED USE

Despite its attractive appearance, axinite's uses in jewelry are limited—its crystals almost never weigh more than five carats (0.035 oz.) and most contain flaws that make cutting impractical. One of the few locations from which faceting-quality axinite has been extracted to date is Crestmore in California.

In chemical terms, axinite is a hydrous borosilicate (a silicate that contains boron) of the metals calcium, manganese, iron, and aluminum.

The axinite group contains several closely related minerals. One of these is tinzenite, which always contains more manganese than iron and up to 1.5 percent calcium. Tinzenite was identified in 1969 at Tinzens, Grisons, Switzerland. It is generally yellow.

Another member of the axinite group is mangan-axinite, a mainly blue mineral that always contains more manganese than iron and more than 1.5 percent calcium. Ferroaxinite, on the other hand, has more iron than manganese but, again, up to 1.5 percent calcium. Magnesioaxinite is a hydrous borosilicate of calcium, magnesium, and aluminum that contains no manganese at all. These related minerals often meld into each other in the Earth to form a complex solid solution series.

AZURITE

This mineral used to be used as a pigment by artists until it was found that it gradually transformed to give a green, rather than a blue, color.

*Azurite is a secondary mineral, formed through the alteration of **bournonite** and other preexistent copper-bearing minerals. It is often found in association with **malachite, cuprite,** and native **copper** itself.*

Main Sources: ◆ *Australia* ◆ *Chile* ◆ *China* ◆ *England* ◆ *France* ◆ *Greece* ◆ *Italy* ◆ *Morocco* ◆ *Namibia* ◆ *Russia* ◆ *Arizona, Nevada, Utah, and Washington, United States*

CHEMICAL FORMULAE	
Azurite:	$Cu_3(CO_3)_2(OH)_2$
Malachite:	$CuCO_3(OH)_2$

A hydrous carbonate of copper, azurite is named for its distinctive sky-blue color. Historically, the main use of this mineral was in artists' pigments—it was ground into powder to make the colors mountain blue and Armenian stone. However, gradually it was discovered that, over a long period of time (sometimes hundreds of years), the mineral would absorb humidity from the air and turn into **malachite**, which is actually green in color. Thus, if we look today at paintings of the 13th and 14th centuries that have not been restored, we may notice that some of them have green skies. This is particularly true of some of the work of the Italian artist Giotto (c1267–1337).

USE IN JEWELRY

The best-looking specimens of azurite are those that contain an admixture of malachite and appear in beautiful combinations of blue and green. Crystals of these colors are often cut and polished for use in jewelry, particularly cameos (brooches with raised designs or images on their surfaces). This usage is despite the fact that azurite crystals are quite soft, scoring only 3½ to 4 on the Mohs Scale of Hardness, and can be easily scratched. Gems of this type are known as azurmalachite (this is a mixture, not a chemical compound).

Massive aggregates of azurite are sometimes used to make ornamental stones. Such specimens are known as chessylite, after Chessy near Lyons, France, where the classic deposits were found.

Below: Blue crystals of azurite on a groundmass of brownish limonite.

BARITE

Although of some use itself, barite is better known as a source of barium, widely used in both industry and medicine.

*The mineral is found in ore veins that have been affected by hydrothermals, in **limestone**, in clays formed from weathered limestones, in **sandstones**, and in extensive beds formed by lake or marine deposits.*

Main Sources: ◆ *Czech Republic* ◆ *England* ◆ *Germany* ◆ *Italy* ◆ *Romania* ◆ *Arizona, California, Colorado, Oklahoma, and South Dakota, United States*

Above: The finest crystals of barite are greatly sought after by mineral collectors.

Also known as heavy spar, barite is the most common mineral of barium. The name is derived from the Greek word *barys*, meaning "heavy"—barite weighs between 4.3 and 4.6 times more than the equivalent volume of water at room temperature.

MAIN SOURCE OF BARIUM

Barite is the world's principal ore of barium, a metal with a wide range of industrial uses. In metallurgy, for example, it lines the walls of vacuum tubes to absorb unwanted residual gases during purification (minerals that perform such a role are known as getters). Barium is also a deoxidizer in copper refining and may be combined with nickel to form an alloy used in sparking plugs. Barium is extracted from barite by electrolysis or by heating in a vacuum with aluminum or silicon.

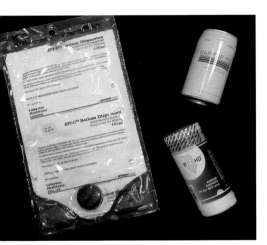

Barite itself is the chief component of the white pigment lithopone. Barite mud is used in oil wells to control the pressure of oil and gas and to prevent drill-hole cave-ins.

Barium is also used in medicine. Meals of barium sulfate (*see* photo, left) are administered to hospital patients who are about to have stomach X-rays. The compound is impervious to X-rays so will show up white on the photographs, providing a contrast against which doctors can view the surrounding organs more clearly.

Barite is not a gemstone—it is not hard enough, beautiful enough, or rare enough. However, the finest brown crystals are sometimes faceted and displayed in mineral collections. The largest crystals can be more than 40 in. (102 cm) long.

BASALT

This dark, igneous rock comprises most of the Earth's surface and is also widespread on the Moon.

Basalt is the most widely distributed rock in the world. It is an extrusive igneous rock formed from volcanic lava that has erupted onto the surface of the Earth.

Main Sources: *One of the most famous deposits is the Giant's Causeway in County Antrim, Northern Ireland. Basalt is common in the United States, especially in Hawaii, Michigan, Oregon, Washington, and Wisconsin.*

More than half of all volcanic rocks are some form of basalt—it may comprise as much as 70 percent of the Earth's surface. The rock is particularly plentiful on the floors of the world's oceans.

DARK, CONSISTENT ROCK

Despite the enormously wide areas over which it is spread, the chemical composition of basalt is remarkably consistent throughout all deposits. It is typically made up of between 45 and 55 percent silica, more than half of which takes the form of plagioclase **feldspar**; the remainder is pyroxene minerals such as **augite**, and up to 10 percent **quartz**.

Basalt is a dark rock, often with large numbers of spherical vesicles (pockmarks) across its surface. It is closely related to **andesite**, but andesite is generally lighter in color and always contains less than 50 percent feldspar.

Basalt is widely used as a building material, in particular to make roads and railway sleeper ballast. It is also the raw material in industrial abrasives such as rock wool and fiber glass.

DIFFERENT COLORS

Basalt is not only found on Earth, but also the Moon. The main difference between lunar and terrestrial specimens is their color. Earth basalt is gray or black when first deposited, but turns brown, green, or red when exposed to air or water in a process known as chemical weathering. The Moon, however, has no atmosphere and so the basalt on its surface retains its original color.

Below: A basalt specimen showing zeolite minerals in the vesicles on its surface.

MOON ROCKS

Although the Moon contains some pyroxene minerals that have never been found on Earth, the two heavenly bodies are otherwise composed largely of the same materials. Geological research suggests that they are both about the same age.

BAUXITE

Bauxite is the world's main industrial source of aluminum—a very light, corrosion-resistant metal.

*Bauxite is not a mineral in the strict sense but, rather, a mixture of several hydrous aluminum oxides, principally **diaspore, gibbsite,** and boehmite. It is formed in tropical climates, the result of the weathering of rocks that contain aluminum silicates.*

Main Sources: ◆ *Australia* ◆ *Brazil* ◆ *France* ◆ *Ghana* ◆ *Greece* ◆ *Guinea* ◆ *India* ◆ *Jamaica* ◆ *Russia* ◆ *Surinam*

Not only a mixture of minerals, bauxite also contains impurities that do not form an essential part of its chemical makeup but nevertheless determine its appearance and texture. The impurities that give bauxite its characteristic form are clay minerals such as dickite and **kaolinite**. **Quartz** and iron hydroxides, such as **siderite**, may also be present.

Bauxite is named for Les Beaux, southern France, where it was first identified in the 19th century.

Aluminum is the world's third most abundant element—it comprises 8.1 percent by weight of the Earth's crust. However, it never occurs in its native state but is always part of a compound. The compound in which aluminum is most abundant, and from which it is most easily extracted, is bauxite. The aluminum is extracted by electrolysis, which removes oxygen and water of crystallization to leave the pure element.

VALUABLE METAL

Aluminum has a number of properties that make it useful in a wide range of industrial applications. It is highly resistant to corrosion and very light—its density at 68° F (20° C), which is room temperature, is only 0.1 pounds/cubic inch. Because of these properties it is used extensively in the construction of aircraft, automobiles (*see* photo, above), and drinks cans. It is a good conductor of electricity, so it is used to make overhead power cables.

Although basically a soft metal, aluminum may be combined with other metals to form alloys that are stronger than any of its parts. The most important alloys of aluminum are those it forms with copper, magnesium, manganese, and zinc.

Aluminum may also be combined with the non-metal silicon to make the hypereutectic (easily melted) wire that is used in welding and semiconductors. A semiconductor is any substance that does not conduct electricity at low temperatures but becomes a conductor when heated or if slightly impure.

Left: Bauxite is typically brown in color but may sometimes appear red, white, or yellowish, depending on the impurities that are present within it.

BAYLDONITE

Usually green in color, bayldonite is a little understood mineral that only occasionally occurs as distinct crystals.

*Bayldonite is a secondary mineral formed in the oxidation zones of copper ore-bearing veins. It usually appears as green or yellow encrustations on the surfaces of other minerals and rocks. Among the minerals with which it is most commonly associated are **azurite**, **conichalcite**, **malachite**, **mimetite**, and **olivenite**.*

Main Sources: ◆ *Australia* ◆ *England* ◆ *France* ◆ *Namibia* ◆ *Arizona, United States*

Bayldonite is a fairly rare arsenate of copper and lead. It is named after John Bayldon, the 19th-century physician who first discovered it in a mine in Cornwall, England.

LITTLE-KNOWN MINERAL

Although classified as a mineral in 1865, it was not until 1956 that the chemical formula for bayldonite was confirmed as $Cu_3Pb(AsO_4)_2(OH)_2$. Even today, mineralogists still have significant gaps in their basic knowledge of this mineral—for example, its streak (*see* box, right) has yet to be determined.

UNUSUAL CRYSTALS

Bayldonite usually forms as granular masses, or as powdery habits, or sometimes crusts, on rock surfaces. Crystallization is in the monoclinic system of symmetry although it is difficult to see the crystal form in these habits.

Distinct crystals of the mineral are unusual, but those that do occur may be polished into smooth, domed cabochons for display in mineral collections. They are subtranslucent—in other words, light will only just pass through them.

Above: A crust of tiny green bayldonite crystals on a groundmass of quartz.

STREAK

Many minerals may appear in more than one color, depending on a range of factors, including the impurities they contain and the light in which they are viewed. However, no matter what color it displays, every mineral has an irreducible color—the color that all specimens would be if they were reduced to powder. In one of the most common identification tests carried out on minerals, this streak, as it is called, is obtained by rubbing a specimen across the surface of an unglazed porcelain tile. The mark, or streak, left behind is always that mineral's basic color.

BENITOITE

Some of the largest and most attractive specimens of this varicolored mineral can be found in California.

Benitoite forms in **schist** *and* **serpentinite**, *where it is commonly associated with bazirite, a silicate of barium and zirconium, and pabstite, a silicate of barium, titanium, and tin. Also present may be joaquinite, another silicate of barium that also contains iron and the rare earth elements cerium and niobium.*

Main Sources: ◆ *Belgium* ◆ *California and Texas, United States*

First discovered at the beginning of the 20th century at the Benito gem mine in San Benito County, California, benitoite is a silicate of barium and titanium. It has a similar chemistry to its main associated minerals, bazirite and pabstite. All three conform to the hexagonal system of symmetry so, in scientific terms, they are said to be isostructural. Among the other minerals with which benitoite commonly occurs are **natrolite** and **neptunite**.

MANY COLORS

Benitoite may appear in a wide range of colors, depending on its location. It is most commonly blue, but may also be purple, pink, white, or colorless. Sometimes two of these colors are seen within a single crystal—this phenomenon is known as dichroism. In addition, benitoite may display a blue fluorescence under ultraviolet light.

Because of its interesting optical properties and relative hardness—6 to 6½ on the Mohs scale—the finest specimens of benitoite are faceted or smoothed into cabochons for display in collections. Careful cutting can bring out the natural lights to even greater advantage. Some of the most beautiful specimens have been extracted from the type locality in the Mount Diablo Range in California. The largest crystals measure more than 2 in. (5 cm) in diameter.

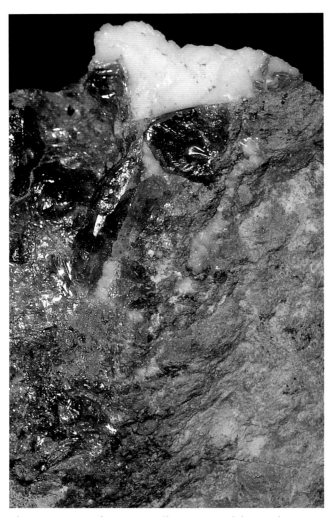

Above: Benitoite forms typically in pyramidal crystals on groundmasses of rock.

CHEMICAL FORMULAE	
Bazirite:	$BaZrSi_3O_9$
Benitoite:	$BaTiSi_3O_9$
Pabstite:	$Ba(Sn,Ti)Si_3O_9$

BERYL

Beryl is important as a source of beryllium. The mineral has several gem varieties, the most valuable of which is emerald.

*Most beryl is found in **pegmatite** dikes, where large crystals are intergrown with **quartz** and **feldspar**. However, the **emerald** variety also occurs in altered **limestone** and in various metamorphic rocks.*

Main Sources: ◆ *Brazil* ◆ *Colombia* ◆ *England* ◆ *India* ◆ *Madagascar* ◆ *Namibia* ◆ *Pakistan* ◆ *South Africa* ◆ *Maine, South Dakota, and Utah, United States* ◆ *Zimbabwe*

AQUAMARINE

The blue variety of beryl derives its coloration from amounts of iron. The depth of the color may be enhanced by heating, and many aquamarine gemstones are in fact ordinary beryl that has been artificially enhanced. Beryl is the birthstone of natives of Pisces (20 February to 20 March).

With bertrandite (beryllium aluminum silicate), beryl is the main commercial ore of beryllium, a metal that does not occur in the free state (unattached to other elements).

Beryllium has several properties that make it of great use in industry. This metal is even lighter and stronger than aluminum, is resistant to corrosion, and has a high melting point of 2,332° F (1,278° C). However, it is so rare and expensive to extract and purify that it costs about twice as much as aluminum.

In terms of its industrial applications, beryllium may be alloyed with copper to make corrosion-resistant springs, electrical contacts (it is less than half as conductive as copper), and, because of its hardness, in spark-proof hammers and wrenches. Beryllium itself is also used as a cladding material for nuclear fuel elements.

RANGE OF COLORS

The color of beryl can vary enormously (*see* photo, left), and several of the precious and semiprecious forms of the mineral have been given their own names. For example, it may be colorless, blue (aquamarine), golden (heliodor), green (emerald), pink (morganite), red, or white.

Beryl forms in prismatic crystals that sometimes terminate in small pyramids. Its crystals can vary in size to a large extent. One weighing 200 tons (204 tonnes) was mined in Minas Gerais, Brazil, and crystals about 20 ft. (6 m) long and 7 ft. (2 m) across have been found in Albany, Maine, and in the Black Hills of South Dakota. Sometimes beryl forms in massive habits that can be mistaken for quartz.

Left: Beryl is a transparent to translucent mineral with a glassy sheen. It is widely distributed in many parts of the Earth, but seldom in large quantities.

BISMUTH

A fairly common element, bismuth has some unusual properties that make it useful in, for example, fire prevention and die-casting.

*Bismuth may occur with **bismuthinite**, **gold**, and **silver**, and in various ores of cobalt, **copper**, lead, nickel, and tin. These are all found together in **gneiss**, **granite**, and **pegmatite** and in veins that have been altered by the action of hydrothermals (hot fluids).*

Main Sources: ◆ *Australia* ◆ *Bolivia* ◆ *Canada* ◆ *Czech Republic* ◆ *Italy* ◆ *Japan* ◆ *Mexico* ◆ *Norway* ◆ *Peru* ◆ *California, Colorado, Connecticut, and South Dakota, United States*

Bismuth is relatively abundant in the Earth, with about 200 parts per million of the crust made up of this metal. Most of it occurs in various oxide, sulfide, or carbonate compounds, but it may also occur in its native state, uncombined with any other elements. The etymology of the English name for this mineral is not certain, but it may come from the German *weisse Masse*, meaning "white mass."

Bismuth is a dense metal with a specific gravity of 9.7 to 9.8. It also has a lower melting point—520° F (271° C)—than any other metal except mercury, which is liquid at room temperature. These properties make it useful in sprinkler systems

(*see* photo, left) and fire detection devices, often combined in alloys with cadmium and tin.

EXPANDS ON FREEZING

Bismuth is one of only two chemical elements that expand on freezing, the other being gallium. As a result bismuth is useful for detailed die-castings and may be used as an intermediate product in the manufacture of acrylic fibers, paints, and plastics.

Much of this element is found in association with lead, which is poisonous to humans. However, bismuth that has been formed in lead-free environments may be used to make iridescent lipstick, mascara, and nail polish.

Left: Crystals of bismuth are seldom distinct, but microscopic examination will reveal that they are often twinned.

PULLING AWAY

If you hold a magnet against a piece of bismuth, the metal will pull in the opposite direction. This unusual property is known as diamagnetism.

BISMUTHINITE

Bismuthinite is mined principally as an industrial source of bismuth, a metal with many industrial applications.

Above: Most bismuthinite is lead gray. It is an opaque mineral with a metallic luster.

Although bismuth does occur in the native state, deposits are seldom large or easily accessible enough to satisfy industrial demand for the metal. As a consequence, the main commercial source of bismuth is bismuthinite, which, like many important ores, is a sulfide. It is sometimes known as bismuth glance, the word "glance" coming from the German *Glanz*, meaning "luster." This refers to the mineral's striking lead-gray metallic sheen.

Some specimens of bismuthinite contain iron and copper, but these are impurities and do not form essential parts of the mineral's makeup. Thus they do not appear in the chemical formula, which is Bi_2S_3.

SIMILAR MINERALS

Bismuthinite is very similar to guanajuatite, a sulfide of bismuth in which some of the sulfur has been replaced by the metal selenium in a ratio of two parts sulfur to every three of selenium. Bismuthinite may also appear similar to **stibnite**, a sulfide of **antimony**. All three minerals have orthorhombic crystals. However, bismuthinite is distinctive because the only acid it will dissolve in is nitric acid. This is one of the main tests used to establish its identity.

*Bismuthinite is formed principally in igneous rocks and in high-temperature hydrothermal veins. It may also occur in tourmaline-bearing **copper** deposits and in veins of **tourmaline** and **quartz**. It is commonly associated with native **bismuth** and the minerals **chalcopyrite**, **galena**, **magnetite**, **pyrite**, and **sphalerite**.*

Main Sources: ◆ *Bolivia* ◆ *England* ◆ *Italy* ◆ *Peru* ◆ *Arizona, California, Connecticut, Dakota, Montana, Utah, and Washington, United States*

CRYSTALS

Distinct crystals of bismuthinite are rare, and most deposits take the form of fairly shapeless massive aggregates. However, of those crystals that do appear, the finest appear as gray, acicular habits (in the shape of tiny needles). If you are lucky enough to acquire such a specimen, you should handle it with great care because it is extremely soft—Mohs scale 2—and can be scratched quite easily, even with a fingernail.

BITUMEN

Formed from the decomposed remains of various living organisms, bitumen occurs in four types, the best known of which is asphalt.

Bitumen is a rock composed of hydrocarbons, waxes, and other highly volatile materials. It is formed from the remains of animals and plants that have accumulated in sedimentary rocks. Fossils are sometimes found in it.

Main Sources: *Bitumen occurs in California and Kentucky, United States. Canada, England, France, Romania, and Trinidad are also leading producers.*

When organisms die, their bodies decompose and secrete oily fluids and waxes. After a while, the pressure in the Earth's crust causes the lighter of these oils to migrate through surrounding permeable rocks until they become trapped together in a single location in an area of lower pressure. Meanwhile, the heavier waxes are left behind at or near the place where they were originally deposited.

VARIOUS TYPES

As a result of the above process, bitumen appears in various forms. The most important of these is asphalt, which is mined commercially and used to make roads (*see* photo, below) and roofing, and in the production of varnishes, paints, and stains. However, there are another three main types of bitumen: albertite, elaterite, and ozokerite.

Albertite is black and shiny. When it breaks up after being hit with a hammer, the marks left behind on its surface resemble the patterns on a seashell. This effect is known as conchoidal fracture.

Above: The edges of this bitumen specimen resemble the edges of a seashell—this is known as conchoidal fracture.

Albertite is named after one of its most productive sources, the Albert Mine, New Brunswick, Canada.

Elaterite is a softer and more plastic form of bitumen, with a rubbery appearance. Its name comes from the Greek *elate*, meaning "pine," the tree from which the resins in the rock are thought to have come. It was first identified in Derbyshire, England.

Ozokerite, meanwhile, is rich in paraffin, a valuable fuel that boils at low temperatures of 130 to 150° F (55 to 66° C). The rock is brown or green, has a waxy appearance, and is often associated with oil deposits. Its name is derived from the Greek *ozein* "to smell" and *keros* "wax."

BOLÉITE

A rare and complex mineral, boléite is reddish or purple in color and usually forms in cube-shaped crystals.

Boléite is a rare mineral that is formed as an alteration product on the surface of sulfide deposits. It may be found especially in zones of lead sulfide that have been weathered by percolating liquids—an effect known as leaching. The two minerals with which it is most commonly associated are cumengéite and pseudoboléite.

Main Sources: ◆ *Australia* ◆ *Germany* ◆ *Iran* ◆ *Mexico* ◆ *Arizona, United States*

CHEMICAL FORMULAE	
Boléite:	$Pb_{26}Ag_{10}Cu_{24}Cl_{62}(OH)_{48}.3H_2O$
Cumengéite:	$Pb_4Cu_4Cl_8(OH)_8.H_2O$
Pseudoboléite:	$Pb_5Cu_4Cl_{10}(OH)_8.2H_2O$

Below: Crystals of boléite may appear as cubes or in eight- or 12-sided shapes.

This secondary mineral, which often forms in precise, symmetrical cubes, is named after the location where it was first discovered—Boléo, near Santa Rosalia, in Baja California, Mexico. Boléite was confirmed as a distinct mineral in 1891.

COMPLEX MINERAL

Boléite is one of the halide group of about 100 minerals, each member of which contains one of the halogens (astatine, bromine, chlorine, fluorine, or iodine). Boléite has a complex chemical structure—it contains 26 atoms of lead, 10 atoms of **silver**, 24 atoms of **copper**, 62 atoms of chlorine, and 48 hydroxyl molecules. It also has three attached molecules of water of crystallization.

Boléite is closely related to pseudoboléite, which has a similar chemical formula but contains no silver. Pseudoboléite often forms on the surface of boléite. When this happens, it is extremely difficult to tell where one species ends and the other begins. Indeed, it was not until 1985 that pseudoboléite was shown to be a distinct species rather than merely a variant form of boléite.

Crystals of boléite conform to the cubic system of symmetry while those of pseudoboléite are tetragonal. Boléite is a deep reddish or purple blue color.

BORACITE

Although this mineral does form naturally when seawater evaporates, most boracite samples have been created artificially.

Left: Boracite is basically white. Although color variations do occur, these are caused by the presence of impurities.

symmetry and are known as α-boracite (alpha-boracite). Specimens formed at lower temperatures have orthorhombic crystals and are known as β-boracite (beta-boracite). Most specimens that exist are the high-temperature type, α-boracite. These have been formed artificially as a byproduct of the industrial process by which **sylvine** is extracted from the Earth to make potash, an agricultural fertilizer.

ERICAITE AND CHAMBERSITE

Boracite forms a solid solution series with ericaite, a mineral that has substantially the same chemical makeup but contains, in addition, more than 36 percent iron and some manganese. This close relative is named after its color, which is the same purple as one of the heather blossoms (genus *Erica*). Ericaite is also closely related to, and often externally indistinguishable from, congolite, another borate, which was first identified near Brazzaville in the Democratic Republic of the Congo (formerly Zaire).

Chambersite, which was first identified at Barber's Hill Salt Dome, Chambers County, Texas, also has almost exactly the same chemical formula as boracite, but contains manganese rather than magnesium. This mineral is therefore described in scientific terms as the manganese analog of boracite.

Boracite is an evaporite mineral—one that crystallizes from dried up salt water in deserts and other arid areas. It is most commonly found in extensive beds, where it is accompanied by many other minerals with similar origins, most notably **gypsum** *and* **halite**.

Main Sources: ◆ *Canada* ◆ *England* ◆ *France* ◆ *Germany* ◆ *Poland* ◆ *California, Louisiana, and Texas, United States*

B oracite is a minor source of boron, a metalloid constituting only three parts per million of the Earth's crust. The main ores of this rare element are **borax** and kernite. Although many evaporites are externally similar, boracite is fairly easy to recognize because it is considerably harder (7 to 7½ on the Mohs scale) than most other minerals of this type.

There are two different types of boracite. Specimens formed at temperatures in excess of 514° F (268° C) conform to the cubic system of

CHEMICAL FORMULAE	
Boracite:	$Mg_3B_7O_{13}Cl$
Chambersite:	$Mn_3B_7O_{13}Cl$
Congolite:	$(Fe,Mg)_3B_7O_{13}Cl$
Ericaite:	$(Fe^{2+},Mg,Mn)_3B_7O_{13}Cl$

BORAX

This white borate mineral has a distinctive, monoclinic crystal form and is the best known source of the element boron.

Borax is an evaporite mineral that is formed when salt-rich waters are dried out by the Sun in arid regions such as salt lakes and playas (the floors of desert basins that sometimes become lakes). It occurs in association with other borates, such as **colemanite.**

Main Sources: ◆ *India* ◆ *Iran* ◆ *Russia* ◆ *Tibet* ◆ *Turkey* ◆ *California, Nevada, and New Mexico, United States*

The most common of the 100–odd minerals that contain boron, borax is the chief ore of this metalloid element. It has been mined since ancient times from salt lakes in Tibet and Kashmir, where it was known as tincal. Its modern English name comes from the Arabic *buraq,* meaning "white."

USES OF BORON AND BORAX

The main use of boron is as an alloy to increase the hardness of steel. It plays an important part in the purification of metals, helping to remove any oxygen and nitrogen impurities they may contain. It is also used to absorb fast neutrons in nuclear reactors.

Under normal conditions, boron has a low electrical conductivity, but this increases greatly as its temperature is raised. As a result, heated boron is a semiconductor that is often added to germanium and silicon to increase their electrical conductivity.

Borax itself is also important in industry. It has long been used in ceramic glazes, in the production of glass (*see* photo, left), and as a soldering flux (a material used to aid fusion). Textiles and wood may be impregnated with borax to make them fireproof. It is also used as a water softener in laundries and as a flux to dissolve oxides in brazing.

In addition, borax is the source of boric acid, used as a mild antiseptic and preservative. However, this product is not entirely harmless to humans and its use in food is prohibited in many countries.

Today, most boron is extracted from large quantities of borax, kernite, and colemanite mined at Borax, Searles, and Kramer lakes in California.

Below: Borax is a white mineral that forms in prismatic crystals with a vitreous (glassy) luster.

BORNITE

A valued ore of copper, bornite's reddish color tarnishes to give an iridescent appearance when exposed to the air.

*Bornite is a secondary mineral formed by the action of hydrothermals (see box, below) in zones of contact metamorphism and in sulfide ore veins. It is commonly associated with **chalcopyrite** and **chalcosite**, which are both more important as ores of copper.*

Main Sources: ◆ *Australia* ◆ *Chile* ◆ *England* ◆ *Mexico* ◆ *Namibia* ◆ *Peru* ◆ *Connecticut and Montana, United States* ◆ *Zambia*

Below: Bornite may tarnish on exposure to the atmosphere and take on a blue, purple, or red coloration.

A common and widespread sulfide of copper and iron, bornite is also a minor ore of copper. It was confirmed as a distinct species in 1845 and named after Austrian mineralogist, Ignaz von Born.

PEACOCK ORE

When bornite is first extracted from the Earth it is reddish brown with a metallic luster. However, it tarnishes and develops a rainbowlike play of colors on its surface when exposed to the atmosphere. Because of this iridescence, it is may be known as peacock ore.

The crystal structure may vary according to the temperature of the hydrothermals from which the bornite was deposited. Most samples are formed from fluids at 572 to 932° F (300 to 500° C) and have cubic crystals. However, some specimens, formed in much cooler conditions, have tetragonal crystals.

HYDROTHERMALS

Hydrothermals are fluids that perform two main functions in the Earth's crust—they carry elements from which vein minerals are crystallized, and they alter preexistent minerals to form new species. Hydrothermals is a general term that takes little account of the exact temperature of each stream. To be more accurate, scientists speak of three categories of subterranean fluid. The coolest are known as epithermals, which form at between 122 and 392° F (50 and 200° C). Mesothermals are hotter fluids within the range 392 to 572° F (200 to 300° C). Strictly, the term hydrothermals should be used only to describe the hottest fluids of this type—572 to 932° F (300 to 500° C). However, for general convenience, all three categories are covered by the blanket term hydrothermals.

BOULANGERITE

More widespread than originally thought, this gray or bluish mineral is often mined with its most common associate, galena.

*Boulangerite is a double sulfide of lead and **antimony** that forms in hydrothermal veins. It is found in association with many other minerals, particularly **galena**.*

Main Sources ◆ *Czech Republic* ◆ *France* ◆ *Germany* ◆ *Italy* ◆ *Mexico* ◆ *Russia* ◆ *Sweden* ◆ *California, Nevada, and Washington, United States*

Confirmed as a distinct mineral species in 1837, boulangerite was named after Charles Louis Boulanger (1810–49), the French mining engineer who originally described it. When it was identified,

Above: Boulangerite is lead gray or bluish gray in color with a dull or metallic luster.

boulangerite was rare. However, since the early 19th century more and more deposits have been discovered, often occurring with galena. The two minerals are now extracted together for their lead and purified by the same roasting process.

Boulangerite is also commonly found with **pyrite**, **sphalerite**, and **stibnite**, and sometimes with **calcite**, **dolomite**, and **quartz**.

ACICULAR OR FIBROUS

The mineral conforms to the monoclinic system of symmetry. Externally, it may appear in long, prismatic crystals that may have an acicular (needle-shaped) habit (appearance). Alternatively, boulangerite forms in massive aggregates with a fibrous or plumous (feathery) habit. It has a two-way cleavage (it breaks in two directions when subjected to pressure) and its crystals may be flexible, which helps to distinguish it from the otherwise similar **jamesonite**. Boulangerite's type locality is at Molières, Gard in France.

HABITS
A mineral's habit is its characteristic appearance. Geologists have a wide range of established terms to describe the various habits, but these are seven of the most frequently used:

Acicular:	needle-shaped
Bladed:	resembles the cutting part of a knife
Botryoidal:	like bunches of grapes
Dendritic:	with a plantlike shape
Massive:	no particular shape discernible
Prismatic:	with parallel sides and polygonal ends
Reniform:	kidney-shaped

BOURNONITE

The finest crystals of bournonite form in extraordinarily shaped masses that are highly prized by mineral collectors.

*A primary mineral, bournonite is crystallized directly from underground fluids when they cool and solidify. It is commonly found in association with **galena, sphalerite,** and other sulfides. The secondary minerals derived from bournonite include **azurite, cerussite,** and **malachite.***

Main Sources: ◆ *Australia* ◆ *Bolivia* ◆ *Canada* ◆ *Czech Republic* ◆ *England* ◆ *France* ◆ *Germany* ◆ *Italy* ◆ *Mexico* ◆ *Peru* ◆ *Spain* ◆ *Arizona, California, Nevada, Utah, and Washington, United States*

This mineral is an important sulfide ore of lead and **copper**, and also contains **antimony**. It is a member of the sulfosalt group (*see* box, below) and is named after Count Jacques Louis de Bournon (1751–1825), the French crystallographer who first described the mineral.

By weight bournonite comprises 42 percent lead, 13 percent copper, 25 percent antimony, and 20 percent **sulfur**, giving the chemical formula $PbCuSbS_3$. It crystallizes in the orthorhombic system as prismatic or tabular crystals and is usually dark gray and metallic looking. The streak is also gray or black.

COGWHEEL ORE

Crystals of bournonite are often twinned, sharing a face or faces with one or more of their neighbors. As a result the mineral often appears in the indented circular shapes that have given rise to its alternative name, cogwheel ore. Bournonite may also be known as endellionite, after Endellion, the site of the mine in Cornwall, England where it was first discovered.

In some deposits, the antimony in bournonite may gradually be replaced by arsenic to form a completely different mineral—a sulfide of lead, copper, and arsenic called seligmannite. The two minerals are the end members of a solid solution series.

Above: Prismatic crystals of bournonite conform to the orthorhombic system of symmetry.

SULFOSALTS

Sulfides are chemical compounds of sulfur. One of the best known examples is **pyrite**, which contains a single metal, iron, and sulfur. Some sulfides, however, contain two or more metals, and these are known as double or triple sulfides or, strictly, as sulfosalts. In addition to bournonite, some of the principal sulfosalts are **boulangerite**, **enargite**, and **tetrahedrite**.

BRECCIA

Distinctive for its angular fragments of various sizes, breccia may be brightly colored red, yellowish, or gray.

Breccia is formed principally through the consolidation of scree—piles of preexistent rock that have accumulated through landslides or as a result of weathering.

Main Sources: *Breccia may be found almost anywhere, but it is most likely to appear at the bottom of cliffs or in collapsed caves. It may also be found near faults in the Earth's surface and around the sites of **meteorite** impact craters. Because of the manner of its formation, the mineralogical composition of each deposit tends to be restricted.*

Breccia is a sedimentary rock made up of large, angular fragments that have become cemented together. The main components may be of any rock type—igneous, metamorphic, or sedimentary. The cement, meanwhile, may be a fine-grained combination of **calcite** and **quartz**, together with the iron oxides **limonite** and **hematite**.

VARIABLE FRAGMENTS

The size of breccia fragments varies a great deal, but within a defined lower limit because particles of coarse-grained rocks—of which breccia is a type—are always more than ⅖ in. (0.2 cm) in diameter. However, there is no upper limit to the size of a fragment and the largest pieces may be great boulders. Although the cementing material may be composed of very small particles indeed, breccia is classed as a coarse-grained rock.

The general appearance and chemical composition of breccia are broadly similar to those of **conglomerate**. However, the two can be distinguished in that fragments of breccia are always angular, whereas those of conglomerate are smooth and rounded. This is because conglomerate has been transported by water, and worn down in the process, whereas breccia is often formed in place.

Below: Breccia is made up of fragments of any size cemented together in a base of silt or sand.

BROCHANTITE

Occasionally mined for its copper, brochantite is distinctive for its bright, emerald-green crystals.

Brochantite is a secondary mineral that forms in oxidation zones through the alteration of primary copper-bearing deposits. It is particularly likely to occur in desert regions, where it may be associated with one or more other sulfates of copper.

Main Sources: ◆ *Algeria* ◆ *Australia* ◆ *Chile* ◆ *England* ◆ *Germany* ◆ *Iceland* ◆ *Italy* ◆ *Namibia* ◆ *Spain* ◆ *Arizona, California, Idaho, New Mexico, and Utah, United States*

A hydrous copper sulfate with the chemical formula $Cu_4SO_4(OH)_6$, brochantite was first identified at a mine near Sverdlovsk in the Ural Mountains of Russia. It was confirmed as a distinct species in 1824 and named after André Brochant de Villiers, professor of mineralogy at *L'école pratique des mines* in Paris, France. Large deposits that are found in association with copper sulfates (*see* box, below) may be mined for their metal content.

FINE, GREEN CRYSTALS

Brochantite is strictly an ore of copper, but only a minor one. What is most interesting about this mineral is the beauty of its finest crystals, which are shiny and green and form in prismatic or acicular shapes. Many are twinned—in other words, they share a face or faces with one or more of their neighbors.

Below: Brochantite may be emerald green or blackish green in color.

COPPER SULFATE MINERALS

There are currently known to be 28 copper sulfate minerals. They are all quite similar but each has a slightly different chemical formula and contains varying amounts of water. Some are sulfates of other metals as well as copper. The best known is **chalcanthite**. Among the others are:

Antlerite:	$Cu_3SO_4(OH)_4$
Bonattite:	$CuSO_4.3H_2O$
Boothite:	$CuSO_4.7H_2O$
Chalcanthite:	$CuSO_4.5H_2O$
Chalcocyanite:	$CuSO_4$
Cyanotrichite:	$Cu_4Al_2SO_4(OH)_{12}.2H_2O$
Devilline:	$CaCu_4(SO_4)_2(OH)_6.3H_2O$
Dolerophane:	Cu_2SO_5
Fedotovite:	$K_2Cu_3O(SO_4)_3$
Kröhnkite:	$Na_2Cu(SO_4)_2.2H_2O$
Langite:	$Cu_4(SO_4)(OH)_6.2H_2O$
Leightonite:	$K_2Ca_2Cu(SO_4)_4.2H_2O$
Natrochalcite:	$NaCu_2(SO_4)_2.6H_2O$
Wroewolfeite:	$Cu_4(SO_4)(OH)_6.2H_2O$

BROOKITE

Confirmed as a distinct mineral species in 1825, brookite is a reddish or brownish form of titanium dioxide.

*Brookite may be found in all three main types of rock— igneous, metamorphic, and sedimentary. It is especially abundant in the metamorphic rocks **gneiss** and **schist**, where it is associated with **feldspar** and **quartz**. It is also common in detrital deposits near the surface of the Earth. In all locations, it is particularly likely to be found with the other two members of its trimorphous series.*

Main Sources: ◆ *Austria* ◆ *Brazil* ◆ *Canada* ◆ *England* ◆ *France* ◆ *Italy* ◆ *Norway* ◆ *Russia* ◆ *Switzerland* ◆ *Arkansas, Colorado, Massachusetts, and New York, United States* ◆ *Wales*

Above: A tabular crystal of brookite on a matrix (base) of igneous **rhyolite**.

Brookite is one of only three naturally occurring forms of titanium dioxide (chemical formula TiO_2). The others are **anatase** and **rutile**. The three minerals are said to be polymorphs of titanium dioxide, which means that they have the same components and may look alike, but they are in fact demonstrably different. Brookite has a white streak but may appear reddish or brownish in color.

TRIMORPHOUS SERIES

Brookite often occurs in association with anatase and rutile but can be distinguished from these close relatives by the internal structure of its crystals and its specific gravity. Both anatase and rutile conform to the tetragonal system of symmetry, while crystals of brookite are orthorhombic. Brookite also weighs between 4.1 and 4.2 times more than the equivalent volume of water at room temperature (its specific gravity). This makes it denser than anatase, which has a specific gravity (SG) of 3.8 to 4.0, and less dense than rutile, which has an SG of 4.23.

Brookite was the latest member of the trio to be recognized. Rutile was confirmed as a distinct mineral in 1800, and anatase followed a year later. It was not until 1809 that brookite was first described and named after geologist Henry James Brooke (1771–1857). After much debate and further examination, the original specimen, which had been found near Mount Snowdon, the highest point in Wales, was confirmed as a mineral in 1825.

BRUCITE

With its high melting point, brucite has many industrial applications and is also an important source of magnesia and magnesium.

*Brucite is found in metamorphic rocks, especially **limestone** and **schist**, in hydrothermal veins, and in layers in sedimentary **clay** with **montmorillonite** and other members of the montmorillonite group. Among the other minerals with which brucite is most commonly associated are **calcite, dolomite, magnesite,** and **talc.***

Main Sources: ◆ *Austria* ◆ *Canada* ◆ *England* ◆ *Italy* ◆ *Russia* ◆ *Scotland* ◆ *Sweden* ◆ *Turkey* ◆ *California, New Jersey, New York, and Pennsylvania, United States*

Brucite is a source of magnesia, a medical antacid and laxative, and one of the four main mineral providers of magnesium—the others are dolomite, magnesite, and **olivine**. The most abundant source of this metal, however, is seawater.

Because brucite itself is virtually impossible to melt, it is also sometimes used in the linings of furnaces, kilns, and ovens.

Brucite was confirmed as a distinct species in 1824 and is named after Archibald Bruce (1777–1818), a physician and professor at Yale University, who first discovered the mineral at Hoboken, New Jersey. Bruce is also known for founding the *American Mineralogical Journal* in 1810.

OFTEN CONTAINS IMPURITIES

In its pure state, brucite is a form of magnesium hydroxide with the chemical formula $Mg(OH)_2$. However, many specimens also contain up to 10 percent by weight of iron oxide, and these are known as ferrobrucite. Other brucite deposits contain impurities of manganese, although even the richest specimens of manganoan brucite still contain five times more magnesium than manganese. Brucite may also sometimes contain zinc.

Above: Brucite is usually white with a waxy, vitreous, or pearly luster. Fibrous varieties of this mineral are silky.

Crystals of brucite conform to the hexagonal system of symmetry and often have a broad, tabular habit (appearance). The basic, irreducible color is white, which may be confirmed by the streak test—that is, by rubbing the specimen across the surface of an unglazed porcelain tile. This gives the color the mineral would be if it were reduced to a powder. However, the presence of the various impurities may cause a specimen to appear blue, brown, gray, or yellow in color. Brucite crystals also sometimes appear in long, thin, greenish threads.

BUSTAMITE

Incorrectly identified and named for a Mexican army general in 1938, bustamite was actually discovered more than 100 years earlier.

Bustamite is a secondary mineral. It is usually found in manganese-bearing ore bodies, where it is formed by metasomatism (chemical changes caused by the introduction of material from an external source).

Main Sources: ◆ *Australia* ◆ *England* ◆ *Japan* ◆ *Mexico* ◆ *Sweden* ◆ *New Jersey, United States*

Bustamite is a silicate mineral that always contains both manganese and calcium, although the exact amount of each metal may vary considerably from specimen to specimen. As a result its chemical formula is written $(Mn,Ca)SiO_3$.

RELATED TO RHODONITE

The mineral is closely related to, but significantly different from, **rhodonite**, a silicate of manganese alone that is sometimes used in jewelry. The two species both conform to the triclinic system of crystal symmetry and are often found in close association with one another.

Apart from the presence of calcium, the key difference between these two minerals is their specific gravity. Bustamite weighs 3.3 to 3.4 times more than the equivalent volume of water at room temperature, while rhodonite is slightly denser, with a specific gravity of 3.5 to 3.7.

INCORRECTLY IDENTIFIED

Bustamite is named after the Mexican army general Anastasio Bustamente (1780–1853). Although he made an important contribution to the mineral's discovery, his role was not quite what he thought it was. The specimen he first unearthed in Real de Minas, Jonotla, in Mexico, was shown in 1938 to be no more than a mixture of rhodonite and johnssen-ite, a silicate of calcium and manganese. Nevertheless, bustamite did exist—it was simply that Bustamente had not correctly identified his own discovery. The genuine original bustamite turned out to be the crystals found at Franklin Furnace, New Jersey, in 1826. This is now the type locality of the mineral, which has retained its original name.

Below: Thin, acicular crystals of bustamite, showing the characteristic reddish-brown coloration of the mineral.

CALCITE

Calcite crystals form in more shapes than any other mineral—as tabular and prismatic crystals, as fibrous aggregates, and many others.

*One of the world's most widely distributed minerals, calcite is the main component of all **limestone**. It may occur as part of other sedimentary rocks and in metamorphic rocks such as **marble**. It forms as a result of seawater precipitation, on the shells of living organisms, and can also be found in caves as stalactites and stalagmites.*

Main Sources: ◆ *England* ◆ *France* ◆ *Germany* ◆ *Carrara, Italy* ◆ *Namibia* ◆ *Colorado, Illinois, Missouri, and Wisconsin, United States*

Calcite is a form of calcium carbonate and because of this is chemically identical to **aragonite**. The defining difference between the two species is the shapes of their crystals: those of aragonite are orthorhombic, while calcite conforms to the hexagonal system of symmetry.

Calcite is widely used as the raw material for all quicklime (calcium oxide) and cement. It is also important in the manufacture of glass and steel.

DOUBLE REFRACTION

One of the basic laws of physics is that whenever light passes from one medium to another, it is deflected. For example, if a pencil is half immersed in water its shaft will seem to bend below the point at which it enters the liquid.

This phenomenon is known as refraction or single refraction. One form of calcite, transparent crystals known as Iceland spar, displays a much rarer optical property known as double refraction. In this case any light that passes through it is split into two distinct beams that move off in separate directions. Some calcite will fluoresce when placed under ultraviolet light—in other words, it will emit a light of its own. The color of this light may vary according to the impurities in the specimen.

Below: Calcite makes up the greater part of most limestones and marbles and may appear in a wide range of shapes and colors. Its basic color, however, is white.

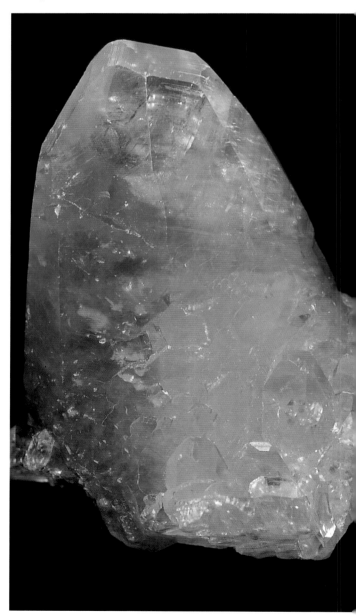

CANCRINITE

A mineral of restricted occurrence, cancrinite is a feldspathoid formed under great pressure deep in the Earth's crust.

Rocks containing feldspathoids are not common, and even within these cancrinite is unusual. It is found almost exclusively in intrusive or plutonic rocks, which are formed at great depth and under enormous pressure. Pressure is crucial to the formation of cancrinite, because it is only this that will force large carbonate ions into its body.

Main Sources: ◆ *Canada* ◆ *China* ◆ *Democratic Republic of the Congo (formerly Zaire)* ◆ *Finland* ◆ *Germany* ◆ *Greenland* ◆ *India* ◆ *Kenya* ◆ *Norway* ◆ *Romania* ◆ *Russia* ◆ *Uganda* ◆ *Colorado, United States*

Above: White cancrinite on a base (matrix) of **syenite**, an intrusive igneous rock.

This rare mineral is usually white but may also be blue, orange, pink, or yellow, depending on inclusions. It was confirmed as a distinct species in 1839 and named after the Russian finance minister of that time, Count Georg von Kancrin (1774–1845).

It is unusual for cancrinite to form as distinct crystals. Prismatic crystals may occur but discrete veins or massive habits are more common.

FELDSPATHOID MINERALS

Cancrinite contains sodium, calcium, and aluminum, together with—unusually for a silicate mineral—two carbonate ions. It is a feldspathoid, one of a group of minerals whose chemistry is similar to that of alkali **feldspar**. However, in contrast with feldspar, feldspathoids occur in rocks that are lacking in **quartz**. If quartz had been present when these rocks were crystallizing, it would have reacted with any feldspathoids present to form a feldspar. Feldspathoid minerals are similar to zeolites such as **analcime** in that their wide, open structures allow large ions to be incorporated into them.

Cancrinite may also contain some percentage of sulfate ions (SO_4) and chlorine ions (Cl). However, these take the form of impurities and as a result do not feature in the mineral's chemical formula, which is $Na_6Ca_2Al_6Si_6O_{24}(CO_3)_2$.

Some scientists believe that cancrinite may form a solid solution series with vishnevite. This mineral is similar, but the carbonate ions present in cancrinite have been replaced by sulfate ions. However, whether or not atomic substitution takes place between the two has yet to be scientifically proven.

CARMINITE

An arsenate mineral valued by collectors for its striking red color, carminite has tiny crystals invisible to the naked eye.

Carminite is a hydrous arsenate that is formed in rich ore veins of iron and lead. It contains both metals. It is a secondary mineral commonly found in association with anglesite, cerussite, goethite, mimetite, pharmacosiderite, quartz, and scorodite.

Main Sources: ◆ *Australia* ◆ *England* ◆ *Germany* ◆ *Mexico* ◆ *Namibia* ◆ *Colorado, Nevada, New Jersey, and Utah, United States*

Below: This carminite was extracted from a lead-rich ore vein deposit.

ARSENATES

Arsenate minerals are compounds of **arsenic** and oxygen that often occur as oxidation products of arsenide ore minerals. For the most part rare, arsenate minerals are deposited at low temperatures in veins and cavities near the surface of the Earth. To date, about 150 different minerals of this type have been identified.

The other arsenates featured in this book are **adamite**, **ceruleite**, **erythrite**, mimetite, **olivenite**, and scorodite.

Carminite derives it name from its coloration—carmine is the red that comes from cochineal insects and is often used as a food dye. The first record of this mineral was from the Luise iron mine at Horhausen in the Rhineland of Germany. It was confirmed as a distinct species in 1850.

With the chemical formula $PbFe^{2+}(AsO_4)_2(OH)_2$, carminite is closely related to gabrielsonite, another arsenate (*see* box, above), formula $PbFe^{2+}AsO_4OH$. Both have orthorhombic crystals, although most specimens are made up of crystals so small that they appear as shapeless massive aggregates. The crystal shapes are usually visible only under a microscope.

HANDLE WITH CARE

Because of its bright red color, carminite is popular with collectors. However, the mineral is readily soluble and easily damaged. As a result, great care must be taken with specimens. If you are lucky enough to own one, you must make sure that you only clean it with distilled water. Tap water should not be used because it contains impurities that may damage or even destroy the carminite.

CARNALLITE

This light mineral can be identified from its granular massive appearance and the ease with which it absorbs water.

*Carnallite forms in marine evaporite deposits where seawater has been concentrated and then dried out over long periods in hot sunshine. It often occurs in association with minerals of the same type, especially other potassium and magnesium evaporites such as **kainite** and **sylvine**.*

Main Sources: ◆ *China* ◆ *England* ◆ *Germany* ◆ *Iran* ◆ *Italy* ◆ *Mali* ◆ *Russia* ◆ *Spain* ◆ *Tunisia* ◆ *Ukraine* ◆ *New Mexico and Texas, United States*

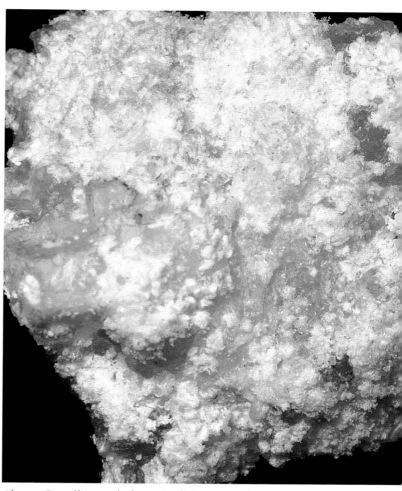

Above: Carnallite rarely forms in distinct crystals—most deposits are granular or massive aggregates such as this.

An important source of potash for fertilizer, carnallite is also a minor ore of magnesium. It is a widespread mineral that forms extensive bedded deposits in many parts of the world. White, or colorless, carnallite may also appear red or yellowish depending on inclusions. It was first identified near Stassfurt, Germany and confirmed as a distinct species in 1856. It is named after Rudolph von Carnall (1804–74), a Prussian mining engineer.

RARE CRYSTALS

Carnallite is a halide mineral, all of which contain one of the halogens. It is composed of magnesium, potassium, and chlorine, together with water of crystallization. Its crystals are rare because they deliquesce, meaning that they absorb water from humid air. This decomposition can be slowed down, if not entirely prevented, by storing specimens of carnallite in a sealed, dry container.

Even though it commonly appears in blanket deposits with many other evaporite minerals, carnallite is relatively easy to distinguish from its neighbors because of its very low specific gravity—it weighs only 1.6 times more than the equivalent volume of water at room temperature. Another good clue to its identity is that when it is held over a bunsen burner, the potassium it contains will turn the flame red. Very few other evaporites contain this metal.

USED AS A FERTILIZER

Carnallite is the second most important mineral source of the fertilizer potash, the most important source being sylvine. Although carnallite's magnesium content is less important industrially, it remains Russia's most significant source of this metal.

CARNOTITE

Often appearing as a powdery yellow coating on host rocks, carnotite is a radioactive mineral that contains uranium and vanadium.

*Carnotite is a secondary mineral formed when oxygenated waters dissolve uranium from primary minerals and the metal is later redeposited in new environments. Many carnotite deposits in **sandstones** are associated with petrified trees and other fossils.*

Main Sources: ◆ *Australia* ◆ *Democratic Republic of the Congo (formerly Zaire)* ◆ *Kazakhstan* ◆ *Morocco* ◆ *Russia* ◆ *Turkestan* ◆ *Arizona, Colorado, New Mexico, Utah, and Wyoming, United States*

CHEMICAL FORMULAE

Carnotite: $K_2(UO_2)_2(VO_4)_2.3H_2O$
Tyuyamunite: $Ca(UO_2)_2V_2O_8.5–8H_2O$

Despite its rarity, carnotite is an important ore of vanadium and uranium. It was confirmed as a mineral in 1899 and named after engineer and chemist, Adolphe-Marie Carnot (1839–1920).

A hydrated vanadate of potassium and uranium, carnotite's closest relative is tyuyamunite. There are, however, important differences between the two: one contains potassium, the other calcium; they have different amounts of water of crystallization; and they conform to separate systems of crystal symmetry.

Despite these differences, the two minerals are often found in close association are practically indistinguishable by ordinary methods.

Carnotite is radioactive, and mineral collectors should cover specimens with a sheet of lead to prevent leakage. In its pure form it contains about 53 percent by weight of uranium and 12 percent by weight of vanadium. When extracted from the mineral ore, uranium is used as a source of nuclear energy. Vanadium is highly resistant to corrosion and is therefore a major component of rustproof alloys, especially those used to make high-speed drills.

Below: Yellowish carnotite in a crust on the surface of an unidentified uranium-bearing rock.

CASSITERITE

For more than 5,000 years, reddish-brown cassiterite has been the world's principal ore of tin.

*Cassiterite occurs in high-temperature hydrothermal veins and is often found in association with **quartz**, **chalcopyrite**, and **tourmaline**.*

Main Sources: ◆ *Australia* ◆ *Bolivia* ◆ *China* ◆ *England* ◆ *France* ◆ *Germany* ◆ *Indonesia* ◆ *Italy* ◆ *Malaysia* ◆ *Mexico* ◆ *Nigeria* ◆ *Portugal* ◆ *Russia* ◆ *South Africa* ◆ *Spain* ◆ *Thailand* ◆ *Zaire*

Above: A cluster of cassiterite crystals, many of which have been twinned.

The best-formed crystals of cassiterite are bright, shiny, and attractive. However, its main importance is as an industrial mineral that is mined for its tin wherever it is found in reasonable quantities.

The chemical formula of cassiterite, SnO_2, shows that each molecule contains twice as many atoms of oxygen as it does of tin. In terms of actual density, however, up to 80 percent of any given specimen may be the pure metal. The oxygen is also fairly easy to remove by heating in a process known as carbon reduction. This, together with cassiterite's widespread distribution in many parts of the Earth, makes it much more important commercially than other tin-bearing minerals such as herzenbergite and berndtite.

The history of cassiterite is closely linked with the rise of human technology in primitive societies. The use of an alloy of tin and **copper** to make tools began in about 2500 B.C. and heralded the start of the Bronze Age. It is thought that the first inclusion of tin in bronze was probably an accidental result of tin ore being found in copper ore.

USEFUL ALLOYS

In addition to bronze, tin is a component of many useful alloys. Pewter, for example, is an alloy of tin hardened with **antimony** and copper. Tin alloys are also used in solder.

Because of its resistance to corrosion, tin is also used as a protective coating for other metals that corrode easily. Most of the tin imported into the United States is used for plating steel. Tin cans, for example, are actually steel cans with a thin coating of metallic tin. Once a portion of the tin coating has been removed, the underlying steel is exposed to the atmosphere and moisture, and corrosion takes place. Tinplate also prevents the organic acids contained in many foods from reacting with the steel can.

The plating or coating of the steel with tin is carried out either by electrolysis or by dipping the steel into molten tin.

WHERE TO LOOK

Tin is relatively rare, making up no more than 0.001 percent by weight of the Earth's crust. About 90 percent of the tin mined each year comes from cassiterite. Just over 200,000 tons (204,000 tonnes) of tin are produced annually worldwide.

CELESTINE

An important source of strontium, celestine is also popular with mineral collectors because it is often an attractive blue color.

*Celestine is formed by high-temperature hydrothermals in **granite** and in **pegmatite**. It occurs in association with **galena** and other sulfides. It may also occur as an evaporite mineral in **sulfur** deposits.*

Main Sources: ◆ *Austria* ◆ *Belgium* ◆ *Canada* ◆ *Egypt* ◆ *England* ◆ *France* ◆ *Germany* ◆ *Italy* ◆ *Madagascar* ◆ *Mexico* ◆ *Russia* ◆ *Switzerland* ◆ *Turkestan* ◆ *Tunisia* ◆ *Arizona, Ohio, Michigan, New York, Texas, and Utah, United States*

Above: Prismatic crystals of celestine. Some specimens are fluorescent when viewed under ultraviolet light.

Also known as celestite, celestine is one of the two main ores of strontium. The other is **strontianite**. The name celestine is derived from the Latin *caelestis*, meaning "of the sky"—this is a reference to the mineral's light blue color. However, it may also be gray, yellow, green, red, brown, or orange.

SOURCE OF STRONTIUM

Strontium is a soft, silvery metal first isolated in 1808 by the great English scientist Sir Humphry Davy (1778–1829). Its chemical and physical properties are similar to those of calcium.

Many radioactive isotopes of strontium are produced in nuclear reactors. One of these, strontium 90, is formed in nuclear explosions. It has a half-life of 28 years and accumulates in human bones. Because of this it is considered to be the most dangerous component of radioactive fallout. Strontium salts impart red color to flames and are widely used in signal flares, fireworks (*see* photo, above), and tracer bullets. They are also used in ceramics, frosted glass, and varnishes.

Celestine has the same orthorhombic structure as **barite** and forms very similar crystals. In fact the two minerals often appear identical, but they may be differentiated by the flame test, carried out by holding the mineral over a bunsen burner. Celestine will produce a red flame, because of its strontium content, while the calcium in barite will cause the flame to burn pale green.

Celestine is very popular with mineral collectors because of its attractive blue color. It also occurs as well-formed crystals, which grow quite commonly to more than 4 in. (10 cm) in length. The largest celestine crystals are over 30 in. (76 cm) long.

CERULEITE

This beautiful sky blue mineral might easily be mistaken for turquoise, but chemically it is an arsenate rather than a phosphate.

Chemically, ceruleite is a hydrous hydrated arsenate of **copper** *and aluminum. It is found in thick concretions in ore veins, where it is associated with copper-bearing minerals such as* **chalcopyrite**, *together with* **barite**, **goethite**, *and* **quartz**.

Main Sources: ◆ *Bolivia* ◆ *Chile* ◆ *England* ◆ *California, United States*

An attractive mineral, ceruleite derives its name from *caeruleus*, the Latin word for the color sky blue. It was first found at the Emma Luisa gold mine in Huanaco, Chile, and was confirmed as a distinct mineral species in 1900.

Ceruleite may also be found in compact, claylike concretions measuring up to 4 in. (10 cm) in diameter. Some of the finest crystals occur as encrustations on sulfur and in crystal-lined rock cavities known as geodes.

CHEMICAL FORMULA

Ceruleite's formula, $Cu_2Al_7(AsO_4)_4(OH)_{13}.11.5H_2O$, requires some explanation because it appears to imply that the mineral has half a molecule of water of crystallization attached to it. Clearly this is impossible because, in nature, atoms and molecules are always whole. The notation simply means that ceruleite almost always forms in pairs or other even-numbered multiples of molecules.

LOOKS LIKE TURQUOISE

Superficially, ceruleite sometimes resembles the precious gemstone **turquoise**. The two minerals not only have a similar sky blue coloration, but also a similar hardness (Mohs scale 5 to 6) and specific gravity (2.7). In addition, they both conform to the triclinic system of crystal symmetry. However, there is a key, chemical difference between the two minerals. Rather than being an arsenate, turquoise is a hydrous hydrated phosphate of copper and aluminum, formula $CuAl_6(PO_4)_4(OH)_8.5H_2O$. It can be seen from this that it contains no **arsenic**.

Below: An encrustation of ceruleite on a groundmass of rock from a copper-bearing ore vein.

CERUSSITE

Cerussite is a popular mineral with collectors because of its varied crystal shapes and the unusual optical properties of some specimens.

---

*Cerussite is a secondary mineral formed in the oxidized zones of ore veins through the alteration of **galena**. It is similar to, and often found with, **aragonite**, and is classified as a member of the aragonite group. It is also commonly associated with **anglesite, barite,** and **calcite**.*

Main Sources: ◆ *Australia* ◆ *Czech Republic* ◆ *Democratic Republic of the Congo (formerly Zaire)* ◆ *Italy* ◆ *Kazakhstan* ◆ *Morocco* ◆ *Namibia* ◆ *New Zealand* ◆ *Russia* ◆ *Scotland* ◆ *Tunisia* ◆ *Arizona, California, Colorado, Montana, Nevada, New Mexico, Pennsylvania, and Utah, United States* ◆ *Zambia*

Below: A cluster of cerussite crystals with striated faces and evident twinning.

As a lead carbonate, chemical formula $PbCO_3$, cerussite is a minor ore of lead. However, the principal industrial source of this metal is galena, and cerussite is mainly of interest to collectors rather than miners. It is collectable because of its beautiful orthorhombic crystals, the finest of which are prismatic or tabular in habit and often end in blunt pyramids. Many such crystals have surface grooves known as striations.

MANY SHAPES

Cerussite can form in a number of geometrically intricate structures, especially spoked star shapes, because of multiple twinning (sharing faces with their neighbors). In addition, some specimens appear as acicular (needle-shaped) crystals. Reniform (kidney-shaped), earthy, and crusty varieties are also found, as are strawlike clusters.

The mineral's English name comes from the Greek *keros*, meaning "wax"—this is a reference to its shiny, translucent crystals.

UNUSUAL PROPERTIES

With a specific gravity of 6.4 to 6.6, cerussite is very dense for a transparent mineral. It also has a high refractive index (2.07), meaning that it bends incident (incoming) light through quite a large angle. Another characteristic is that some specimens contain impurities that may cause the mineral to display a yellow fluorescence under ultraviolet light.

The United States has abundant deposits of cerussite, some of the largest of which are found in New Mexico. However, the most valuable deposits come from Arizona. In particular, crystals from the Mammoth Mine in Pinal County display a distinctive optical effect that resembles the slit in a cat's eye. This is known as chatoyancy.

CHABAZITE

A zeolite mineral widely used as a chemical sieve (a filter for gases), chabazite is usually found in association with many other minerals.

*Chabazite forms principally in the vesicles (petrified bubbles) of volcanic rocks, and in some **limestones** and metamorphic rocks, for example **schists**. It may also be precipitated in and around hot spring deposits.*

Main Sources ◆ *Australia* ◆ *Canada* ◆ *Czech Republic* ◆ *England* ◆ *Faroe Islands* ◆ *France* ◆ *Germany* ◆ *Greenland* ◆ *Hungary* ◆ *Iceland* ◆ *India* ◆ *Italy* ◆ *New Zealand* ◆ *Northern Ireland* ◆ *Russia* ◆ *Scotland* ◆ *Switzerland* ◆ *California, New Jersey, Oregon, and Wyoming, United States*

Left: These crystals of chabazite in a **basalt** groundmass make it is easy to see how the mineral got its name.

Chabazite is used as a filter to clean a variety of gases. It is particularly important in the extraction of methane from the gases that are given off when bacteria react with decaying organic waste. Its English name is thought to be a misreading of the Greek word *khalazios*, meaning "hailstones," because this is what the finest crystals often look like.

In addition to chabazite, the vesicles of the volcanic rocks where it forms may contain a wide range of other minerals. These include **apophyllite**, **calcite**, **heulandite**, **natrolite**, **quartz**, **scolecite**, and **stilbite**.

Some of the finest crystals of chabazite have been found in the vesicles of volcanic rocks at Pune, India, where they are associated with many other zeolites and exotic minerals.

Chabazite conforms to the trigonal system of symmetry. Twinning is common, especially twinning by penetration rather than the more common contact form. Externally, the crystals often appear in dicelike cube shapes (rhombohedra).

CHEMICAL SIEVE

As a member of the zeolite group of minerals (*see* **analcime**), chabazite's structure has a typical zeolite openness that allows large ions and molecules to reside and actually move around inside the atomic framework. Hence it contains open channels that allow water and large ions to travel into and out of the crystal structure. The size of these channels governs the size of the molecules or ions that can pass through. As a result, a zeolite such as chabazite can act as a chemical sieve, allowing some ions to pass through while blocking others.

CHALCANTHITE

Chalcanthite is an ore of copper that forms from the action of ground-water on preexistent minerals such as bornite.

*Chalcanthite is a secondary mineral formed near the surface of the Earth in the oxidation zones of **copper** ore belts. It usually forms late in the development of these deposits. It is commonly associated with **aragonite**, **brochantite**, **calcite**, **chalcopyrite**, and **malachite**.*

Main Sources: ◆ *Chile* ◆ *England* ◆ *France* ◆ *Germany* ◆ *Ireland* ◆ *New Zealand* ◆ *Spain* ◆ *Arizona, Arkansas, California, Montana, Nevada, New Mexico, Tennessee, and Utah, United States*

Below: Bluish chalcanthite on a groundmass of copper-bearing rock.

An ore of copper, chalcanthite takes its name from the Greek *khalkos*, meaning "copper," and *anthos*, meaning "flower."

Chalcanthite is one the few sulfate minerals that are soluble in water. Deposits may crystallize, dissolve, and recrystallize over and over again.

In wet regions, chalcanthite is rare, but in arid areas the mineral is abundant and a major ore. Indeed, in the copper mines of the Atacama Desert in Chile, it may be seen forming blue encrustations, crystal aggregates, and stalactites on the sides of the shafts. This process is caused by sulfate-rich ground-water that removes copper from other minerals. Later, when the water evaporates, the solids it contains recrystallize as chalcanthite.

DIFFICULT TO KEEP

Rich blue crystals of chalcanthite are popular with mineral collectors, but most of these are difficult to preserve in good condition because they dissolve so easily in water. In general, specimens should be kept with desiccants (drying agents) in tightly sealed containers to prevent them from being damaged by water in the atmosphere.

However, some chalcanthite crystals are surprisingly insoluble. These appear to be the ones that contain iron, an impurity left over from **bornite**. This is, despite itself being a secondary mineral, the preexistent mineral from which much chalcanthite is formed.

CHALCANTHITE GROUP	
Chalcanthite:	$CuSO_4.5H_2O$
Jokokuite:	$MnSO_4.5H_2O$
Pentahydrite:	$MgSO_4.5H_2O$
Siderotil:	$FeSO_4.5H_2O$

CHALCEDONY

Chalcedony is famed for its variable shapes and colors and for its many gemstone varieties including agate, jasper, and onyx.

*Chalcedony is a cryptocrystalline form of **quartz** that comes in a wide range of shapes and colors. It usually develops at low temperature in rock cavities.*

Main Sources: ◆ *Agate: Brazil, England, Germany, Scotland, and Uruguay* ◆ *Bloodstone: India* ◆ *Carnelian: England and India* ◆ *Chrysoprase: Australia, Austria, Brazil, Russia, and California, United States* ◆ *Jasper: France, Germany, India, Russia, Scotland, California, United States, and Venezuela* ◆ *Onyx: India*

Many varieties of chalcedony are semiprecious gemstones. The name may be derived from that of the ancient port of Khalkedon in Asia Minor (modern Turkey), where some of the earliest deposits are thought to have been unearthed.

GEMSTONE VARIETIES

Agate is distinguished from other forms of chalcedony by the curving, parallel colored bands that appear inside it when it is cut open. These are caused by the presence of various impurities. There are many forms of agate, such as agatized wood, formed when fossilized trees have their organic matter replaced by striped chalcedony, and fortification agate, which has concentric angled bandings that resemble the plan of a castle. Another type, moss agate, contains iron and manganese inclusions that make the stone appear as if it has green vegetation growing in it.

Onyx, sard, and sardonyx are similar to agate but feature straight, rather than curved, bands. The name onyx comes from the Greek for "fingernail," a reference to the width of the bandings.

Above: Chalcedony often forms in varicolored bands that follow the shape of the exterior of the specimen.

Bloodstone, also known as heliotrope, is the opaque, spotted form of chalcedony. Its green coloration is caused by the presence of iron oxides. Another gemstone variety, plasma, is also green and may have yellow spots.

Carnelian, or cornelian, is the translucent, reddish orange form of chalcedony quartz. It, too, is colored by iron oxide impurities. Some people believe that it will help the wearer to remain calm under stress.

Another gemstone variety, jasper, is frequently red, but may appear blue, green, yellow, or a combination of all these colors. When it is worn, as jewelry, for example, some people believe that it will protect against sight defects and the effects of drought.

Finally, the most precious form of chalcedony is chrysoprase, which is colored apple-green by the presence of nickel.

CHALCOPYRITE

Although not the richest source of copper, chalcopyrite is so plentiful that it has become the world's most important copper-bearing ore.

*Chalcopyrite is a sulfide of **copper** and iron with the chemical formula $CuFeS_2$. It is not particularly rich in copper, which takes up only about 35 percent of its mass, but it is by far the most plentiful and widely distributed ore of this metal. It is found in hydrothermal veins in almost all sulfide ore deposits.*

Main Sources: *◆ Australia ◆ Austria ◆ Canada ◆ Chile ◆ Czech Republic ◆ England ◆ France ◆ Germany ◆ Italy ◆ Japan ◆ Mexico ◆ Norway ◆ Peru ◆ Russia ◆ Serbia ◆ South Africa ◆ Spain ◆ Sweden ◆ Arizona, Montana, New Mexico, Tennessee, and Utah, United States ◆ Zambia*

Above: A compact aggregate of chalcopyrite showing the characteristic brassy yellow coloration of this mineral.

Chalcopyrite is the most important ore of copper—more than half of the world's output of the metal comes from this source. Its name comes from the Greek *khalkos*, meaning "copper," and "**pyrite**" because of its similarity to this mineral.

Copper has been used by humans since at least 5000 B.C. Greeks and Romans obtained much of their copper from Cyprus—the island's name actually means "copper." Copper is used to make roofing, piping, electric cables, wires, ornaments, and statues (*see* photo, right). It is also an important component of more than 1,000 alloys. When combined with zinc, for example, it forms brass, and when mixed with tin it forms bronze.

EXTRACTING COPPER

To extract copper, the chalcopyrite is first crushed. The powder is then placed in a flotation tank where it is agitated with foaming water containing an agent to make the copper-bearing particles water-repellent. The particles accumulate on the surface and are skimmed off and heated to about 1,472° F (800° C) to remove some of the water and impurities. The residue is then mixed with silica and melted in a furnace at 2,552 to 2,732° F (1,400 to 1,500° C). This produces two liquid layers: a lower layer of copper matte (cuprous sulfide mixed with iron sulfide and oxides), and an upper layer of slag, which is drawn off. The remaining copper sulfide is reduced to molten copper by heating in a controlled amount of air. The final stage of the purification is electrolysis, which yields copper of at least 99.95 percent purity.

CHALCOSITE

Although it is rich as copper, chalcosite is not particularly widespread and may be difficult to identify because of frequent pseudomorphism.

Although chalcosite is both a primary and a secondary mineral, most deposits fall into the latter category, since they are formed through the alteration of primary **copper** *minerals in oxidation zones above the water table.*

Main Sources: ◆ *Australia* ◆ *Chile* ◆ *Czech Republic* ◆ *England* ◆ *Germany* ◆ *Italy* ◆ *Mexico* ◆ *Namibia* ◆ *Norway* ◆ *Peru* ◆ *Russia* ◆ *Spain* ◆ *Alaska, Arizona, California, Connecticut, Montana, Nevada, Tennessee, and Utah, United States*

Above: Chalcosite is an opaque, dark gray mineral with a metallic luster.

A dark gray or black sulfide mineral, chalcosite has been mined for centuries for its copper content. Its chemical formula, Cu_2S, shows that, atomically, two thirds of the mineral is copper. In fact, by weight the amount of this valuable metal it contains is even greater—typically 80 percent of chalcosite is copper.

The mineral is easily purified by smelting and would be copper's principal ore if only it were more abundant and widely distributed. As it is, the main industrial source of copper is **chalcopyrite**.

Copper ore bodies commonly have a layer of chalcosite that corresponds to the level of a present or a previous water table. This feature is known as a chalcosite blanket.

PSEUDOMORPHISM

In many deposits, chalcosite appears as a pseudo-morph (false form) of other minerals. In other words, it replaces the other species atom by atom but leaves their original crystal shapes intact. This results in mineral deposits that have the outward form of the original species but the chemical composition and structure of chalcosite. Among the minerals infiltrated by chalcosite in this way are **bornite**, which forms in the tetragonal system of crystal symmetry, chalcopyrite (trigonal), **covellite** (hexagonal), **enargite** (orthorhombic), **galena** (cubic), **pyrite** (cubic), and **sphalerite** (cubic). Pseudomorphism can make mineral identification extremely difficult.

Chalcosite itself conforms to the monoclinic system of symmetry, and twinning is common. However, distinct chalcosite crystals are rare and most deposits take the form of massive aggregates. The few crystals that do occur appear as pseudo-hexagonal star shapes with heavy surface striations. These are much sought after by collectors and are often very expensive.

CHALK

A useful rock with a wide range of industrial and agricultural uses, chalk is also of interest because of the fossils it often contains.

*Chalk is formed when tiny marine organisms die and their remains settle at the bottom of shallow seas. In time the deposits are broken down into a mud that is cemented by precipitating **calcite**, and then compacted into rock.*

Main Sources: *Chalk is found in large quantities in every land mass that was once covered by sea water.*

A type of sedimentary rock, chalk is a pure variety of fine-grained **limestone**. Many of the world's finest chalk deposits were formed during the Cretaceous Period, 140 to 65 million years ago. The English word Cretaceous comes from the Latin *creta*, meaning "chalk." Chalk is soft and porous and contains very little silt or mud, which is unusual considering the circumstances of its formation. It is usually pure white, although some deposits are stained red by iron oxides.

Above: Chalk is easily recognizable by its predominantly white coloration and its crumbly (friable) composition.

FOSSILIZED ORGANISMS

The main components of chalk are minute fossilized fragments of algae, or single-celled organisms known as foraminifera. It may also contain larger organisms such as bivalve shells, and crystals of calcite. Most of the marine fossils are so small that they may be seen only under a microscope, but some are visible to the naked eye. Among the largest are ammonites, brachiopods, and sea urchins. These remains provide scientists with a wealth of information about life on Earth before recorded history. Some chalk beds, such as those in western Kansas, the United States, even contain the preserved skeletons of long-extinct mammals.

Usually, more than 50 percent of chalk is composed of calcium carbonate. This is because calcite and many of the fragments of the marine organisms are composed of this compound. The calcium carbonate composition is sometimes as high as 98 percent. Other minerals present in chalk include various types of **clay**, **hematite** and other iron oxides, **marcasite**, **mica**, **quartz**, and **pyrite**. Chalk may also contain **aragonite**, another mineral form of calcium carbonate.

Chalk has a wide range of uses. It is used in the manufacture of rubber goods, paint (*see* photo, above), putty, polishing powders, and portland cement, and as a soil conditioner.

CHAMOSITE

Occurring mainly in compact, massive aggregates, chamosite is thought to have two different crystal forms.

*Chamosite forms in various sedimentary rocks, for example in some **clay** deposits and in **ironstone**. It occurs in association with **quartz** and **siderite**.*

Main Sources: ◆ *Czech Republic* ◆ *England* ◆ *France* ◆ *Germany* ◆ *Japan* ◆ *Peru* ◆ *Switzerland* ◆ *California, Colorado, and Pennsylvania, United States*

Below: Chamosite is a translucent mineral. Specimens may be greenish or black in color.

Named after its discovery locality, Chamoson, near St. Maurice in the Swiss Alps, chamosite is usually dark green in color, although some specimens may be black. Crystals of chamosite conform to the monoclinic system of symmetry. Externally, however, the mineral almost always appears in massive aggregates, distinct crystals being virtually unknown.

Many specimens of chamosite have a structure closely allied to that of **kaolinite**, which conforms to the triclinic system of crystal symmetry. These are known as K–type chamosite.

TWO CRYSTAL FORMS

There appear to be two polymorphs of this mineral, meaning that it seems to have two distinct crystal forms. The accredited species is monoclinic, but the variant form, orthochamosite, is orthorhombic.

For many years a mineral named berthierine was thought to exist in two crystal forms—hexagonal and monoclinic. Some geologists now believe that monoclinic berthierine is in fact chamosite, in which case it may soon need to be recategorized.

Chamosite forms a solid solution series with **clinochlore**, with the the ferric iron (Fe^{3+}) in chamosite being gradually replaced by magnesium in clinochlore. Both species are members of the chlorite group, these all being hydrated silicates of magnesium, iron, and aluminum.

CHLORITE GROUP
Berthierine: $(Fe^{2+},Fe^{3+},Mg,Al)_{2-3}(Si,Al)_2O_5(OH)_4$
Chamosite and Orthochamosite: $(Fe^{2+},Mg,Fe^{3+})_5Al(Si_3Al)O_{10}(OH,O)_8$
Clinochlore: $(Mg,Fe)_5Al(Si_3Al)O_{10}(OH)_8$
Kaolinite: $Al_2Si_2O_5(OH)_4$

CHERT

Originally formed from silica on seabeds, chert is a hard, gray rock found in many parts of the world.

Above: The individual crystals of chert are so tiny it is only possible to see them clearly under a microscope.

Chert is formed as a result of the accumulation of silica, which is often organic in origin but may be derived from inorganic pebbles.

Main Sources: *Chert is found all over the world, wherever* **limestone** *is deposited.*

A fine-grained sedimentary rock, chert is composed mainly of silica. Silica occurs in many minerals, the most widespread of which is **quartz**. Chert usually contains a form of quartz called **chalcedony,** in greatest abundance. Indeed, many cherts contain nothing else and are described as monomineralic. Some cherts also contain agate and jasper, two of the semiprecious gem varieties of chalcedony.

Chert is usually structureless, and cryptocrystalline (crystalline, but extremely fine-grained) deposits may contain lumps of flint, another variety of silica. The defining difference between chert and flint is fracture—in other words, the way each breaks up when hit with a hammer or subjected to pressure. Flint splits into pointed shards, while chert fractures unevenly into flat, blunt layers.

Deposits of chert are found in many parts of the world. The most extensive are quarried to make the concrete aggregates used in highway construction (*see* photo, below). The most beautiful specimens, on the other hand, may be polished into ornamental slabs.

RADIOLARIAN CHERT

Chert formed originally on seabeds from colloidal (*see* box, below) suspensions of silica. Because of the rock's marine origin, some deposits are rich in the fossils of radiolaria—tiny protozoan sea creatures that were named for the radial patterns on their shells.

Both chert and flint are much harder than the limestone that often surrounds them. The softer rock is therefore worn away a lot faster, leaving the chert and flint protruding.

SUPERSATURATED SEAWATER

All rivers carry dissolved silica into the sea. But the sea already contains large quantities of this form of silicon dioxide, and this extra material may coalesce into a fine ooze. If this solidifies, it forms chert.

CHILDRENITE

Named for the doctor who helped identify it, childrenite is externally almost identical to its closest relative, eosphorite.

*Both childrenite and its relative eosphorite form in **granite pegmatites** that have been altered by the action of hydrothermals. They are most commonly found in association with **chalcopyrite** and **quartz**.*

Main Sources: ◆ *Australia* ◆ *Brazil* ◆ *England* ◆ *Germany* ◆ *Rwanda* ◆ *Connecticut, North Carolina, and South Dakota, United States*

Above: Brown childrenite on a groundmass of granite pegmatite rock.

This mineral is named after English doctor and naturalist John George Children (1777–1852), who helped to identify it. Childrenite was confirmed as a distinct mineral species in 1823 and its classic location is Tavistock, Devon, in England. Its closest relative, eosphorite, was identified rather later, in 1878. Its type locality is at Branchville, Connecticut.

IRON REPLACES MANGANESE

Chemically, the difference between these two minerals is that childrenite contains more iron than manganese, while eosphorite features more manganese than iron. The metals gradually take each other's place within a single deposit—the two minerals form the end members of a solid solution series as a result of this atomic substitution.

Between these two extremes, some crystals have been found that contain almost equal quantities of iron and manganese. Such specimens are known as childro-eosphorite, but they are not a distinct species, merely a variant form of the two basic minerals.

CHEMICAL FORMULAE

Childrenite:	$(Fe,Mn)Al(PO_4)(OH)_2 \cdot H_2O$
Eosphorite:	$(Mn,Fe)AlPO_4(OH)_2 \cdot H_2O$

Childrenite and eosphorite are isomorphous, which means that while they may appear externally identical—brown or yellow with a vitreous luster—the two minerals are actually quite different. Microscopic examination will reveal that they conform to different systems of crystal symmetry—childrenite has orthorhombic crystals while crystals of eosphorite conform to the monoclinic system.

CHROMITE

Although of some industrial use itself, chromite is better known as an important source of chromium, a metal with a wide range of uses.

An oxide of chromium and iron, chromite is a member of the **spinel** *group. It is formed mainly in igneous rocks such as* **peridotite** *and* **serpentinite** *but may also occur in alluvial sands, gravels, and in stony iron* **meteorites***.*

Main Sources: ◆ *Albania* ◆ *Austria* ◆ *Brazil* ◆ *Finland* ◆ *India* ◆ *Italy* ◆ *New Caledonia* ◆ *Philippines* ◆ *Poland* ◆ *Russia* ◆ *South Africa* ◆ *Turkey* ◆ *California, Maryland, New York, North Carolina, Pennsylvania, Washington, and Wyoming, United States* ◆ *Zimbabwe*

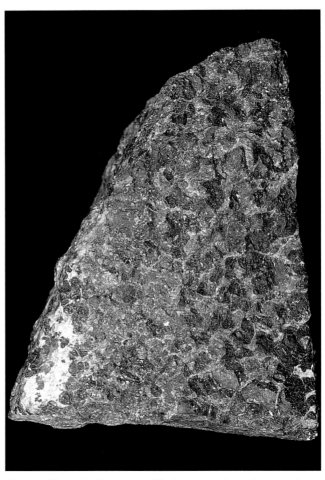

Above: Chromite has a metallic luster, and specimens often have a smooth surface, a result of weathering.

The only industrially important ore of chromium, chromite is also used to make refractory (heat–resistant) bricks for furnace linings.

EXTRACTING CHROMIUM

Chromium is a metal that makes up 0.1 to 0.3 parts per million of the Earth's crust. It seldom occurs in isolation but may be extracted from chromite by reducing the ore in a blast furnace with carbon (coke) or silicon. This forms an alloy of chromium and iron called ferrochrome and is used as the starting material for the many alloys of iron that use chromium.

The most important use of this metal is in chrome plating, which creates attractive hard, shiny, wear-resistant surfaces over brass, bronze, and steel. Chrome plating is performed by immersion in the molten metal or by electrolysis.

IMPORTANT ALLOYS

Chromium is also alloyed with iron to increase its hardness and its resistance to corrosion. Genuine stainless steel always contains both chromium and nickel. Super corrosion-resistant types of steel, such as those used for furnaces and burner heads, contain about 30 percent chromium.

Another of the many important chromium alloys is stellite, which also contains cobalt and tungsten and is used in cutting, lathing, and milling tools. There is also nickel-chromium (nichrome)—used in resistance wire in electrical heaters, irons, and toasters. The world's first chromite mine was dug in the Bare Hills near Baltimore, Maryland, the United States, and began working in the mid-19th century.

CHRYSOBERYL

Widely used in jewelry, chrysoberyl provides several attractive gemstones with unusual optical properties.

*Chrysoberyl occurs mainly as crystals or as loose, rounded grains in granitic **pegmatite**, and in metamorphic rocks such as **gneiss** and **schist**. The most precious specimens have been found as rounded waterworn pebbles in alluvial gravel.*

Main Sources: ◆ *Australia* ◆ *Brazil* ◆ *Canada* ◆ *China* ◆ *Czech Republic* ◆ *Finland* ◆ *Germany* ◆ *Ireland* ◆ *Italy* ◆ *Japan* ◆ *Madagascar* ◆ *Myanmar (Burma)* ◆ *Russia* ◆ *Sri Lanka* ◆ *Switzerland* ◆ *Tanzania* ◆ *Zimbabwe*

Chrysoberyl is a hard, durable form of beryllium aluminum oxide that is widely used as a gemstone. It is yellowish green, green, or brown in color, and has a vitreous (glassy) luster.

The largest chrysoberyl crystals ever discovered weigh over 60 carats (about ½ oz.). The crystals may be cut in a wide range of styles to bring out their natural lights to even greater advantage. The two most precious varieties of chrysoberyl are alexandrite and cymophane, which is also known as cat's eye.

ALEXANDRITE AND CYMOPHANE

First discovered in 1830 in Russia on the birthday of Alexander II (1818–81), alexandrite was named after the Russian Tsar. The stone is valuable because it is very rare and because it has the capacity to change color from green in daylight to red, mauve, or brown

under incandescent light—for example, when lit by a normal domestic electric bulb. Today, alexandrite is manufactured synthetically for use in the windows of spacecraft (*see* photo, left) because it can filter out potentially harmful cosmic rays.

Cymophane is distinctive for the vertical line in the shape of a cat's pupil across its face when it is cut *en cabochon*. This effect, which gives the stone the name cat's eye, is caused by impurities of **rutile** within the crystal structure. The most valuable stones of this type are dark and light brown, giving a "milk and honey" effect.

Below: In its plain, non-precious form, chrysoberyl is a transparent to translucent mineral with a vitreous luster. Crystals are often twinned.

CHRYSOCOLLA

Although pure chrysocolla is very soft, more resilient varieties, intergrown with other, stronger minerals, may be used in jewelry.

*Found mainly in **copper** mining areas, chrysocolla is a secondary product of oxidation. It commonly occurs in association with **azurite**, **cuprite**, **hemimorphite**, **malachite**, **smithsonite**, **turquoise**, and **variscite**.*

Main Sources: ◆ *Australia* ◆ *Chile* ◆ *Democratic Republic of the Congo (formerly Zaire)* ◆ *England* ◆ *Italy* ◆ *Mexico* ◆ *Russia* ◆ *Arizona, California, Montana, Nevada, New Mexico, Pennsylvania, and Utah, United States* ◆ *Zambia*

The English name of this gemstone is derived from the Greek *chrysos*, meaning "gold," and *kolla*, meaning "glue." This refers to its use in classical antiquity as a flux for soldering the precious metal.

EILAT STONE

Chrysocolla that has intergrown with malachite and turquoise is known as Eilat stone, Eilat being a port in the Sinai peninsula of modern Israel. According to legend, this variety was originally unearthed in King Solomon's mines.

A hydrous silicate of copper and aluminum, chrysocolla is hydrated by an indefinite amount of water of crystallization. Its chemical formula is $(Cu,Al)_2H_2Si_2O_5(OH)_4 \cdot nH_2O$.

In its pure form, chrysocolla is too soft to be used in jewelry. With a score of only 2 on the Mohs Scale of Hardness, it is easily scratched.

HARDER VARIETIES

Precious varieties are those that have formed intergrowths with more resilient minerals such as **chalcedony**, **opal**, and **quartz** (*see* box, above). The presence of such materials in a chrysocolla specimen may increase its hardness to Mohs scale 4.

Chrysocolla that is strong enough to be turned into jewelry is usually cut *en cabochon* (fashioned into a domed shape) or smoothed in mechanical tumblers to make beads. Some specimens are made into cameo or intaglio brooches.

Specimens of this gemstone are predominantly green or blue in color. The brown patches that sometimes appear on the crystal surfaces are copper ores. Chrysocolla forms in microcrystals belonging to the orthorhombic system of symmetry. Intergrowths, however, conform to other systems.

Left: A botryodial (grapelike) aggregate of greenish blue chrysocolla from the oxidation zone of a copper deposit.

CHRYSOTILE

This fibrous mineral used to be the main industrial source of asbestos, a fireproof material that is now banned for health reasons.

Chrysotile is formed through the alteration of **serpentinite** *that is rich in* **olivine**.

Main Sources: ◆ *Canada* ◆ *England* ◆ *Poland* ◆ *Russia* ◆ *Arizona and California, United States*

A hydrous silicate of magnesium, chrysotile was the source of more than 90 percent of the asbestos formerly used all over the world as a fireproof building material and in brake linings.

FIRST REGULATED MATERIAL

The English name for this mineral comes from the Greek *krysos*, meaning "gold," and *tilos*, meaning fiber. In the 1970s, doctors discovered that tiny fibers of asbestos, if inhaled by humans over long periods, cause asbestosis, a form of lung cancer.

In 1971 asbestos became the first material to be regulated by the United States Occupational Safety and Health Administration (OSHA). In 1989, the Environmental Protection Agency (EPA) ordered that the manufacture and use of asbestos be reduced by 94 percent over the next seven years.

Asbestos is now banned almost worldwide, although it remains in some older buildings. This is partly through inertia on the part of town and city officials but also because it is feared that removing it would be more dangerous than leaving it where it is.

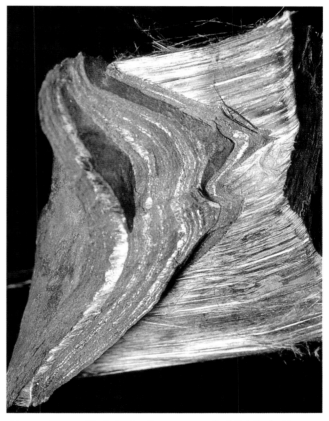

Above: Chrysotile is typically composed of tightly knit masses of thin fibers.

Nevertheless, some scientists maintain that the dangerous form of asbestos actually comes from amphibole, a group of closely related but different silicate minerals, and that chrysotile asbestos is not a hazard to human health.

Chrysotile crystals appear in readily flexible threads, which are often long enough and strong enough to be woven. The mineral is classified as a serpentine—a group of naturally occurring silicates of magnesium, iron, or nickel. It is usually grouped by mineralogists with its closest relative, **kaolinite**.

CHEMICAL FORMULAE

Chrysotile:	$Mg_3Si_2O_5(OH)_4$
Kaolinite:	$Al_2Si_2O_5(OH)_8$
Serpentine:	$A_3Si_2O_5(OH)_4$ (a general formula in which A may be Mg, Fe^{2+} or Ni)

CINNABAR

This mineral is the world's principal source of mercury, a metal with a number of unusual and useful properties.

Occurring in areas of recent volcanic activity, cinnabar is precipitated from alkaline solutions in veins, hot-spring deposits, and porous volcanic rocks. It is associated with **barite, calcite, chalcedony, marcasite, opal, pyrite, quartz, realgar,** *and* **stibnite.**

Main Sources: ◆ *Chile* ◆ *China* ◆ *Germany* ◆ *Italy* ◆ *Mexico* ◆ *Peru* ◆ *Serbia* ◆ *Slovenia* ◆ *Spain* ◆ *Arkansas, California, Nevada, Oregon, Texas, and Washington, United States*

Above: If viewed under a hand lens, it would be possible to see that many of these crystals of cinnabar are twinned.

Cinnabar is the only common ore of the metal mercury. A sulfide of mercury with the chemical formula HgS, its name in English comes from the Arabic word *zinjafr,* or the Persian *zinjifrah,* both meaning "dragon's blood"—a reference to its scarlet or red-brown color. Cinnabar was also the original source of vermilion, the artists' red pigment.

The world's most important cinnabar deposit is at Almaden in Spain. It is also thought to be the oldest, having been mined continuously for its mercury since at least 500 B.C.

EXTRACTING MERCURY

Mercury is extracted from cinnabar by roasting. When the mineral reaches about 1,076° F (580° C), oxygen in the air combines with the sulfur in the mineral to give off sulfur dioxide gas. The residue of mercury vapor is condensed by washing it in nitric acid and then distilling it into pure liquid metal.

Mercury freezes at –38° F (–38.9° C) and boils at 675° F (357° C). In normal atmospheric conditions of between about –4° F (–20° C) and 104° F (40° C), it expands and contracts visibly and uniformly. It is this unusual property that has led to the frequent use of mercury in thermometers. It is also used in electrical switches that need to turn on or off at certain temperatures, such as those in thermostats and some doze-alarm-type alarm clocks.

Mercury also dissolves numerous metals to form amalgams and is thus used to extract gold dust from rocks by dissolving the gold and then boiling off the mercury. The amalgam used in dental fillings contains tin and silver (and sometimes gold) dissolved in mercury. Mercury vapor lamps are widely used because they are powerful and cheap sources of ultraviolet and visible light.

CLAY

A fine-grained sedimentary rock, the use and value of clay varies widely depending on grain size and the impurities it contains.

*Clay formation occurs in many different geological environments. The most extensive layers are formed in areas that are now, or once were, seas or lakes (marine or lacustrine deposits), in moraines left behind by receding glaciers, and in zones of **granite** that have been altered by the action of hydrothermal fluids. It also forms from volcanic dust.*

Main Sources: ◆ *China* ◆ *England* ◆ *Florida, Georgia, Michigan, and Nevada, United States* ◆ *Wales*

SHALE AND CLAY

Clay is the main component of the sedimentary rock **shale**. Although shale contains many clay minerals, clay and shale are different sedimentary rocks. While shale is dried and layered, clay is wet and has no obvious layers.

Below: The texture of clay is so fine that its particles are invisible to the naked eye.

Clay is a widespread sedimentary rock with grains too fine to be seen by the naked eye. Its name comes from the Old English *clæg*, which is related to the Latin *glus*, meaning "glue," and the Greek *gloios*, meaning "sticky oil."

Most clay contains the mineral **kaolinite**. It is also likely to feature one or more of the minerals **feldspar**, **gypsum**, **mica**, and **quartz**. Clays that were formed originally in seawater may, in addition, contain numerous well-preserved fossils.

The richest and most extensive clays are quarried for use in the manufacture of bricks (*see* photo, left), pipes, pottery, tiles, and terra cotta. Clay is also an important component of lightweight aggregates, cement, concrete, and mortar.

The properties of clay vary widely, depending on the grain size of its component particles. The most industrially valuable clay is plastic (easily molded) and retains its own or painted colors after firing (heating in a kiln). The least useful clay is that which contains soluble impurities of **halite** (rock salt), **calcite**, and **pyrite**. Pyrite will make it explode when it is fired.

CLINOCHLORE

A member of the chlorite group of minerals, clinochlore may appear colorless, white, yellow, or deep green to olive green.

Above: Transparent crystals of clinochlore with hexagonal cross-sections.

Clinochlore is found in many metamorphic rocks, most particularly in **schist**.

Main Sources: ◆ *Austria* ◆ *India* ◆ *Italy* ◆ *Japan* ◆ *New Zealand* ◆ *Russia* ◆ *Switzerland* ◆ *California, Colorado, Montana, New York, Pennsylvania, South Dakota, and Vermont, United States*

The English name for this mineral—taken from the Greek words *klinein*, meaning "to incline," and *chloros*, meaning "green"—alludes to the oblique angles of its optic axes around which it must be rotated in order to determine its symmetry and its

color. Clinochlore forms in the monoclinic system of crystal symmetry and may appear colorless, white, yellowish, or, as its name suggests, green.

Clinochlore forms a solid solution series with **chamosite**, and both minerals are members of the chlorite group—silicate minerals that are rich in magnesium and iron. All chlorites are forms of **mica**.

THE CHLORITE GROUP

In addition to their chemical makeup and color, chlorite minerals share several other properties in common. They are mainly soft (Mohs scale 2 to 2½) and form flat, flakelike crystals with perfect cleavage. Their specific gravity ranges from 2.6 to 3.3, depending on the amount of iron that they contain. Clinochlore itself may feature varying amounts of this metal, and this is reflected in the mineral's specific gravity, which is between 2.63 and 2.98.

GREENSTONES

Members of the chlorite group are typical components of magnesium- and iron-rich metamorphic rocks formed at fairly low temperatures of up to about 932° F (500° C). Such rocks are known as greenstones or greenschists because of the color imparted by chlorite and other iron and magnesium silicates. Chlorites may also be formed by the action of hot water on magnesium-bearing igneous rocks such as **basalt** and **peridotite**. Chlorite minerals are fairly resistant to chemical weathering and are thus common in sedimentary rocks.

Chlorites are also known as sheet silicates because of the arrangement of their component atoms. Flat layers of silica are bonded to flat layers of magnesium ions to form a magnesium silicate "sandwich." Iron and aluminum ions may be substituted for magnesium, and aluminum for silicon.

CLINOZOISITE

Of varied external appearance, clinozoisite may form as prismatic, needlelike crystals or in shapeless, fibrous, or granular aggregates.

Clinozoisite is found mainly in regional metamorphic rocks and in smaller contact zones of altered **limestone**. *It may also occur as a secondary mineral through the alteration by heat of calcium-rich plagioclase* **feldspar**.

Main Sources: ◆ *Austria* ◆ *Canada* ◆ *Czech Republic* ◆ *India* ◆ *Ireland* ◆ *Italy* ◆ *Madagascar* ◆ *Mexico* ◆ *Switzerland* ◆ *California, Colorado, and Nevada, United States*

Above: Pink crystals of clinozoisite on a groundmass of metamorphic rock.

A hydrous silicate of calcium and aluminum, clinozoisite was confirmed as a distinct mineral species in 1896. Its name is derived from the Greek *klinein*, meaning "to lean"—a reference to its crystal shapes—and **zoisite**, its closest relative. Zoisite was discovered almost a century earlier.

RELATED SPECIES

Clinozoisite is an end member of a solid solution series in which some of its aluminum is gradually substituted by ferric iron. The other end member of the series is **epidote**.

Chemically, clinozoisite and zoisite are almost identical, apart from the fact that their atoms of silicon and oxygen are arranged slightly differently. However, there are significant differences between the two minerals, the two most important of which are their crystallography and their specific gravity. These differences are sufficient to justify them being categorized as separate species.

Clinozoisite, epidote, and zoisite are often indistinguishable externally, so in scientific terms are said to be isomorphous. Identification is further hindered by the fact that they are all insoluble in acids.

COMPARE AND CONTRAST

	Clinozoisite	Epidote	Zoisite
Chemical formula	$Ca_2Al_3(SiO_4)_3(OH)$	$Ca_2(Al,Fe^{3+})_3(SiO_4)_3OH$	$Ca_2Al_3(SiO_4)_3OH$
Crystal system	Monoclinic	Monoclinic	Orthorhombic
Hardness	6½	6 to 7	6½ to 7
Specific gravity	3.21 to 3.38	3.35 to 3.50	3.55
Streak	Colorless	Colorless	Colorless

COAL

An essential fossil fuel, most of the world's electricity supplies are generated by burning coal.

Coal is a rock formed from vegetable matter that has fallen to the ground and then been compressed and heated and thus metamorphosed over long periods.

Main Sources: *The world's top coal-producing nations are China (about 1,323 billion tons/1,200 billion tonnes a year), and the United States (1,034 billion tons/938 billion tonnes). Behind them come Russia, India, Germany, Australia, Poland, South Africa, Kazakhstan, and North Korea.*

The degree of compression and metamorphism of the vegetable matter that makes up coal determines the amount of carbon that is present in a deposit. The carbon content, in turn, determines the coal's efficiency as a source of energy—the more carbon it contains, the better it will burn.

DIFFERENT GRADES OF COAL

The first stage in the formation of coal takes place on the surface of the Earth as the original vegetable matter is decomposed into **peat**. Peat is a low-grade fuel but not a form of coal itself. It is highly absorbent—up to 75 percent of the body weight of peat may be moisture.

If peat is to turn into coal, it must be covered with a layer of further sediment. This sediment produces heat through pressing down on the peat and reducing its moisture.

Low-rank coal, closely related to peat but with less moisture, is classed as **lignite**, or brown coal. It has a low carbon content. Coal with still less moisture is known as bituminous coal, and the driest and most compressed coal is called anthracite. With the highest carbon content, anthracite is high-grade coal.

Bituminous coal is used as a fuel in the production of coal tar and coke, while anthracite is also a domestic fuel. Another form, cannel coal, is a highly volatile variety of bituminous coal that burns with a bright flame. Much of the world's electricity is generated by burning coal.

Coal is generally abundant worldwide; the United States has approximately 31 percent of known recoverable reserves. At the present rate of production, serious depletion of this fuel will take several hundred years. However, coal is a nonrenewable natural resource and deposits will eventually run out.

Below: The archetypal fossil fuel, coal is formed from tightly compacted vegetable matter.

COBALTITE

Also known as cobalt glance, cobaltite is the main ore of cobalt, a valuable metal with many industrial applications.

Formed in metamorphic rocks and hydrothermal veins, cobaltite is usually found in association with other arsenides and sulfides.

Main Sources: ◆ *Australia* ◆ *Canada* ◆ *Democratic Republic of the Congo (formerly Zaire)* ◆ *England* ◆ *Germany* ◆ *India* ◆ *Mexico* ◆ *Morocco* ◆ *Russia* ◆ *Sweden* ◆ *California, Colorado, Idaho, and Nevada, United States*

Above: Although crystals of cobaltite often appear in cubic shapes, they in fact conform to the orthorhombic system.

With a cobalt content of up to 35 percent by weight, cobaltite is the chief ore of this valuable metal. Cobalt may also be obtained from **erythrite**, linnaeite, and smaltite.

A cobalt sulfarsenide with the chemical formula $CoAsS$, cobaltite is also a minor source of **arsenic**. It may additionally contain up to 10 percent iron and some nickel in the form of impurities.

Crystals of cobaltite are basically orthorhombic, but may appear in pseudocubic shapes. Under normal conditions, the arsenic and **sulfur** elements are strictly ordered within the molecular structure. However, they become disordered during a process known as annealing, when the mineral is heated strongly and then gradually cooled, after which these elements conform to the cubic system of symmetry.

VALUABLE METAL

Cobalt occurs in one or two parts per 1,000 of the Earth's crust and is also a part of many meteorites. It is found in the atmosphere of the Sun and other stars. The largest producer of cobalt is the Democratic Republic of the Congo (formerly Zaire).

The metal is an important component of several alloys. It is combined with iron to form hyperco, which is used as the nucleus for strong electro-magnets. Alloys of titanium, aluminum, cobalt, and nickel, such as alnico and ticonal, can be made permanently magnetic. Stellite—an alloy of cobalt, chromium, tungsten, and molybdenum—retains its hardness even at high temperatures. Cobalt is also used in cutting tools, combustion-engine valves, and parts for gas turbines. Isotopes of cobalt are used in hydrogen bombs and as a source of X-rays.

COLEMANITE

Colemanite, named after the American industrialist W. T. Coleman, is a source of boron, which is used in heat-resistant glass.

*The mineral colemanite forms in evaporite deposits such as those found in volcanic hot springs or salt lakes and is sometimes found in association with elongated red crystals of **realgar**.*

Main Sources: ◆ *Argentina* ◆ *Canada* ◆ *Kazakhstan* ◆ *Russia* ◆ *Turkey* ◆ *California and Nevada, United States*

Above: A cluster of white, translucent, prismatic crystals of colemanite, a widely distributed evaporite mineral.

Named after William Tell Coleman (1824–93), a mine owner and founder of the California borax industry, colemanite was confirmed as a distinct mineral species in 1863. Its type locality is Death Valley, California—it is against a specimen taken from the Thompson Mine there that all subsequent finds are tested for authenticity.

Chemically, colemanite is a hydrated borate of calcium, with the formula $Ca_2B_6O_{11}.5H_2O$. It is a secondary mineral that forms either in volcanic hot-spring deposits or in dried-up lakes of borate salts in desert regions. The latter are known in English as *playas*, the Spanish word for "beaches." In such locations, colemanite may form in encrustations up to several yards thick.

RARE GEMSTONE CRYSTALS

Colemanite crystals conform to the monoclinic system and have one perfect cleavage. They are usually short, but can appear in prismatic shapes up to 8 in. (20 cm) long. These are greatly prized by collectors. The mineral can also appear compact, massive, or granular. It has above average hardness for a borate (4 to 4½ on the Mohs scale). Although colemanite is quite brittle, it can be cut and polished as a gemstone. However, crystals of this quality are rare.

A SOURCE OF BORON

Colemanite is a commercial source of boron, an element that comprises about 16 percent of its mass. The most important ore of boron is **borax**.

Boron is a rare element that occurs in only about three parts per million of the Earth's crust. It was first isolated in 1808 by famous English scientist Sir Humphry Davy (1778–1829) and, independently at about the same time, by two Frenchmen, Joseph Louis Gay-Lussac (1778–1850) and Louis Jacques Thénard (1777–1857).

Boron is immensely resistant to heat—it melts at 3,774° F (2,079° C). This property makes it useful in the manufacture of heat-resistant glass, such as that used in Pyrex dishes.

COLUMBITE

The most common ore of the metal niobium, columbite is used as an alloy to produce highly strengthened steel.

Above: This massive aggregate of columbite may also contain significant quantities of the closely related tantalite.

*Columbite occurs with **tantalite** in granitic **pegmatite** that is rich in lithium and phosphorus minerals—columbite is concentrated on the edges, tantalite at the core. Both are often associated with **amblygonite, apatite, beryl, cassiterite, quartz, spodumene,** and **tourmaline**.*

Main Sources: ◆ *Afghanistan* ◆ *Argentina* ◆ *Australia* ◆ *Brazil* ◆ *Canada* ◆ *Democratic Republic of the Congo (formerly Zaire)* ◆ *Finland* ◆ *France* ◆ *Germany* ◆ *India* ◆ *Italy* ◆ *Japan* ◆ *Madagascar* ◆ *Namibia* ◆ *Norway* ◆ *Russia* ◆ *Sweden* ◆ *California, Colorado, Idaho, Maine, South Dakota, and Virginia, United States* ◆ *Zambia*

Columbite takes its name from Columbium— an old name for America and an alternative modern name for niobium (Nb). It is the most widespread ore of niobium, a metal used in alloys to make specially strengthened steel.

Columbite forms a solid solution series with tantalite in which the niobium in the former is gradually replaced by tantalum in the latter. Another important difference between the two minerals is that tantalite weighs over eight times more than the equivalent volume of water at room temperature, while the specific gravity of columbite is only 4.6.

In addition, the amounts of iron and manganese in columbite may vary considerably from specimen to specimen, as one or both of these metals is substituted by magnesium. Strictly, then, columbite is not one mineral but a series of three: ferrocolumbite, manganocolumbite, and magnocolumbite.

CHEMICAL FORMULAE	
Columbite:	$(Fe,Mn)(Nb,Ta)_2O_6$
Tantalite:	$(Fe,Mn)(Ta,Nb)_2O_6$
Manganocolumbite:	$(Mn,Fe^{2+})(Nb,Ta)_2O_6$
Ferrocolumbite:	$Fe,Mn)(Nb,Ta)_2O_6$
Magnocolumbite:	$(Mg, Fe^{2+},Mn)(Nb,Ta)_2O_6$

NIOBIUM

Niobium is a shiny, soft, white metal that was first identified in 1801 by the English chemist Charles Hatchett (1765–1847) in a sample of columbite sent to England more than 100 years previously by the first governor of Connecticut. It was isolated in 1864 by Swedish chemist Christian Blomstrand (1826–97). Despite the adoption of the name niobium by the International Union of Pure and Applied Chemistry, the alternative name columbium is still used by metallurgists in the United States.

CONGLOMERATE

Conglomerates are sedimentary rocks in which pebbles have built up through the action of strong water currents.

Conglomerates are accumulations of pebbles, such as those that are found on beaches, in flood plains, and in the outwash fans of rivers.

Main Sources: *Conglomerates form around the shores of lakes, rivers, and seas. They are often associated with other sedimentary rocks such as **arkose** and **sandstone**.*

Conglomerates are rocks composed of particles that have been smoothed by the action of turbulent shallow rivers or seas, or by melting glaciers or ice sheets. They are rudaceous (coarse-grained) sedimentary deposits in which more than 30 percent of the particles must always exceed ½ in. (2 mm) in diameter. Their environment of deposition (the place where they are formed) is on rocky beaches. They are also prevalent wherever flooding onto the land has occurred. Conglomerates may contain almost any mineral or preexistent rock.

What distinguishes a conglomerate from the loosely related **breccia** is the roundedness of its component particles. Both conglomerates and breccias may be classified in three ways, according to the amount of gravel they contain, the chemical makeup of the matrix (base) in which these particles are set, and the composition of the particles themselves.

COMPONENTS

Deposits containing more than 80 percent pebbles, cobbles, or boulders are known as conglomerates proper, while those containing between 30 and 80 percent of these ingredients are said to be either arenaceous (sandy) or argillaceous (shaley). The matrix between the layers of coarse particles will sometimes be calcareous, meaning than they contain calcium carbonate, or sideritic (containing iron

Above: Conglomerates are sedimentary rocks containing large fragments that may be of any rock type.

carbonate). The most common matrix components are **clay**, sand, **shales**, mudstones, and other fine-grained sediments, which fill the gaps between the rounded fragments. However, tough rocks such as **quartz** are often the predominant ingredient. Fossils are rarely found in conglomerates. The conglomerates in Witwatersrand, South Africa, contain valuable quantities of native **gold**.

Conglomerates containing pebbles of few rock types are classified as oligomictic, while deposits with many types of rock are said to be polymictic.

CONICHALCITE

Often brilliant green in color, this adelite group mineral forms two solid solution series and appears in a number of habits.

*Conichalcite is a secondary mineral that forms in the oxidation zones of **copper** ore bodies. It often forms encrustations on rocks composed mainly of **limonite**, where it is associated with **adamite, azurite, bayldonite, linarite, malachite, olivenite,** and **smithsonite.***

Main Sources: ◆ *Chile* ◆ *Democratic Republic of the Congo (formerly Zaire)* ◆ *England* ◆ *France* ◆ *Germany* ◆ *Mexico* ◆ *Morocco* ◆ *Namibia* ◆ *Poland* ◆ *Russia* ◆ *Spain* ◆ *Arizona, Nevada, South Dakota, and Utah, United States*

ADELITE GROUP	
Adelite:	$CaMg(AsO_4)OH$
Austinite:	$CaZn(AsO_4)OH$
Bayldonite:	$Cu_3Pb(AsO_4)_2(OH)_2$
Calciovolborthite:	$CaCu(VO_4)OH$
Cobaltaustinite:	$CaCo(AsO_4)(OH)$
Conichalcite:	$CaCu(AsO_4)OH$
Duftite:	$PbCu(AsO_4)OH$
Gabrielsonite:	$PbFe^{2+}(AsO_4)OH$
Parabayldonite:	$(Pb,Cu)_7(AsO_4)_4(OH)_2.0.5H_2O$
Staszicite:	$Ca(Cu,Zn)(AsO_4)OH$

Although it is sometimes a minor ore of copper, conichalcite is of interest mainly to mineral collectors because of its beautiful grass green color.

A hydrous arsenate of calcium and copper, conichalcite was confirmed as a distinct species in 1849. The type locality of this mineral is Hinojosa de Cordoba in Andalucia, Spain. Its name—which is taken from the Greek words *konia*, meaning "powder," and *chalkos*, meaning "copper,"—refers to its typical habit (external appearance) and composition.

Crystals of conichalcite conform to the orthorhombic system and appear in acicular (needlelike) or short prismatic shapes. Botryoidal masses (that resemble bunches of grapes) or reniform (kidney-shaped) crusts with a fibrous structure may also occur. Conichalcite is normally yellow, or a bright emerald green color.

SEVERAL VARIANT FORMS

Part of the adelite group (*see* box, above), conichalcite is the end member of two solid solution series. In one, the copper present in the mineral is gradually replaced by zinc to form a distinct species, austinite. Between these two end extremes is staszicite, which contains both copper and zinc.

Another variant form of conichalcite contains lead rather than calcium and is also slightly hydrated. This form is known as parabayldonite. Many other specimens of conichalcite have been found to contain phosphorus oxide (chemical formula P_2O_5) in the form of impurities. In a second solid solution series, conichalcite's arsenic is substituted by vanadium to form calciovolborthite.

Below: A beautiful green encrustation of conichalcite on the surface of an unidentified rock.

CONNELLITE

Connellite is an attractive blue mineral, the finest specimens of which are highly sought after by collectors.

Left: The distinctive blue coloration of connellite is derived from its copper content.

Confirmed as a distinct mineral in 1850, connellite was named after a geology professor at St. Andrew's University, Scotland, Arthur Connell (1794–1863). It was Connell who first examined a specimen extracted in the 1790s from a copper mine in Cornwall, England.

FORTUITOUS ORE OF COPPER

In chemical terms, connellite is a hydrated copper chloride sulfate hydroxide with the chemical formula $Cu_{19}Cl_4(SO_4)(OH)_{32}.3H_2O$. Although this mineral is quite rare, it is sometimes used as an ore of copper when it is accidentally unearthed during mining for other, more important, sources of the metal, for example chalcopyrite.

Connellite is closely related to buttgenbachite, a hydrous hydrated chloride nitrate of copper with the formula $Cu_{19}Cl_4(NO_3)_2(OH)_{32}.2H_2O$. The two minerals are isostructural, having the same external shape, and form a solid solution series.

COLLECTABLE BUT FRAGILE

Crystals of connellite conform to the hexagonal system of crystal symmetry. Externally, they often appear in acicular (needlelike) clusters or in feltlike aggregates with striations (surface grooves). The crystals are usually blue or blue green in color with a vitreous luster, meaning that they look a little like pieces of broken glass.

The finest specimens are highly collectable, but great care must be taken when handling them because they are very fragile and easily broken by the slightest pressure. They should be cleaned with distilled, rather than tap, water.

*Connellite is a secondary mineral formed in the oxidation zones of **copper** deposits. In addition to **chalcopyrite**, it is often associated with **atacamite**, **brochantite, cuprite, limonite, malachite, quartz,** and **selenite,** a variety of **gypsum.***

Main Sources: ◆ *Algeria* ◆ *Austria* ◆ *Brazil* ◆ *Democratic Republic of the Congo (formerly Zaire)* ◆ *England* ◆ *France* ◆ *Germany* ◆ *Greenland* ◆ *Italy* ◆ *Namibia* ◆ *South Africa* ◆ *Arizona, California, and Utah, United States*

COPIAPITE

Externally similar to other members of the copiapite group, this yellow mineral should be stored carefully to prevent dehydration.

*Copiapite is a secondary mineral formed through the oxidation of iron sulfide deposits. At times it has been known to form rather quickly as a crust on exposed ore bodies in mines and coal dumps. It is most commonly associated with **pyrite**.*

Main Sources: ◆ *Bulgaria* ◆ *Chile* ◆ *China* ◆ *Czech Republic* ◆ *France* ◆ *Germany* ◆ *Poland* ◆ *Russia* ◆ *Spain* ◆ *Alaska, Arizona, California, Nevada, and Utah, United States*

COPIAPITE GROUP

Aluminocopiapite:
$$AlFe^{3+}_4(SO_4)_6O(OH).20H_2O$$
Calciocopiapite:
$$CaFe^{3+}_4(SO_4)_6(OH)_2.10H_2O$$
Copiapite: $Fe^{2+}Fe^{3+}_4(SO_4)_6(OH)_2.20H_2O$
Cuprocopiapite:
$$CuFe^{3+}_4(SO_4)_6(OH)_2.20H_2O$$
Ferricopiapite:
$$Fe^{3+}_5(SO_4)_6O(OH).20H_2O$$
Magnesiocopiapite:
$$MgFe^{3+}_4(SO_4)_6(OH)_2.20H_2O$$
Zincocopiapite:
$$ZnFe^{3+}_4(SO_4)_6(OH)_2.18H_2O$$

A hydrous hydrated sulfate of both forms of iron—ferrous iron (chemical symbol Fe^{2+}) and ferric iron (Fe^{3+})—copiapite is named after its type locality, Copiapó in Chile.

Externally, crystals of copiapite appear in tabular shapes, in platelike aggregates of microcrystals, or in powdery encrustations on the surface of rocks and other minerals. The finest specimens are an attractive yellow or orange color when freshly extracted from the Earth. However, the mineral dehydrates easily and it should be stored in a closed container, ideally with a small pot of water to help it retain its water of crystallization.

HARD TO DISTINGUISH

It is difficult to distinguish copiapite from other similar hydrated iron sulfates without X-ray analysis. The copiapite group includes several closely related minerals with similar chemistry and the same triclinic crystals (*see* box, above). In each, the ferrous iron of copiapite itself has been replaced by one of the metals aluminum, calcium, copper, magnesium, or zinc. In scientific terms, they are all analagous with copiapite. This means that aluminocopiapite is described as the aluminum analog of copiapite, calciocopiapite the calcium analog, and so on.

Left: Copiapite is mainly yellowish and often forms in association with the similarly colored pyrite.

COPPER

Second only to iron in its industrial usefulness, copper's many important properties include being highly resistant to chemical attack.

*Native copper is, paradoxically, only a minor source of copper. It is found with **calcite**, **malachite**, and **silver**.*

Main Sources: ◆ *Antarctica* ◆ *Australia* ◆ *Bolivia* ◆ *Canada* ◆ *Chile* ◆ *Cyprus* ◆ *Democratic Republic of the Congo (formerly Zaire)* ◆ *England* ◆ *India* ◆ *Italy* ◆ *Namibia* ◆ *Peru* ◆ *Poland* ◆ *Russia* ◆ *Scotland* ◆ *Arizona, Michigan, Montana, and New Mexico, United States* ◆ *Zambia*

A lthough most of the world's copper is extracted from mineral ores, especially **chalcopyrite**, the metal also occurs in the native state (on its own) in nature, albeit in small quantities. Copper constitutes 70 parts per million of the Earth's crust and is also present in seawater. It is thought to have been the first metal to be used by humans, with the earliest recorded workings dating back to at least 5000 B.C. Its range of uses is second only to iron.

CORROSION-RESISTANT METAL

Copper has several important physical properties. One of its outstanding features is its resistance to chemical attack—water, steam, and dilute hydrochloric and sulfuric acids have little effect on it. It is, however, slowly susceptible to moist air, which causes the surface to become covered with a green patina of **malachite**.

In a vacuum, copper melts at 1,980° F (1,083° C) and boils at 4,653° F (2,567° C). It also weighs 8.96 times more than the equivalent volume of water at room temperature, which is about 68° F (20° C). The element has a Mohs scale rating of 2½ to 3.

Copper has a bright metallic luster and a cubic crystal structure, and is malleable and ductile. It is also a good conductor of heat and is second only to silver as a conductor of electricity.

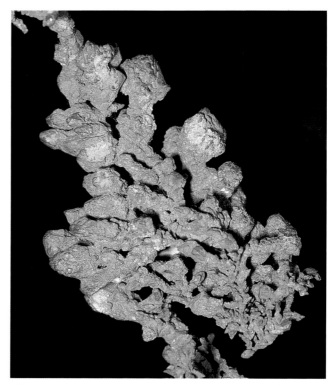

Above: Specimens like this aggregate of copper with vaguely treelike shapes are said to be dendritic.

LAKE COPPER

For many years the world's finest native copper was extracted from the region surrounding Lake Superior. "Lake copper," as it was known, was so pure that it only required melting with a flux before being ready for industrial use. This source became the world standard for the metal. But this once abundant supply is now close to exhaustion. Today, more than 80 percent of all copper mined is derived from low-grade ores containing two percent or less of the element.

CORDIERITE

Cordierite occurs in various forms including an attractive, semi-precious gem variety, sometimes known as water sapphire.

*Most cordierite forms in massive aggregates or in compact grains embedded in metamorphic **gneiss**, **pegmatite**, and **schist**. The gemstone variety, iolite, is found as smooth, transparent, waterworn pebbles in alluvial deposits.*

Main Sources: ◆ *Antarctica* ◆ *Australia* ◆ *Brazil* ◆ *Canada* ◆ *England* ◆ *Finland* ◆ *Germany* ◆ *Greenland* ◆ *India* ◆ *Japan* ◆ *Madagascar* ◆ *Myanmar (Burma)* ◆ *Norway* ◆ *Scotland* ◆ *Sri Lanka* ◆ *California, Colorado, Connecticut, New Hampshire, New York, South Dakota, and Wyoming, United States*

CHEMICAL FORMULAE	
Cordierite:	$(Mg,Fe)_2Al_4Si_5O_{18}$
Indialite:	$Mg_2Al_4Si_5O_{18}$
Sekaninaite:	$(Fe,Mg)_2Al_4Si_5O_{18}$

This silicate of magnesium, iron, and aluminum is named after Pierre Louis Antoine Cordier (1777–1861), the French geologist who first described it. The finest specimens, a semiprecious violet-tinged blue gemstone known as iolite, is also known as water sapphire because of its superficial resemblance to this precious form of **corundum**.

Another name for the gem variety is dichroite, a reference to its unusual optical properties. However, the name is inaccurate—a dichroic mineral shows two colors while cordierite is strongly pleochroic and shows at least three. Its color changes from violet blue to yellowish gray or light blue, depending on the direction of the light source and the angle from which it is viewed. Some specimens appear colorless.

Cordierite crystals are rare, but those that do occur are prismatic and twinning in pseudo-hexagonal habits is common. Their natural lights may be enhanced by cutting and the preferred styles include cabochons and cubes.

Pure cordierite contains more magnesium than iron. However, atomic substitution in some deposits causes a reversal in the proportions of these metals to form sekaninaite, the iron-rich analog of cordierite. Where this occurs, the two species are end members of a solid solution series.

Externally, cordierite may appear identical to indialite, an artificial product first found when coal seams were burned in a mine in India. Later, naturally occurring deposits of this silicate of magnesium and aluminum were discovered in fused sediments in North Dakota and in cordierite veins in Japan.

Below: Blue cordierite with a strong vitreous luster. This mineral may also appear brown, gray, green, or yellow.

CORNETITE

A hydrous phosphate of copper, cornetite is a brittle mineral with a similar chemical composition to turquoise.

*Cornetite is a rare secondary mineral that is formed in the weathered oxidation zones of copper sulfide ore bodies. It is found in association with **brochantite, chrysocolla, libethenite, limonite, malachite,** and **pseudomalachite**.*

Main Sources: ◆ *Australia* ◆ *Democratic Republic of the Congo (formerly Zaire)* ◆ *South Africa* ◆ *Arizona and Nevada, United States* ◆ *Zambia*

COPPER HYDROUS PHOSPHATES

Andrewsite:	$(Cu,Fe^{2+})_3Fe^{3+}_3(PO_4)_4(OH)_{12}$
Chalcosiderite:	$CuFe^{3+}_6(PO_4)_4(OH)_8.4H_2O$
Cornetite:	$Cu_3(PO_4)(OH)$
Hentschelite:	$CuFe_2(PO_4)_2(OH)_2$
Libethenite:	$Cu_2(PO_4)(OH)$
Ludjibaite:	$Cu_5(PO_4)_2(OH)_4$
Nissonite:	$Cu_2Mg_2(PO_4)_2(OH)_2.5H_2O$
Phosphofibrite:	$KCuFe^{3+}_{15}(PO_4)_{12}.12H_2O$
Planerite:	$(Cu,Ca)Al_6(PO_4)_4(OH)_8.H_2O$
Pseudomalachite:	$Cu_5(PO_4)_2(OH)_4.H_2O$
Reichenbachite:	$Cu_5(PO_4)_2(OH)_4$
Sieleckiite:	$Cu_3Al_4(PO_4)_2(OH)_{12}.2H_2O$
Turquoise:	$CuAl_6(PO_4)_4(OH)_8.4H_2O$
Zapatalite:	$Cu_3Al_4(PO_4)_3(OH)_9.4H_2O$

First described in 1912, cornetite was confirmed as a distinct mineral species in 1917 and named after Belgian geologist Jules Cornet (1865–1929).

Cornetite is one of 14 naturally occurring hydrous phosphates of copper (*see* box, right), the best known mineral with this chemical composition being **turquoise**. In addition to this composition, some specimens of cornetite may contain small amounts of cobalt in the

form of impurities. Cornetite crystals conform to the orthorhombic system of symmetry. Externally they often appear as diamond-shaped prisms, sometimes as prisms with dome-shaped ends, or as fibrous crusts or masses on the surface of rocks. The mineral is dark green or blue in color with a vitreous luster.

NO CLEAVAGE

Cornetite is a brittle mineral. This means that when it is hit with a hammer or subjected to pressure, it will shatter, rather than break along certain lines determined by its atomic structure. In scientific terms, therefore, cornetite is said to display no cleavage. The type locality for this mineral is L'Etoile de Congo copper mine in Katanga, the Democratic Republic of the Congo (formerly Zaire).

Left: A fibrous crust of blue cornetite on the surface of a rock in a copper ore deposit.

CORUNDUM

Known in the Orient since antiquity, corundum reached the West in the 18th century, when crystals from China were powdered for use as abrasives.

*Corundum occurs as an accessory mineral in silica-poor igneous rocks, in recrystallized **limestone**, in placer sands, and in aluminum-rich metamorphic rocks. It is found along with **calcite**, **feldspar**, **garnet**, **mica**, and **zoisite**.*

Main Sources: ◆ *Afghanistan* ◆ *Australia* ◆ *Brazil* ◆ *Cambodia* ◆ *Canada* ◆ *Colombia* ◆ *England* ◆ *France* ◆ *Greece* ◆ *India* ◆ *Italy* ◆ *Japan* ◆ *Kenya* ◆ *Madagascar* ◆ *Malawi* ◆ *Myanmar (Burma)* ◆ *Nigeria* ◆ *Norway* ◆ *Pakistan* ◆ *Russia* ◆ *Scotland* ◆ *South Africa* ◆ *Sri Lanka* ◆ *Sweden* ◆ *Switzerland* ◆ *Tanzania* ◆ *Thailand* ◆ *Alabama, California, Colorado, Connecticut, Georgia, Massachusetts, Montana, New Jersey, North Carolina, Pennsylvania, South Carolina, Virginia, and Wyoming, United States* ◆ *Vietnam*

Above: A small, dull-colored prismatic corundum crystal. The hexagonal cross-section of this crystal can be seen in the photo below right.

Corundum is fairly easy to combine with other chemical compounds, and most of the material used industrially under the names ß-alumina, fused bauxite, or fused alumina is produced synthetically. Emery is a mixture of corundum and either **hematite** or **magnetite**.

In addition to its use as an abrasive, corundum is employed in the manufacture of scratch-resistant glass, especially as a coating on expensive watches, and in the windows of spacecraft and satellites.

A widely distributed oxide of aluminum with the chemical formula Al_2O_3, corundum scores 9 on the Mohs Scale of Hardness. Indeed, it is the Earth's second hardest naturally occurring material—the hardest is **diamond**—so may be ground to make various industrial abrasive and polishing agents, including emery. Corundum is also unaffected by acids and resistant to the passage of ultraviolet light rays.

The basic color of corundum is dull brown, but it may be brightly colored by a range of impurities. The precious forms of this mineral are the gemstones **ruby** and **sapphire**, which are red and blue respectively.

The English name corundum comes from *kurundam*, the Tamil word for the mineral, which is in turn derived from *kuruvinda*, the Sanskrit for ruby.

COLOR CODES

Corundum is basically white, but small impurities of ferrous iron (chemical symbol Fe^{2+}) give it a brown color, while unusually large concentrations of this metal may turn it into blue sapphire. Tiny impurities of ferric iron (Fe^{3+})—between 0.5 and 1.0 percent by weight—are sufficient to turn the mineral yellow, while only 0.1 percent of chromium is enough to create a precious ruby.

COVELLITE

A minor ore of copper, covellite is mainly of interest to collectors when it forms attractive indigo crystals with an iridescent tarnish.

Covellite is both a primary and a secondary mineral formed by seeping hydrothermal fluids in parts of **copper** *veins. It is commonly associated with* **bornite, chalcosite, cuprite,** *and* **pyrite.**

Main Sources: ◆ *Argentina* ◆ *Austria* ◆ *Bolivia* ◆ *Chile* ◆ *England* ◆ *Germany* ◆ *Greece* ◆ *Italy* ◆ *Namibia* ◆ *New Zealand* ◆ *Peru* ◆ *Philippines* ◆ *Serbia* ◆ *Alaska, California, Colorado, Idaho, Montana, New Jersey, South Dakota, Utah, Washington, and Wyoming, United States*

A sulfide of copper, covellite is named after Niccolo Covelli (1790–1829), who first discovered it on the slopes of the Italian volcano Mount Vesuvius. The mineral is also known as covelline.

Although it is generally neither widespread nor abundant, covellite is sometimes mined for its copper content. However, this is only economically viable when it occurs in association with **chalcopyrite** and other more productive ores of the metal.

Some covellite contains fairly substantial impurities of iron—up to 5.7 percent by weight—and of **silver**—up to 16.7 percent.

RAINBOW COLORS

The main attraction of covellite is its appearance and the finest specimens may be sought after by mineral collectors for this reason. Its beautiful indigo blue crystals have a metallic luster and display a tarnish in the form of a play of colors—mainly yellow and red—about their surface. This rainbowlike optical phenomenon is known as iridescence. The crystals conform to the hexagonal system and may appear in thin, tabular, six-sided plates with hexagonal striations (surface grooves) on the base.

Most deposits of covellite occur as massive, foliated aggregates (in very thin sheets, like the pages of a book) and crystals are rare. Nonetheless, some fine specimens have been unearthed, in particular from the Calabona mine, Alghero, in Sardinia, Italy.

If covellite is hit with a hammer, it will split into laminae (thin, flexible plates), so it is said to display perfect, basal cleavage. This property distinguishes covellite from bornite, while its color distinguishes it from another associated mineral, chalcosine.

Left: A foliated mass of covellite showing the characteristic play of colors (iridescence) about its surface.

CRISTOBALITE

A polymorph of trigonal quartz, cristobalite is distinctive for its crystal system and the temperatures at which it forms.

Microcrystals of cristobalite are common in volcanic rocks. However, larger well-formed crystals are rare, and good specimens are confined to the vesicles (cavities and crevices) of host rocks.

Main Sources: ◆ *Czech Republic* ◆ *France* ◆ *Germany* ◆ *Hungary* ◆ *India* ◆ *Italy* ◆ *Japan* ◆ *Mexico* ◆ *New Zealand* ◆ *California, Colorado, Oregon, and Wyoming, United States*

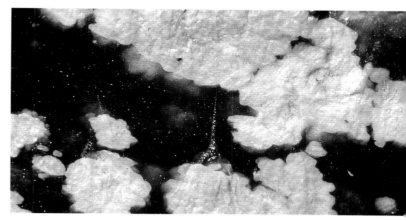

Above: White crystals of cristobalite on a groundmass of volcanic rock.

A form of silicon dioxide, cristobalite has the same chemical formula as **quartz**. However, it has tetragonal rather than trigonal crystals, so is defined as a polymorph of quartz. It was confirmed as a distinct species in 1887 and named after its discovery locality, Cerro San Cristobal in Pachuca, Mexico.

The difference between the two minerals arises from the fact that cristobalite is deposited at both higher and lower temperatures than quartz.

Quartz is formed at between 1,067° F (575° C) and 1,598° F (870° C). Cristobalite may be formed at temperatures of up to 514° F (268° C)—this variety is known as low cristobalite. Alternatively it may start to crystallize at temperatures above this,

becoming stable only after it has been heated to between 2,678° F (1,470° C) and its melting point, 3,142° F (1,728° C). This second form is known as high or ß–cristobalite. Hence the presence of cristobalite gives petrologists an indication of the range of temperatures at which the host rock was crystallized.

Cristobalite appears in pseudo-octahedral crystals that are usually no more than ⅙ in. (4 mm) long. Most deposits are botryoidal (grapelike), fibrous aggregates, stalactitic, or spherulitic crusts.

THE QUARTZ GROUP		
Mineral	**Crystal system**	**Comment**
Coesite:	Monoclinic	Naturally occurring
Cristobalite:	Tetragonal	Naturally occurring
Keatite:	Tetragonal	Synthetic
Lechatelierite:	Amorphous	Naturally occurring supercooled glass
Stishovite:	Tetragonal	High temperature
α-Tridymite:	Monoclinic	Naturally occurring—pseudohexagonal
β-Tridymite:	Hexagonal	Naturally occurring—hexagonal

CROCOITE

A rare and extremely fragile mineral, crocoite crystals are dark orange in color and form as long, thin prisms.

*Crocoite is a chromate of lead with the chemical formula $PbCrO_4$. It is a secondary mineral formed where veins containing **galena** cut through chromium-bearing host rocks to bring together all three elements of the mineral. Among the other minerals with which it may be associated are **cerussite**, **limonite**, **pyromorphite**, **vanadanite**, and **wulfenite**.*

Main Sources: ◆ *Australia* ◆ *Brazil* ◆ *Philippines* ◆ *Romania* ◆ *Russia* ◆ *Arizona and California, United States* ◆ *Zimbabwe*

First discovered in mines at Sverdlovsk in the Ural Mountains of Russia, crocoite is a rare mineral. Its English name comes from the Greek word *krokos*, meaning "saffron." This refers to its distinctive reddish orange coloration, which is similar to that of the stigmas of the crocus—the flower from which saffron is obtained. Crocoite has long been used by painters to provide a striking orange pigment.

CHROMIUM

Although **chromite** is now the major source of chromium, crocoite played an important part in its original isolation. When this metallic element, which is found naturally only in combination, was first isolated by the French chemist L.N.Vaquelin in 1798, the mineral with which he started was crocoite.

Crocoite weighs about six times more than the equivalent volume of water at room temperature. This high specific gravity is accounted for by the fact that another of crocoite's constituent elements is lead.

ATTRACTIVE CRYSTALS

Crystals of crocoite conform to the monoclinic system. Although they can be found in massive or granular habits, its crystals often appear as long, thin

Above: Prismatic crystals of crocoite, distinctive for their strong red coloration and vitreous to adamantine luster.

prisms with squarish cross-sections. Many are over 2 in. (5 cm) long. The largest crocoite crystal ever found measures 4½ in. (11.4 cm) long by 1¾ in. (4.4 cm) across. It now forms part of the Swoboda Collection in Los Angeles, California. The source of this, and most other good crocoite specimens, is the Dundas District of Tasmania, Australia. This region is also the type locality for the mineral. The finest crystals may be faceted or fashioned to make cabochons.

Crocoite is very fragile and should also be protected from intense light, which will cause it to pale and lose its distinctive adamantine (diamondlike) to vitreous luster.

CRYOLITE

A colorless mineral, cryolite is unusual in that it occurs mainly in only one locality in Greenland. Deposits elsewhere are very limited.

*Cryolite forms in **pegmatite** through the precipitation of fluoride-rich fluids. It is found in association with a wide range of other minerals, including **astrophyllite**, **cassiterite**, **chalcopyrite**, **columbite**, **fluorite**, **galena**, **molybdenite**, **quartz**, **siderite**, **topaz**, **wolframite**, and **zircon**.*

Main Sources: ◆ *Canada* ◆ *Greenland* ◆ *Nigeria* ◆ *Russia* ◆ *Spain* ◆ *Colorado, United States*

Above: Cryolite is colorless with a vitreous or greasy luster.

Cryolite often appears as white, translucent crystals. This explains its name, which is derived from the Greek *kruos*, meaning "icy."

USES

Cryolite was originally used in industry as a flux (a kind of solvent) to help refine **bauxite** into pure aluminum. Although this function is now performed mainly by fluorite (calcium fluoride) or sodium aluminum fluoride, cryolite is still used to make glazes for glass and pottery (*see* photo, below).

A member of the halide group, this mineral is a fluoride of sodium and aluminum with the chemical formula Na_3AlF_6. However, some specimens have been found to be slightly deficient in sodium and to contain water rather than fluorine.

One unusual property of cryolite is that it is almost invisible in water. This is partly because of its color but mainly because the two substances have a similarly low index of refraction—in other words, they both disperse and reflect incident light to much the same degree. This means that even a specimen of cloudy cryolite will become more transparent and its edges will appear less distinct when it is placed in water. It will actually resemble a piece of ice under these conditions, the only difference being that cryolite does not float.

PSEUDOCUBIC

Although cryolite crystals conform to the monoclinic system, they often take the external shape of dice. As a result, they are said to be pseudocubic. Twinning is common, and many crystals share a face or faces with one or more of their neighbors. Many cryolite crystals also have striations (surface grooves).

Cryolite was first discovered at Ivigtut on the west coast of Greenland and was confirmed as a distinct mineral species in 1799. It has since been found elsewhere, but only in very limited quantities, so it is close to being a one-locality mineral.

CUPRITE

Cuprite is a popular feature of many mineral collections, although care must be taken to keep it away from strong light sources.

Abundant and widely distributed, cuprite is formed by the oxidation of sulfide minerals in the upper zones of veins containing **copper***. It is also commonly found with* **azurite, chalcosite, chrysocolla, limonite,** *and* **malachite***.*

Main Sources: ◆ *Australia* ◆ *Bolivia* ◆ *Chile* ◆ *Democratic Republic of the Congo (formerly Zaire)* ◆ *England* ◆ *France* ◆ *Germany* ◆ *Hungary* ◆ *Japan* ◆ *Mexico* ◆ *Namibia* ◆ *Romania* ◆ *Russia* ◆ *Arizona, California, Colorado, Idaho, Montana, Nevada, New Mexico, Pennsylvania, Tennessee, Utah, and Washington, United States*

After **chalcopyrite**, cuprite is the chief ore of copper. Specimens typically contain up to 88.8 percent by weight of the pure metal. The copper can be extracted fairly simply, by heating the mineral with carbon in a furnace. The chemical formula of cuprite is Cu_2O.

The finest cuprite crystals are deep red with an almost black interior. These are sometimes used as semiprecious gemstones, although they are strictly for display only. With a Mohs scale rating of only 3½ to 4, the crystals are not hard enough to withstand the wear and tear of everyday use as jewelry.

A form of cuprite that appears in fine tufts of acicular (needlelike) crystals is known as chalcotrichite. This variety also has a beautiful red coloration and a special sparkle that makes it a popular feature of mineralogists' collections.

PSEUDOMORPHISM

All cuprite specimens have to be stored in cabinets, away from strong light. This is because prolonged exposure to light may cause the formation of a green patina on the surface of the mineral. This thin film is malachite. If the malachite formation is not halted, the other mineral may eventually take over the structure of the cuprite entirely in a process known as pseudomorphism. Cuprite may sometimes lose its oxygen and decompose into native copper.

Crystals of cuprite conform to the cubic system of symmetry and may appear as cubes, but are more often octahedrons, dodecahedrons, or combinations of these forms. Massive aggregates, granular, or compact habits are also common. Red deposits of this type are known as tile ore.

Left: Red cuprite. Crystals of this valuable ore mineral are sometimes twinned, but most are distinct and individual.

DANALITE

A member of the helvite group, danalite forms an unusual solid solution series with helvite itself and genthelvite.

Above: A granular aggregate of grayish danalite. Most deposits are mixed with other closely related species.

Danalite is found mainly in granitic **pegmatite**, and in hydrothermal veins. It may also form in zones of metasomatism (alteration by chemical fluids).

Main Sources: ◆ Canada ◆ England ◆ Japan ◆ Russia ◆ Sweden ◆ Arizona, Colorado, Massachusetts, and New Hampshire, United States

Danalite was first discovered at Rockport, Cape Ann, Massachusetts, and was confirmed as a distinct mineral in 1866. James Dwight Dana (1813–95), in whose honor danalite is named, was a professor at Yale University and a preeminent mineralogist. He was editor, with his father-in-law, Benjamin Silliman, of the *American Journal of Science* from 1840 and author of the textbook *Manual of Mineralogy* (1848).

UNUSUAL TRIO

This mineral is the iron-rich member of the helvite group, which comprises three beryllium silicates with sulfide (*see* box, below). Atomic substitution may cause the replacement of the iron in danalite—either by zinc, to form genthelvite, or by manganese to create helvite itself. Hence, the trio forms an unusual

solid solution series in which none of the minerals is a midway point. Rather, all three minerals are end members of the series, and each may be converted into either of the other two.

It should be noted that, although the members of any such series were originally formed from and with each other, they do not necessarily occur in close association with one another today. This is because, in at least some cases, the atomic substitution that takes place between members of a solid solution series is now complete and pervasive throughout the whole deposit.

All three helvite group minerals crystallize according to the cubic system of symmetry. Externally, danalite appears in octahedra, dodecahedra, or as granular masses. It may be gray, yellow, red, or brown in color and it has a vitreous (glassy) or resinous (greasy) luster.

HELVITE GROUP			
	Formula	Specific gravity	Hardness
Danalite:	$Fe^{2+}{}_4Be_3(SiO_4)S$	3.3 to 3.4	5½ to 6
Genthelvite:	$Zn_4Be_3Si_3O_{12}S$	3.6	6 to 6½
Helvite:	$Mn_4Be_3(SiO_4)_3S$	3.1 to 3.3	6

DANBURITE

Danburite, named after its discovery site in Connecticut, has enjoyed increased popularity with mineral collectors.

*The mineral and gemstone danburite occurs with **feldspar** in **dolomite**, granitic **pegmatites**, and nonmarine evaporites. It is commonly associated with **apophyllite**, **cassiterite**, **calcite**, **chalcopyrite**, **corundum** (especially ruby), **fluorite**, **pyrite**, **sphalerite**, and **quartz**.*

Main Sources: ◆ *Czech Republic* ◆ *Japan* ◆ *Madagascar* ◆ *Mexico* ◆ *Myanmar (Burma)* ◆ *Switzerland* ◆ *Connecticut and New York, United States*

Above: This beautiful transparent crystal of danburite shows its characteristic wedgelike shape.

Danburite is a borosilicate of calcium with the chemical formula $CaB_2(SiO_4)_2$. It is named after the locality where it was discovered—Danbury, Connecticut. The site at which it was originally found in the early 19th century is now entirely covered with buildings.

CLEAR AND LUSTROUS

Danburite is often colorless, but may sometimes appear light yellow, gold, pale pink, brown, or white. It nearly always has a striking glassy or greasy sheen. When cut, the stone is clear and brilliant.

Although not generally well-known, danburite has become increasingly popular among mineral collectors because it forms attractive clusters of transparent crystals with diamond-shaped cross-sections and wedgelike terminations that resemble a steeply inclined dome. Its crystals range from completely transparent to translucent and resemble **topaz**. The smaller crystals are rather thin, but some of the largest individual crystals are acicular and may be up to 1 ft. (30 cm) long and several inches in diameter. Many have vertical parallel striations along their faces that can be either white or colorless.

Danburite is quite a hard mineral (Mohs scale 7 to 7.5) and has a very low sensitivity to heat—in

other words, it melts only at very high temperatures. As a result, the best specimens may be faceted or cut *en cabochon* to enhance their appearance. Its specific gravity of 3.0 is average for a mineral.

At the present time, there are known to be 51 borosilicate minerals, including **tourmaline**.

DESCLOIZITE

The rare mineral descloizite has a sister mineral—mottramite. The two are often differentiated only by the amount of copper and zinc found in their compositions.

---

*Descloizite is a rare secondary mineral that forms in the oxidation zones of lead and zinc ore deposits and veins. It is principally associated with **mottramite**, but may also occur with **calcite, cerussite, mimetite, pyromorphite, vanadinite,** and **wulfenite**.*

Main Sources: ◆ *Algeria* ◆ *Argentina* ◆ *Austria* ◆ *Brazil* ◆ *Democratic Republic of the Congo (formerly Zaire)* ◆ *England* ◆ *France* ◆ *Germany* ◆ *Italy* ◆ *Mexico* ◆ *Namibia* ◆ *Tunisia* ◆ *Arizona, Nevada, New Mexico, South Dakota, and Utah, United States* ◆ *Zambia* ◆ *Zimbabwe*

Although sometimes a minor ore of lead and zinc, descloizite is mainly of interest to mineralogists and collectors. It is named after the man who first described it—Alfred Louis Olivier Legrand des Cloizeaux (1817–97), professor of mineralogy at the University of Paris, France.

Descloizite is a hydrous vanadate. The main metal it contains is lead, but it also features zinc and **copper**, although always more of the former than the latter. Descloizite's closest relative is mottramite, which has almost the same chemical composition but always contains more copper than zinc. The two minerals form the end members of a solid solution series in which one of these metals gradually replaces the other in a process known as atomic substitution.

Mottramite and descloizite are so similar that they can often be distinguished from each other only by scientific analysis of the relative amounts of copper and zinc in each specimen.

CHEMICAL FORMULAE	
Descloizite:	$Pb(Zn,Cu)(VO_4)OH$
Mottramite:	$Pb(Cu,Zn)VO_4OH$

Descloizite can form well-shaped crystals with an attractive luster. Its color, although always striking, is variable: zinc-rich specimens are typically reddish brown or black, but with increasing copper content they may appear yellow, orange, or dark green. Descloizite displays a yellowish orange or reddish brown streak.

Crystals of both descloizite and mottramite conform to the orthorhombic system of symmetry. Their external appearance is typically small, flat platelets with rounded, triangular, or pyramidal ends that resemble spears. Descloizite may also appear in microcrystalline crusts and stalactitic masses. It is a relatively soft mineral, rating only 3 to 3½ on the Mohs scale, and melts easily at high temperatures.

Below: An aggregate of reddish brown descloizite crystals from an oxidated lead ore vein.

DIABASE

Diabase is formed from magma that has cooled just underneath the Earth's surface and is sometimes found as intrusions in older rock.

*Diabase is made up of plagioclase **feldspar**, pyroxene, and **quartz**. In addition to these essential components, this rock can also contain **chalcopyrite**, **hornblende**, **ilmenite**, and **pyrrhotite**.*

Main Sources: *Diabase is often found in plugs that have formed in the necks of old volcanoes.*

Diabase is a dark, intrusive, basic igneous rock made of plagioclase feldspar crystals, surrounded by smaller grains of pyroxenes such as augite, and up to 10 percent quartz.

Igneous rocks may be classified in many ways: one is according to the size of their component particles. The coarsest-grained basic rock is **gabbro**, which is created at great depth under enormous pressure and is thus said to be a plutonic formation.

The finest-grained basic igneous rock is **basalt**, which is formed from lava extruded onto the surface of the Earth during volcanic eruptions.

Diabase lies between these two extremes—it is formed from magma that has solidified close to, but not on, the surface and often occurs as small intrusions, such as dikes and sills that have entered surrounding rocks when molten, in fissures. Rock of this type is said to be hypabyssal—the word means "moderately deep-seated."

Any rock containing significant quantities of magnesium- and/or iron-bearing minerals such as these is said to be mafic, a word derived from the first two letters of magnesium and the first letter of the chemical symbol for iron (Fe).

Igneous rocks are also defined by the amount of silica they contain. Those richest in silica are labeled acidic; the next grade down is intermediate, then basic, and finally ultrabasic. With a relatively low silica content (45 to 55 percent), diabase is classified as a basic igneous rock.

Diabase dike and sill structures often stand proud of softer country rocks that have been weathered. One of the finest examples is the Palisade sill on the Hudson River.

Left: Although diabase is a mainly dark-colored rock, it also features lighter, sparkling crystals of feldspar.

DIAMOND

As the hardest natural substance on Earth, diamonds make excellent cutting and drilling tools, as well as priceless jewels and adornments.

Above: An uncut crystal of diamond. Specimens like this may be cut into hugely valuable gemstones.

*Most diamonds are extracted from kimberlite—an ultra-mafic igneous rock composed mainly of **olivine** that forms pipelike intrusions, which can go down about 60 miles (97 km) beneath the Earth's surface. Diamond is also found in **meteorites**.*

Main Sources: ◆ *Angola* ◆ *Australia* ◆ *Borneo* ◆ *Botswana* ◆ *Brazil* ◆ *Ghana* ◆ *Guinea* ◆ *Guyana* ◆ *India* ◆ *Namibia* ◆ *Russia* ◆ *Sierra Leone* ◆ *South Africa* ◆ *Tanzania* ◆ *Arkansas, California, Colorado, Georgia, Idaho, North Carolina, Oregon, Virginia, Washington, Wisconsin, and Wyoming, United States* ◆ *Venezuela*

Most people know that diamond is the hardest natural substance on Earth. What fewer realize is that it is four times harder in real terms than the next hardest mineral, **corundum**. Diamond is also the world's best conductor of heat—five times more effective than the next best, **silver**—and has a higher melting point than any other mineral.

The main industrial use of diamond is as a cutting and drilling tool, as it is can cut anything. The diamonds used for this purpose are dull and opaque, but the clearest crystals are the most precious of all gemstones. Some of the largest weigh over 1,000 carats (7 oz.) and are used in royal jewelry.

But diamond does have some weaknesses. It has four directions of cleavage—if it receives a sharp blow in one of these directions, it will split. Jewelers shape and mount diamonds in such a way as to protect these flaws when the diamond is put in an ornamental setting.

Diamond is an allotrope or polymorph of the element carbon, as is **graphite**. Diamond and graphite share the same chemistry, but have very different structures and properties. Diamond is hard, transparent, an excellent electrical insulator, and the best natural abrasive. Graphite is soft, opaque, a good electrical conductor, and an effective lubricant.

But graphite is a more stable form of carbon than diamond. In fact, all diamonds at or near the surface of the Earth are currently undergoing an extremely slow but sure transformation into graphite.

DIAMOND—THE BIRTHSTONE

Because of the great clarity of the finest specimens, diamonds are believed to give those who wear them the power to speak the truth. Diamond is the birthstone of natives of Aries—people born between 21 March and 20 April.

DIASPORE

Diaspore is similar to boehmite, but much harder and heavier, making it better suited as a gemstone for jewelry.

*Diaspore occurs in **bauxite**—a sedimentary deposit—within **clay**, as well as in chlorite **schist** and **marble**, which are metamorphic formations. It is found in association with many minerals, including **corundum**, **dolomite**, **magnetite**, and **spinel**.*

Main Sources: *◆ China ◆ France ◆ Germany ◆ Greece ◆ Greenland ◆ Hungary ◆ Italy ◆ Japan ◆ Norway ◆ Russia ◆ South Africa ◆ Sweden ◆ Switzerland ◆ Turkey ◆ Arizona, California, Colorado, Connecticut, Massachusetts, Missouri, North Carolina, Pennsylvania, Utah, and Washington, United States*

Above: The white lines on the surface of this diaspore specimen are the planes of fracture along which the mineral has broken off from its original base.

Diaspore is one of the largest constituents of bauxite, the principal ore of aluminum. It is itself an important industrial source of this metal.

The mineral's name is derived from the Greek word *diaspora*, which means "scattering," and alludes to the way it decrepitates (crackles) when heated strongly with air from a blowpipe.

Diaspore is closely related to boehmite. The two minerals have exactly the same crystal structure (orthorhombic) and chemical formula, which is AlO(OH). They may appear identical and are therefore said to be dimorphous. Diaspore was confirmed as a distinct mineral in 1801; boehmite was not positively identified until 1927.

The main differences between the two species, however, are their specific gravity and their hardness —with an SG of 3.3 to 3.5 and a Mohs scale rating of 6½ to 7, diaspore is both a heavier and harder mineral than boehmite.

Diaspore appears in a wide variety of external forms. It can take the shape of acicular (needlelike), tabular, or platy (thin and flattened) crystals, as well as massive, foliated, scaly, and stalactitic habits. Some columnular formations can be up to 8 in. (20 cm) long. Diaspore is often polished and used in jewelry. It is typically colorless, but some specimens may be brown, green, gray, pink, light or dark red, purple, white, or yellow, depending on the impurities involved (for instance, a high manganese content will produce a dark red tint). It is transparent or translucent, with pearly lines that mark out the cleavage along which it has been broken. Diaspore cannot be dissolved by liquid or melted by heat.

DIOPSIDE

Diopside means "two views," a name that expresses one of this mineral's most interesting characteristics—its crystals appear to change shape when looked at from different angles.

CHEMICAL FORMULAE	
Diopside:	$MgCaSi_2O_6$
Hedenbergite:	$CaFe^{2+}Si_2O_6$
Johannsenite:	$CaMnSi_2O_6$

Diopside is an important rock-forming mineral that is a common feature in several metamorphic and igneous rocks. It is also found in **meteorites**. *Among the minerals with which diopside is most commonly associated are* **actinolite**, *calcite, dolomite, fluorite, grossular* **garnet**, *olivine, and* **vesuvianite**.

Main Sources: ◆ *Austria* ◆ *Brazil* ◆ *Canada* ◆ *Finland* ◆ *Germany* ◆ *India* ◆ *Italy* ◆ *Madagascar* ◆ *Myanmar (Burma)* ◆ *Pakistan* ◆ *Russia* ◆ *South Africa* ◆ *Sri Lanka* ◆ *Sweden* ◆ *Switzerland* ◆ *California, Montana, and New York, United States*

The English name of this mineral is taken from the Greek *di* ("double") and *opsis* ("view") because its prismatic crystals appear in different shapes when viewed from different angles.

Pure diopside is typically white or green with a glassy luster. However, there are many variant forms. The finest of these are sometimes polished or cut for use as beads, when they are massive, or gemstones, if they are transparent.

Bright green crystals of this species are colored by impurities of chromium and are known as chrome diopside. Violet-blue crystals, colored by manganese, are known as violane.

There are several other forms of diopside, including a green cat's eye containing minute inclusions of **rutile**, which reflect light in such a way as to produce luminscence within the crystal.

Some specimens have rutile needles that are aligned to produce a four-pointed star. Dark green to black specimens of this type can be found in southern India. This star effect may be enhanced by cutting the stone *en cabochon*.

MEMBER OF THE PYROXENE GROUP

Diopside belongs to the pyroxene group. Pyroxenes are silicates with the general formula $X_2Si_2O_6$, in which X may be one or more of the metals aluminum, calcium, iron, lithium, magnesium, manganese, sodium, or titanium. All pyroxenes have two intersecting perpendicular cleavages.

Diopside is the magnesium-rich end member of a solid solution series of minerals that also includes **hedenbergite** and johannsenite.

Below: Diopside is often green, but it may also be black, brown, gray, or white. It may also be colorless.

DIOPTASE

Originally mistaken for emerald due to its vivid green color, dioptase is a gemstone but is too soft and brittle for reliable use in jewelry.

*Dioptase forms in parts of **copper** veins that have been oxidized by air or water and in some of the surrounding cavities. It is often associated with **azurite, calcite, cerussite, chrysocolla, dolomite, limonite,** and **wulfenite.***

Main Sources: ◆ *Chile* ◆ *Democratic Republic of the Congo (formerly Zaire)* ◆ *Iran* ◆ *Kazakhstan* ◆ *Namibia* ◆ *Russia* ◆ *Arizona and California, United States*

Above: Sparkling green crystals of diopside. It is easy to see how such specimens were mistaken for emeralds.

Dioptase is a deep green mineral that superficially resembles **emerald** (the precious form of **beryl**). However, it is seldom used as a gemstone because, with a Mohs scale rating of 5, a specific gravity of 3.3, and perfect cleavage, it is much softer and more brittle than emerald. Usually only very small stones can be cut from this mineral.

Crystals of dioptase are transparent, and it is from this property that its English name is derived—it is taken from the Greek prefix *dia*, meaning "through," and *optazein*, meaning "visible."

CHANGING COLOR

Some specimens of dioptase are weakly dichroic. This means that they appear to change color, depending on the direction of the light source and the angle from which they are viewed. Although cutting may enhance this effect, it is rarely attempted because the mineral is fragile and the effort is unlikely to be rewarding. However, some specimens of dioptase are highly prized for their rich emerald-green color, sometimes with a bluish tint. When the color is particularly vivid, the stone becomes translucent rather than transparent.

Dioptase is one of the few silicate minerals that crystallize in the trigonal system of symmetry. The others include dolomite and **willemite**. As a result

of this peculiarity, dioptase crystals may take on rhombohedral external forms. Their prismatic faces are sometimes so dark and reflective that the basic green color may appear cloudy and even black.

A CASE OF MISTAKEN IDENTITY

Historically, the most abundant source of dioptase was in Kazakhstan. Specimens mined in this country were wrongly identified as emeralds and sent to the Russian Tsar.

DIORITE

Diorite is often described as the intrusive equivalent of the extrusive rock andesite because of their similar compositions.

*Diorite is an intrusive igneous rock that often forms in discordant layers (dikes) running across the general direction of surrounding bedding layers. It is formed mainly from crystallized magma, but some deposits are produced by chemical reactions between magma and preexistent rocks such as **gabbro**.*

Main Sources: *Diorite is widely distributed throughout the world. In the United States, there are notable formations in California and Minnesota.*

A medium- to coarse-grained intrusive intermediate igneous rock that is closely related to **andesite** and **syenite**, diorite is sometimes used to make building stones.

There are two main types of igneous rock. Extrusive igneous rocks are formed from molten volcanic material that has flowed out onto the surface of the Earth and resolidified, typically as vast sheets. Intrusive igneous rocks, on the other hand, are formations that have forced themselves into preexistent strata, usually along a clearly defined structural feature such as a bedding plane or joint.

DIFFICULTIES IN DEFINING

Diorite is difficult to define, especially where it shades imperceptibly into **granite**—although diorite is generally a darker color than granite. The exact point at which one ends and the other begins is hard to determine with any degree of scientific accuracy. However, as a rule of thumb it is generally agreed that diorite should contain between 55 and 65 percent total silica, of which no more than 10

percent is **quartz**. In addition, diorite may include up to 33 percent **feldspar**. Other minerals that may occur in diorite are **biotite**, **mica**, and **pyroxenite**. When the percentage of quartz rises above the 10 percent level, the rock is redefined as monzonite; with increased amounts of feldspar, the rock becomes known as **granodiorite**.

The general makeup of diorite is broadly similar to that of andesite, and it is thus described as the plutonic (intrusive) equivalent of this extrusive rock.

Diorite may contain phenocrysts—large crystals set in a finer-grained matrix (rock base). Some of the finest of these are **hornblende**.

Below: The light-colored areas of this diorite are composed of plagioclase feldspar.

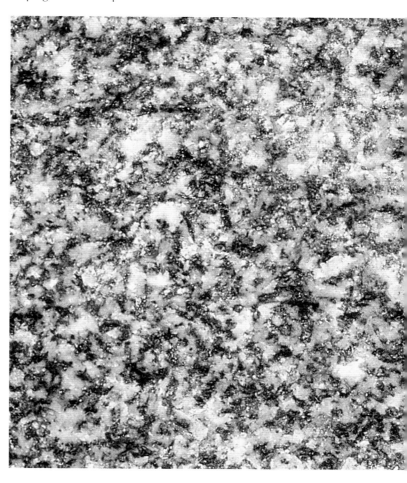

DOLOMITE

Dolomite is an important ore from which magnesium is extracted and used as a metal alloy in goods from snowshoes to horseshoes.

Above: Crystals of dolomite are often twinned. Specimens with curved faces are said to be "saddle-shaped."

*Dolomite is a rock-forming mineral that is created by magnesium-bearing solutions acting on limestone. It is found in hydrothermal veins with **galena** and **sphalerite**.*

Main Sources: ◆ *Canada* ◆ *England* ◆ *Ireland* ◆ *Italy* ◆ *Mexico* ◆ *Norway* ◆ *Scotland* ◆ *Spain* ◆ *Sweden* ◆ *Switzerland* ◆ *Iowa and New York, United States* ◆ *Wales*

One of the most important ores of magnesium, dolomite is a carbonate of this metal and calcium. It is named after Déodat Guy de Dolomieu (1750–1801), one of the scientists who accompanied French emperor Napoleon Bonaparte on his ill-fated expedition to Egypt in 1798. He was captured and imprisoned in Messina, Sicily, for 21 months, during which time he wrote two mineralogical works—a treatise and a memoir—in the margins of his Bible.

Before Dolomieu described its characteristics and occurrence, dolomite was classified as a form of **calcite**, because geologists mistakenly believed that the magnesium was an impurity rather than an integral part of the chemical composition.

Dolomite forms a solid solution series with two other species: **ankerite** and **kutnohorite**. Ankerite forms when some of dolomite's magnesium is substituted by iron and some manganese, whereas calcium carbonate with more manganese than iron is called kutnohorite.

Magnesium—the eighth most abundant element on Earth—is extracted from dolomite either by roasting with ferrosilicon (an alloy of iron and silicon) or by electrolysis. The metal obtained is used in home water-heaters and oil tanks, and as a galvanic anode to prevent corrosion in ships' hulls (*see* photo, right).

Finely divided magnesium burns in air with an intense white light, so it is used in flash-bulbs and fireworks. It is also used in bombs and in the production of titanium and zirconium.

Dolomite may be used as a gemstone when it is found as distinctive colorless, white, pink, or yellow crystals with curved faces. However, being very soft with perfect cleavage, it is rarely faceted.

CHEMICAL FORMULAE	
Ankerite:	$Ca(Fe,Mg,Mn)(CO_3)_2$
Dolomite:	$CaMg(CO_3)_2$
Kutnohorite:	$Ca(Mn,Mg,Fe^{2+})(CO_3)_2$

DOLOSTONE

Dolostone, a rock composed of at least 50 percent dolomite, is formed from limestone deposits and is popular as a building stone.

Dolostone is formed from preexistent deposits of **limestone**, *a rock composed principally of* **calcite**. *In addition to the essential ingredient of* **dolomite**, *dolostone often features the accessory minerals* **bitumen**, **clay**, *and* **quartz**, *and sometimes* **marcasite** *and* **pyrite**. *Silica may also be present in the form of* **chert**.

Main Sources: ◆ *England* ◆ *Texas, United States.*

A sedimentary rock composed mainly of the mineral dolomite, dolostone, by definition, must contain at least 50 percent of this carbonate of calcium and magnesium.

Dolostone is a product of limestone that has been immersed for long periods in seawater and become saturated with magnesium (seawater contains about 0.13 percent magnesium). Indeed, dolostone is the most important industrial source of this metal. The rock is sometimes known alternatively as magnesian limestone and is used to make building stones.

A RESERVOIR FOR OIL
During the chemical process of magnesium saturation—which is known as dolomitization—the rock undergoes a reduction in volume of about 12 percent. It becomes highly porous, with large and visible pores, which may become a reservoir for oil and natural gas.

Dolostone may preserve the texture of its antecedent limestones, and the outlines of skeletal fragments may still be recognizable within it. These, however, are rare, as most dolostones have undergone almost complete replacement and are therefore extensively recrystallized. Any fossils the limestones may once have contained tend to be completely eradicated in the process.

Above: A compact, earthy mass of dolostone with an even crystalline texture.

Dolostone is a creamy, gray, or white color with a generally even and crystalline texture, but it can turn a brown or pink color when weathered. Its masses are compact and earthy. It is usually a fine- to medium-grained rock, and the joints of the rock are highly visible.

DUMORTIERITE

A favorite with mineral collectors, dumortierite is also used in the manufacture of fine ceramics and as a decorative stone.

*Dumortierite is commonly found in aluminum-rich metamorphic rocks, in contact metamorphic regions, and in some forms of **pegmatite**. In some locations it may lose its iron and boron and be altered to **pyrophyllite**.*
*It is also associated with **andalusite, kyanite, quartz, sillimanite**, and **staurolite**.*

Main Sources: ◆ *Australia* ◆ *Brazil* ◆ *Canada* ◆ *France* ◆ *India* ◆ *Madagascar* ◆ *Mexico* ◆ *New Zealand* ◆ *Norway* ◆ *Russia* ◆ *Suriname* ◆ *Arizona, California, Colorado, Montana, Nevada, New York, and Washington, United States*

Above: This dumortierite aggregate is brown, but the mineral may also be blue, pink, or violet in color.

Used as an ornamental stone and in high-grade ceramics and porcelain, dumortierite is also a popular mineral with collectors.

Dumortierite was confirmed as a distinct species in 1881 and named in memory of the French paleontologist Eugène Dumortier (1802–73).

The mineral is a borosilicate, often with an attractive and unusual deep violet to blue color. It is not often used as a gemstone because of the size of its crystals, which are rarely more than 1/25 in. (1 mm) in diameter. Yet it does have good hardness—Mohs scale 8½—and massive dumortierite can be carved into beads, cabochons, eggs, sculptures, and spheres.

Crystals are pleochroic, changing from red to blue to violet, depending on the direction of the light source and the angle from which they are viewed. They are also fluorescent—most give off a blue light of their own when placed under an ultraviolet lamp, but others fluoresce yellow or white.

The quartz variety called dumortierite quartz is massive quartz colored blue by dumortierite crystals. It is cut and polished for decorative stone.

Dumortierite may sometimes be mistaken for other ornamental stones, such as **lazulite, lazurite,** and **sodalite**. Blue sodalite has more white portions and is much less dense—the specific gravity of dumortierite is 3.4—and, unlike dumortierite, lazulite and lazurite are not fibrous. In China, some dumortierite has been used as an imitation lapis lazuli in carvings.

CHEMICAL FORMULAE	
Dumortierite:	$(Al,Fe)_7BO_3(SiO_4)_3O_3$
Pyrophyllite:	$Al_2Si_4O_{10}(OH)_2$

EMERALD

Emerald is one of the world's most precious gemstones. It is the green variety of beryl (beryllium aluminium silicate).

*Emeralds are found mainly in **granites** and **pegmatites**, although some specimens have been turned up in open cast mines near the surface of metamorphic rocks.*

Main Sources: ◆ *Australia* ◆ *Austria* ◆ *Brazil* ◆ *Colombia* ◆ *Egypt* ◆ *India* ◆ *Norway* ◆ *Pakistan* ◆ *Russia* ◆ *South Africa* ◆ *North Carolina, United States* ◆ *Zimbabwe*

Above: One or two small, green emeralds embedded in a rock mass.

Pure **beryl** is colorless—the beautiful green of emerald comes from the presence of various impurities within the body of the gemstone. Brazilian emeralds contain **calcite** or **pyrite**; South African and Russian emeralds nearly always contain **mica**.

Despite their great beauty and preciousness, emeralds are seldom perfect. They nearly always have flaws of some kind, usually liquid droplets, gas bubbles, or minuscule cubes of rock salt (halite). These imperfections can sometimes be disguised by clever stonecutters to improve the appearance of the gem and increase its commercial value in jewelry (*see* photo, above right).

HISTORY

Emeralds have been known since ancient times. The earliest recorded specimens were unearthed in the Sikait-Zabara region on the coast of the Red Sea. Abundant new supplies were discovered in the New World in 1537 during the Spanish invasion of Colombia under Gonzalo Jiménez de Quesada (c.1497–1579). The Spanish then shipped their specimens back to Europe, where they sold them at vast profit to the rulers of the Murghal and Ottoman empires.

FAMOUS EXAMPLES

The world's greatest emerald collection is stored in the Republic of Bogota Bank in Colombia. The five largest crystals of this collection weigh between 220 and 1,795 carats (1½ and 12½ oz.). The most beautiful emeralds actually on display are those in the Topkapi Palace, Istanbul (Turkey), the American Museum of Natural History in New York, and the Smithsonian Institution in Washington, D.C.

ASTROLOGY

Emerald is ruled by the Moon and is the most precious of the lucky gemstones of people born under the sign of Gemini, between 22 May and 21 June. It is believed that anyone who wears or carries an emerald will be more faithful or loyal, and the stone may therefore be given by one lover to another before an enforced separation.

ENARGITE

Enargite is a rare sulfide mineral that is often found in association with other copper-bearing species.

*Enargite is sometimes found with **chalcopyrite** and may also be associated with **bornite, chalcosite, covellite, galena, pyrite, quartz,** and **sphalerite.***

Main Sources: ◆ *Argentina* ◆ *Austria* ◆ *Bolivia* ◆ *Chile* ◆ *Czech Republic* ◆ *England* ◆ *Germany* ◆ *Hungary* ◆ *Italy* ◆ *Mexico* ◆ *Namibia* ◆ *Peru* ◆ *Philippines* ◆ *Serbia* ◆ *Taiwan* ◆ *Alaska, Arkansas, Arizona, California, Colorado, Louisiana, Missouri, Montana, Nevada, Utah, and Washington, United States*

CHEMICAL FORMULAE	
Enargite:	Cu_3AsS_4
Luzonite:	Cu_3AsS_4
Wurtzite:	$(Zn,Fe)S$

Although it never occurs in large enough quantities to be mined on its own account, enargite can be extracted fortuitously with chalcopyrite, and may then be used as an ore of **copper**. Its English name is taken from the Greek word *enarge*, which means "distinct." This is a reference to the mineral's perfect cleavage.

Externally, enargite may appear identical to luzonite, another sulfide of **arsenic** and copper—the two minerals are therefore said to be dimorphous. The main difference between them is that luzonite is tetragonal, while crystals of enargite conform to the orthorhombic system of symmetry. Enargite is also related to **wurtzite**.

Crystals of enargite are usually small, tabular, compact, and granular. They are seldom well formed, but fine clusters do occur. These are often pseudo-hexagonal, having six sides but not six identical sides. Twinning may result in the formation of star-shaped cyclic twins. This process is known as trilling.

UNUSUAL PROPERTY

The most unusual property of enargite crystals is that they are hemimorphic, a term derived from the Greek, the prefix *hemi-* ("half") and the noun *morphe* ("shape"). This means that the crystals may have different shapes at either end.

The exposed terminations of enargite crystals are typically flat faces, but twinning is so common that the other end is almost always concealed by one or more of its neighbors. Consequently, it is impossible to tell what shape the crystal might be if it were distinct. One of the few other minerals that display this phenomenon is **hemimorphite**.

Left: Enargite is a dark gray or black color with crystals that often show deep vertical striations.

ENSTATITE

Enstatite has a variety of uses, depending on the quality of its crystals—from lustrous gemstones to efficient oven linings.

Enstatite is found in metamorphic rocks, especially granulite, and some igneous rocks, as well as in stony and iron meteorites.

Main Sources: ◆ *Germany* ◆ *Japan* ◆ *Madagascar* ◆ *Russia* ◆ *Scotland* ◆ *South Africa* ◆ *Sri Lanka* ◆ *Switzerland* ◆ *Tanzania* ◆ *Arizona, California, Colorado, Delaware, Maryland, Montana, New York, North Carolina, and Pennsylvania, United States*

Above: Enstatite is a transparent to nearly opaque mineral with a vitreous or pearly luster.

Enstatite has a very high melting point, and its name is therefore taken from the Greek *enstates*, meaning "opponent" (of heat). It has a hardness of 5 to 6 on the Mohs scale. The finest crystals are cut in a wide range of styles for use as gemstones; lesser crystals are used to line kilns, ovens, and furnaces.

Enstatite is an orthopyroxene, one of a group of silicates of iron or magnesium. It forms a solid solution series with ferrosilite, as the magnesium it contains is gradually substituted by atoms of iron. The specific gravity of enstatite increases when there is a large amount of iron contained within it and can therefore range between 3.2 and 4. Specimens with an intermediate composition, containing approximately equal amounts of iron and magnesium, are known as hypersthene. However, it should be noted that hypersthene is classified as no more than a variant form of enstatite or ferrosilite, rather than as a mineral in its own right.

Another characteristic of orthopyroxenes is that they all have orthorhombic symmetry. At high temperatures, however, enstatite's structure changes to a structure with a monoclinic symmetry. It has therefore turned into a clinopyroxene and such specimens are known as clinoenstatite. The two species are polymorphous. In other words, they have the same chemistry but different structures.

Enstatite usually forms from the alteration and dehydration of anthophyllite, an amphibole mineral with the chemical formula $(Mg, Fe^{2+})_7Si_8O_{22}(OH)_2$.

Among the ornamental and gemstone forms of enstatite are bronzite, a brown variety containing up to 10 percent iron, and chrome-enstatite, which is colored emerald green by impurities of chromium.

CHEMICAL FORMULAE	
Enstatite:	$Mg_2Si_2O_6$
Ferrosilite:	$Fe^{2+}_2Si_2O_6$

EPIDOTE

Epidote's pistachio-green crystals are too delicate for everyday jewelry, but they are still cut, polished, and sold for display.

*The mineral epidote forms in regionally metamorphosed igneous and sedimentary rocks and through the alteration of plagioclase **feldspar**. It is commonly associated with the minerals **actinolite**, **calcite**, **garnet** (andradite variety), and **hornblende**.*

Main Sources: ◆ *Australia* ◆ *Austria* ◆ *Brazil* ◆ *Czech Republic* ◆ *Finland* ◆ *France* ◆ *Italy* ◆ *Japan* ◆ *Madagascar* ◆ *Mexico* ◆ *Mozambique* ◆ *Myanmar (Burma)* ◆ *Norway* ◆ *Russia* ◆ *South Korea* ◆ *Switzerland* ◆ *Alaska, California, Colorado, Connecticut, Idaho, Massachusetts, Michigan, New Hampshire, and Washington, United States*

Above: The finest crystals of epidote are sometimes removed from their bases (matrices) and cut as gemstones.

Epidote, or pistacite, is sometimes used as a gemstone, but not often because it is rather brittle and has a distinct cleavage. Its name—which is taken from the Greek *epidosis*, meaning "increase"—refers to the fact that one side of the base of its rhombohedral prism is noticeably longer than the others.

Minerals with a similar crystal shape are classed as members of the epidote group. These include **clinozoisite**, **piemontite**, and **zoisite**.

Epidote is a hydrous silicate of calcium, aluminum, and iron with the chemical formula $Ca_2(Al,Fe^{3+})_3(SiO_4)_3OH$. At the heart of the atomic structure are parallel chains of aluminum oxide molecules; minerals formed in this way are known as sorosilicates. These chains are linked by silicate ions (SiO_4).

Crystal of epidote tend to be long, prismatic, or tabular and terminate in wedge shapes or pyramids. Many clusters show slender striated (grooved) crystals or acicular (needle-shaped) sprays. Deposits may also be massive, fibrous, or granular.

The unusual green color of the finest epidote is sometimes described as pistachio, because of its similarity to that of the nut. However, the mineral is strongly pleochroic—its color may change from green to yellow or brown, depending on the direction of the light source and the angle from which it is viewed.

Rocks composed mainly of epidote may be polished or tumbled and then sold under the name "unakite." The finest epidote crystals are cut in a variety of styles, but mainly for display. They are easily flawed and therefore ill-equipped to withstand everyday use as jewelry.

There are known to be three variant forms of epidote with substantial impurities: fouqueite, which features up to 10 percent iron; tawmawite, which contains chromium; and withamite (a variety of piemontite), a manganese-bearing epidote.

Epidote can be mistaken for **tourmaline**, except that it has poor cleavage, unlike epidote.

EPSOMITE

Epsomite, usually found clinging to the walls of mines and limestone caves, is well-known for its use as a laxative in Epsom salts.

*Epsomite forms as an efflorescence (a precipitation from vapors) on **limestone** cave walls and in mines. It is found in deposits from hot springs and fumaroles such as on Mount Vesuvius, Italy, and in the oxidized zones of **pyrite** deposits. Other minerals with which it is associated include **aragonite, gypsum, calcite,** and **pyrrhotite.***

Main Sources: ◆ *Canada* ◆ *Czech Republic* ◆ *England* ◆ *France* ◆ *Germany* ◆ *Italy* ◆ *South Africa* ◆ *Arizona, California, Indiana, Kentucky, Montana, Nevada, New Mexico, Tennessee, Utah, Washington, and Wyoming, United States*

An important source of magnesium salts, epsomite is a laxative that is commonly known as Epsom salts. It is also an ingredient of sizing—the thin, gelatinous coating applied to cotton and silk to make them waterproof. The mineral is named after its type locality, Epsom in Surrey, England, where it forms around mineral springs.

As can be seen from its chemical formula of $MgSO_4.7H_2O$, epsomite is a sulfate of magnesium. The attached molecules of water of crystallization give rise to epsomite's alternative name, heptahydrite, which comes from the Greek *hepta*, meaning "seven."

Unusually for a hydrated mineral, the amount of water attached to a molecule of epsomite is intimately connected with its overall structure. Epsomite has orthorhombic crystals, but if it loses only one of these seven molecules of water of crystallization, it turns into a distinct mineral species called hexahydrite, which conforms to the monoclinic system.

Enormous crystals of epsomite have been found in the salt lakes of the Kruger Mountains in Washington, and at Carlsbad, New Mexico, the United States. The largest crystals are more than 10 ft. (3 m) long. But these large crystals are extremely rare. Epsomite is more generally found as encrustations and massive aggregates on the surface of other minerals and rocks. Typical habits include fibrous, acicular, stalactitic, botryoidal, and granular.

Epsomite is readily soluble in water. Specimens should therefore be stored in a glass or plastic case with a small packet of silica gel to protect them from attack by liquid in the atmosphere.

Below: Epsomite forms typically in white fibrous masses of acicular (needle-shaped) microcrystals.

ERYTHRITE

Erythrite, named for its vivid shades of red (erythros means "red" in Greek), acts as a signpost for prospectors seeking cobalt-bearing ore.

*Erythrite is a secondary mineral formed through the oxidation of **cobaltite** in veins. It may also be associated with **silver** and **skutterudite**.*

Main Sources: ◆ *Australia* ◆ *Austria* ◆ *Canada* ◆ *Chile* ◆ *Czech Republic* ◆ *Democratic Republic of the Congo (formerly Zaire)* ◆ *England* ◆ *France* ◆ *Germany* ◆ *Italy* ◆ *Mexico* ◆ *Morocco* ◆ *Sweden* ◆ *Switzerland* ◆ *Arizona, California, Idaho, Nevada, New Mexico, Utah, and Washington, United States*

Erythrite is sometimes a minor ore of cobalt, but only when it is extracted from the Earth along with cobaltite—the main industrial source of this metal. Erythrite is principally of interest to mineral collectors because of its extraordinary color, which ranges from pale pink to deep purple.

The mineral's geological name is derived from the Greek *erythros*, meaning "red." Miners, however, commonly know it as cobalt bloom. Erythrite has the same structure as nickel bloom—part of the **annabergite** series—but a different chemistry; the two minerals are thus said to be isostructural. They are also both members of the **vivianite** group and the hornesite series.

The distinctive color of erythrite is a useful indicator for prospectors looking for cobalt-bearing ore veins. Where weathered cobalt and nickel ores are found together, so too are erythrite and annabergite—they are both important marker minerals.

In some deposits, the cobalt in erythrite may be gradually substituted by nickel to form annabergite and by magnesium to form hörnesite. These three minerals form a solid solution series.

Also isostructural with erythrite is **köttigite**, a hydrated arsenate with the chemical formula $Zn_3(AsO_4)_2.8H_2O$. But this mineral does not form

Above: Bladed aggregates of erythrite crystals, showing the mineral's characteristic purple and vivid pink coloration.

part of the solid solution series because the zinc it contains will only change places with cobalt on a very limited basis.

Crystals of erythrite are monoclinic; externally, they appear in prismatic or acicular (needlelike) shapes. Erythrite has perfect cleavage, but it is a soft mineral—only 1½ to 2½ on the Mohs scale.

CHEMICAL FORMULAE	
Annabergite:	$Ni_3(AsO_4)_2.8H_2O$
Erythrite:	$Co_3(AsO_4)_2.8H_2O$
Hörnesite:	$Mg_3(AsO_4)_2.8H_2O$

ETTRINGITE

This predominantly yellow and sometimes colorless mineral is named for the locality, Ettringen, in Germany, where it was discovered.

*Ettringite forms in metamorphosed **limestone** and is found mainly in vesicles (bubble-shaped cavities) in lava, where it may be associated with **calcite** and zeolites such as **analcime**.*

Main Sources: ◆ *Germany* ◆ *Israel* ◆ *Morocco* ◆ *Northern Ireland* ◆ *South Africa* ◆ *Sweden* ◆ *Arizona, California, and New Jersey, United States*

Above: Small but beautifully formed crystals of ettringite make an attractive addition to any mineral collection.

Named for the town where it was first found—Ettringen, 20 miles (32 km) southwest of Augsburg, Germany—ettringite was confirmed as a distinct species in 1874.

Ettringite is a hydrous hydrated sulfate of calcium and aluminum. The ettringite group consists of ettringite plus five other minerals with the same basic chemical composition but a variety of other elements that have partly or completely replaced the aluminum in ettringite—boron, chromium, iron, manganese, and silicon. In the mineral thaumasite, some of the aluminum has been replaced by a carbonate radical.

All but one of these minerals conform to the hexagonal system of symmetry. The exception is sturmanite, which has trigonal crystals.

Ettringite has a very low specific gravity of only 1.7. This is because more than half of its atoms are water of crystallization.

SMALL, BEAUTIFUL CRYSTALS

Ettringite crystals are small—seldom more than ¼ in. (6 mm) in length—but they are often beautifully formed. Their habits include hexagonal prisms ending in hexagonal pyramids. Terminations can also be domelike or flat. Flattened rhombohedrons, acicular (needlelike) and fibrous forms are also seen.

ETTRINGITE GROUP

Bentorite:
  $Ca_6(Cr,Al)_2(SO_4)_3(OH)_{12}.26H_2O$
Charlesite:
  $Ca_6(Al,Si)_2(SO_4)_2B(OH)_4(OH,O)_{12}.26H_2O$
Ettringite:
  $Ca_6Al_2(SO_4)_3(OH)_{12}.26H_2O$
Jouravskite:
  $Ca_3Mn^{4+}(SO_4,CO_3)_2(OH)_6.13H_2O$
Sturmanite:
  $Ca_6(Fe^{3+},Al,Mn^{2+})_2(SO_4)_2[B(OH)_4](OH)_{12}.25H_2O$
Thaumasite:
  $Ca_3Si(CO_3)(SO_4)(OH)_6.12H_2O$

EUDIALYTE

Doubts still remain about the exact composition of this colorful mineral, although it was first discovered nearly 200 years ago.

*Eudialyte forms in **pegmatite** and **syenite**. It is often associated with **aegirine**, **arfvedsonite**, **calcite**, **feldspar** (especially **albite**), **natrolite**, **nepheline**, and **quartz**.*

Main Sources: ◆ *Canada* ◆ *Greenland* ◆ *Ireland* ◆ *Madagascar* ◆ *Norway* ◆ *Russia* ◆ *Sweden* ◆ *Arkansas and Montana, United States*

Above: Eudialyte is mainly pink, but the mineral may also appear in brownish-red or yellowish-brown colors.

One of the distinguishing characteristics of this rare and complex silicate mineral is that it is easily soluble in acids. Its name is in fact derived from the Greek meaning "well-dissolved."

Eudialyte crystals are trigonal and appear in prismatic or table-top shapes. They are classically pink in color, but sometimes appear yellowish brown.

The two main sources of eudialyte are the Kola Peninsula of Russia, where it was first discovered, and Kangerdlugssuaq in Greenland, which is now recognized as the type locality.

CONTAINS UNUSUAL METALS

Both these locations are unusually rich in metals that have unusual electrical charges. Examples include barium, beryllium, cerium, niobium, strontium, thorium, yttrium, and zirconium. Elements such as these do not fit easily into widespread and common-place minerals. The few minerals that do contain these elements tend to crystallize late in any cooling process.

Eudialyte is a good example of the type. It is rich in sodium, but also contains zirconium, cerium, and yttrium. In addition, eudialyte is considered to be a potential source of zirconium, although its scarcity and the inaccessibility of most known deposits mean that it has yet to be exploited industrially.

Although eudialyte was confirmed as a distinct mineral as long ago as 1819, there still remains doubt about its exact composition. *Hey's Mineral Index*, the mineralogist's bible, gives the chemical formula $Na_4(Ca,Ce)_2(Fe^{2+}, Mn,Y)ZrSi_8O_{22}(OH,Cl)_2$. Yet, here, as in many references, it is followed by a question mark.

Eucolite is a variant form of eudialyte with a greater concentration of calcium.

FELDSPAR

The 20 members of the feldspar group of minerals together make up more than 50 percent of the Earth's crust.

Feldspars are widely distributed in igneous, metamorphic, and sedimentary rocks.

Main Sources: ◆ *India* ◆ *Russia* ◆ *Sri Lanka*

The feldspars are a group of aluminum silicate minerals. The two main types are orthoclase feldspar and plagioclase feldspar. Orthoclase varieties contain potassium while plagioclase feldspars contain sodium, calcium, or a combination of both. There are also some rare barium feldspars.

Plagioclase feldspars form a solid solution series in which calcium is replaced by sodium to form a range of distinct feldspars. The calcium–rich plagioclases crystallize at higher temperatures and are found in **basalt**. Sodium plagioclases are formed at lower temperatures and occur in rocks such as **granite**.

Orthoclase feldspars also form a solid solution series in which potassium is gradually replaced by sodium. The sodium–rich feldspar is anorthoclase while the potassium-rich end member of this series is albite. Minerals in between these two extremes are usually known simply as orthoclase.

There are several precious forms of feldspar. These include amazonite (the green gem variety of microcline), labradorite (albite), and moonstone (a milky, opalescent variety of adularia orthoclase).

Often, feldspars are referred to simply as plagioclase and orthoclase. However, once they have been identified, some feldspar minerals are found to have distinctive characteristics and are therefore classified as distinct species.

ORTHOCLASE FELDSPARS
Sanidine (potassium-rich)
Orthoclase
Albite (sodium-rich)

PLAGIOCLASE FELDSPARS
Albite (sodium-rich)
Oligoclase
Andesine
Labradorite
Bytownite
Anorthite (calcium-rich)

CHEMICAL FORMULAE
The general formula of feldspar is $X(Al,Si)_4O_8$, in which X may be calcium, potassium, sodium or, sometimes, barium.

Below: This specimen is the albite form of feldspar, which has a play of color, known as a shiller, about its surface.

FLUORITE

A mineral that occurs in many colors, fluorite may be faceted and polished. However, its use as a gemstone is limited by its fragility.

Fluorite forms under a variety of conditions—in lead and silver veins, where it is produced by hydrothermal precipitation, as beds and cavities in sedimentary rocks, in hot spring deposits, and in pegmatite. Associated minerals include apatite, barite, calcite, chalcopyrite, galena, pyrite, quartz, sphalerite, willemite, and witherite.

Main Sources: ◆ *Brazil* ◆ *Canada* ◆ *China* ◆ *England* ◆ *France* ◆ *Germany* ◆ *Italy* ◆ *Mexico* ◆ *Morocco* ◆ *Russia* ◆ *Spain* ◆ *Switzerland* ◆ *Colorado, Illinois, Indiana, Kentucky, New Hampshire, New Mexico, New York, Ohio, and Tennessee, United States*

Fluorite has a wide range of industrial uses—as a flux (added to aid fusion) in iron smelting, as a source of fluorine and hydrofluoric acid, in ceramics, and in special optical lenses. The finest crystals make rare and attractive, if rather fragile, collector's items.

Fluorite is a fluoride of calcium with the chemical formula CaF_2. Its cubic crystals may appear in many shapes—cubes, octohedra, and dodecahedra are common. The mineral's name is derived from the Latin *fluere* ("to flow"), this being a reference to its low melting point.

MULTIPLE COLORS

The colors of fluorite are variable. Blue, green, purple, and yellow are most common, but some specimens are black, pink, red, or colorless. Most specimens have a single color, but a few have multiple colors arranged in bands or zones with shapes that correspond to the internal shape of the crystals. As a result it is possible to see cubic crystals within crystals, each with a different color.

FLUORESCENT MINERALS

Fluorite is the classic example of a fluorescent mineral. Indeed, this physical property takes its name from that of the mineral. When subjected to ultraviolet light, cathode or X-rays, it will give off a strong pink or violet light of its own. However, fluorescence is not a consistent or reliable phenomenon. The colors produced may differ from one specimen to another, and some specimens of supposedly fluorescent minerals will not fluoresce at all.

BLUE JOHN

Fluorite is still sometimes known by its old name, fluorspar. One local variant of the mineral from Derbyshire, England, was used in the 19th century to make beautiful vases. This form of fluorite is known as Blue John, possibly a corruption of the French *bleu jaune*, meaning "blue yellow."

Above: Crystals of fluorite form in cubes and octohedra and are often twinned.

FRANKLINITE

Franklinite takes its name from a place in New Jersey that is one of its major sources.

*Franklinite is formed in crystalline **limestone** through metasomatism (chemical alteration through the introduction of material from external sources). It is associated with **calcite, magnetite, rhodonite, willemite,** and **zincite.***

Main Sources: ◆ *Romania* ◆ *Sweden* ◆ *New Jersey, United States*

Above: Black franklinite in association with red zincite from the mines at Franklin, New Jersey.

An important ore of zinc and manganese, this mineral is one of many useful, interesting, and unusual species that occur in large quantities or were first identified at the mines in Franklin, New Jersey (*see* box, below). The only important sources of franklinite are here and at Sterling Hill, Ogdensburg, also in New Jersey, although it does occur elsewhere.

Franklinite is an oxide of zinc, manganese, and iron. It is a member of the spinel group, which also includes gahnite, hercynite, magnesiochromite, magnetite, and **spinel** itself.

Crystals of franklinite belong to the cubic system of symmetry. Externally, they appear as octahedrons, often with dodecahedral faces modifying the edges of a shape that nevertheless remains basically eight-sided. Franklinite's other main habits are massive and granular. Some of the largest specimens measure almost 1 ft. (30 cm) in diameter.

INCREASED MAGNETISM

One of the key tests to distinguish franklinite from similar minerals is that its weak magnetism is greatly increased when it is heated in a flame.

HIGHLY SOUGHT AFTER

When franklinite is surrounded by calcite, willemite, and zincite, the white, green, and red colors of the specimens combined are greatly sought after by collectors. They make no attempt to separate the minerals because they look so good together.

FRANKLIN MINE

The mines at Franklin and nearby Sterling Hill in Ogdensburg, New Jersey, were the main—and, in some cases, the only—source of over 300 different minerals. Franklinite is one of 60 species that have these mines as their type locality. Although mining here has now ceased and most of the workings are filled with water and rock, tourists can still take guided tours into some of the old mine shafts. There are also opportunities to look for minerals in the remaining spoil tips.

GABBRO

This dark, coarse-grained rock is mined for its accessory minerals, which may be copper, titanium, and other valuable ores.

Gabbro is the intrusive equivalent of the extrusive **basalt**. *Gabbros occur as plutons (deep-seated rock for-mations) or as small individual intrusions such as sills and dikes. Occasionally, they form in lopoliths—huge concave sheets that may extend for hundreds of miles.*

Main Sources: *Gabbro is a country rock, in other words, an extensive and widely distributed formation.*

A coarse-grained, basic igneous rock (one that is formed from molten material), gabbro is usually speckled gray or black but may sometimes have a bluish or greenish tinge. The etymology of its English name is uncertain, but it is thought to derive from the Latin word *glaber*, meaning "smooth."

Gabbro is a plutonic rock (one formed deep beneath the surface of the Earth). It always contains more than 50 percent of calcium-rich plagioclase **feldspar**, together with pyroxene minerals such as **augite**—these are its essential mineralogical components. In addition, gabbro may contain a large number of accessory minerals, such as **apatite**, **chromite**, **garnet**, **hornblende**, **ilmenite**, **magnetite**, **olivine**, **rutile**, and **zircon**. Gabbro is poor in silica compared to granite, containing as it does between 45 and 55 percent, including 10 percent **quartz** or less.

DIFFERENT FORMS

There are many different forms of gabbro. Some, such as hornblende gabbro and quartz gabbro, are named after their main accessory minerals. Others have their own names. One of the best known of these is norite, a gabbro with an even higher than usual concentration of plagioclase feldspar. Another is troctolite, a strongly speckled variety that is also known as troutstone.

Some gabbros are layered, with alternating dark and light bands, each measuring from 1 in. (2 cm) or less up to 1 yd. (90 cm) in thickness. These layers may be inclined, sometimes quite steeply. This is a result of movements of the Earth's plates, as a result, for example, of folding or faulting.

The gabbros in Liguria, Italy, and Cyprus in the Mediterranean are rich in ores of **copper**. Other deposits have an abundance of other valuable ores. Those that contain ilmenite and magnetite, for example, are mined for their titanium and iron ore respectively. Elsewhere, gabbros are mined for their chromium, nickel, and platinum content.

Left: The light parts of gabbro are plagioclase feldspar, while the dark areas are pyroxenes.

GADOLINITE

A mineral with a large number of possible elemental components, gadolinite may be greenish gray, gray, brown, or black in color.

*Gadolinite is found in igneous rocks, especially **syenite**, in **pegmatite**, and in metamorphic **schist**.*

Main Sources: ◆ *Australia* ◆ *Austria* ◆ *Greenland* ◆ *Italy* ◆ *Japan* ◆ *Norway* ◆ *Russia* ◆ *Scotland* ◆ *Sweden* ◆ *Switzerland* ◆ *Arizona, Colorado, and Texas, United States*

Above: This gadolinite has no clear overall shape—deposits such as this are known as massive aggregates.

Gadolinite is an important ore of three metals—beryllium, thorium, and yttrium. There are now known to be two forms of gadolinite. The basic variety, a silicate of yttrium, iron, and beryllium, was confirmed as a distinct species in 1802. It was named after Johan Gadolin (1760–1852), the Finnish chemist who discovered yttrium and isolated the oxide of another metal, gadolinium.

Then, in 1978, scientists identified a variant form of gadolinite containing all the above elements together with cerium, lanthanum, and/or neodymium—this last element may replace the yttrium. This mineral was named gadolinite-(Ce). The original variety is now referred to as gadolinite-(Y).

RADIOACTIVE

Although thorium is not a chemical component of gadolinite, it often occurs as an impurity within the body of the mineral. Thorium is a radioactive metal that may be converted into fissionable uranium-233, so it is an important source of atomic fuel. The gadolinite specimens that contain thorium are also radioactive.

The metal yttrium, meanwhile, is used to provide the red color in color television sets (*see* photo, left). The industrial uses of the third metal, beryllium, are described in the entry on **beryl**.

Gadolinite conforms to the monoclinic system of symmetry but distinct crystals are rare. Most deposits are massive or compact aggregates.

CHEMICAL FORMULAE	
Gadolinite-(Ce):	$(Ce,La,Nd,Y)_2Fe^{2+}Be_2Si_2O_{10}$
Gadolinite-(Y):	$Y_2Fe^{2+}Be_2Si_2O_{10}$

GALENA

Galena is the most important source of lead—a metal with a wide range of uses, although these are limited because of its toxicity.

*Formed in hydrothermal veins, galena is found in association with **fluorite, quartz, calcite, sphalerite,** and **pyrite.***

Main Sources: ◆ *Australia* ◆ *Austria* ◆ *Belgium* ◆ *Bolivia* ◆ *Canada* ◆ *Chile* ◆ *Czech Republic* ◆ *England* ◆ *France* ◆ *Germany* ◆ *Ireland* ◆ *Italy* ◆ *Mexico* ◆ *Namibia* ◆ *Peru* ◆ *Romania* ◆ *Russia* ◆ *Scotland* ◆ *Arizona, California, Colorado, Idaho, Illinois, Iowa, Kansas, Montana, Missouri, New York, Oklahoma, South Dakota, Tennessee, Texas, Utah, Washington, Wisconsin, and Wyoming, United States* ◆ *Wales* ◆ *Zambia*

This mineral is the most important ore of both lead and **silver**. Although silver does not appear in the chemical formula of galena, it may be substituted for the lead and can make up as much as one percent of the total weight of a specimen. Lead is extracted from galena by roasting the ores and then reacting the lead oxide that is obtained with carbon. This forms carbon dioxide gas and isolates the metal.

Above: Cubic crystals of galena. Note the bright metallic luster and the clearly defined lines of cleavage.

MODERN USES

The principal modern uses of lead are in accumulator batteries and solder, an alloy with a low melting point that is used to join metals. Lead is also a major component of bullets (*see* photo, left).

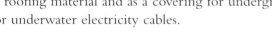

The metal is soft, easily hammered out into sheets, and is also highly resistant to corrosion. These properties make it industrially useful, for example as a roofing material and as a covering for underground or underwater electricity cables.

Lead absorbs radiation so it is also used as a protective shield around nuclear reactors and X-ray equipment. Mineralogists may use sheets of it to protect themselves from the harmful rays given off by radioactive minerals such as **autunite** and **gadolinite**.

POISONOUS METAL

Lead was once an important component of children's toys and water pipes. However, it was then discovered that prolonged exposure is poisonous to humans—it causes plumbism, a disease that is fatal in 25 percent of cases. As a result, lead is no longer used for either of these purposes. Its use as an additive in some grades of automobile gas is also discouraged in many parts of the world.

GARNET

The many different colors of garnet depend on the mineral's chemical composition and the presence of impurities.

Garnets form under high temperatures and/or pressures and are relatively common in highly metamorphosed rocks and in some igneous formations.

Main Sources: ◆ *Almandine: Australia, Brazil, Canada, Greenland, India, Japan, Sri Lanka, Madagascar, Norway, Sweden, Tanzania, Uruguay, United States* ◆ *Andradite: Australia, Czech Republic, Greenland, Italy, Norway, Romania, Russia, Sweden, Switzerland, Uganda, United States* ◆ *Grossular: Australia, Brazil, Canada, Italy, Kenya, Mexico, Pakistan, Russia, Sri Lanka, Switzerland, Tanzania, United States* ◆ *Pyrope: Australia, Czech Republic, India, South Africa, United States* ◆ *Spessartine: Afghanistan, Australia, Brazil, Czech Republic, England, Finland, Madagascar, New Zealand, Pakistan, United States, Wales* ◆ *Uvarovite: Canada, Finland, Norway, Russia, South Africa, Turkey, United States*

Above: Crystals of andradite, a yellow variety of garnet that is sometimes used as a gemstone.

Garnets are a group of silicates with the general formula $X_3Y_2(SiO_4)_3$—the X may represent calcium, ferrous iron, magnesium, or manganese, while the Y may represent aluminum, chromium, ferric iron, or titanium. All garnets crystallize in the cubic system.

There are six main types of garnet—almandine, andradite, grossular, pyrope, spessartine, and uvarovite. The finest specimens are used as gemstones.

The English name is derived from the Old French *grenat*, meaning "red"—the color of many varieties. Almandine may be used to color stained glass windows (*see* photo, above left).

Both pyrope and almandine are red, although pyrope is generally lighter. The color of both these minerals is derived from the presence of iron. While the iron is an integral part of almandine, it is an impurity in pyrope. The green colors of andradite and uvarovite are derived from the presence of chromium impurities. Yellow varieties of andradite are known as topazolite, while dark red or black crystals are called melanite. The best grossular garnet is also green, but specimens may appear in a wide range of colors. Orange or brown specimens may be known as hessonite. Finally, spessartine is orange. The exact intensity of this coloration is determined by the amount of iron in each specimen.

CHEMICAL FORMULAE	
Almandine:	$Fe^{2+}_3Al_2(SiO_4)_3$
Andradite:	$Ca_3Fe^{3+}_2(Si_4O_3$
Grossular:	$Ca_3Al_2(SiO_4)_3$
Pyrope:	$Mg_3Al_2Si_3O_{12}$
Spessartine:	$Mn_3Al_2(SiO_4)_3$
Uvarovite:	$Ca_3Cr_2(SiO_4)_3$

GARNIERITE

Characterized by its brilliant green coloration, garnierite is a layer silicate, often containing a high percentage of nickel.

Garnierite is formed in igneous rocks through the alteration of nickel sulfides by hydrothermal fluids. It may be associated with the two main ores of nickel, **pentlandite** *and* **pyrrhotite**.

Main Sources: ◆ *Italy* ◆ *Madagascar* ◆ *Russia* ◆ *South Africa* ◆ *North Carolina and Oregon, United States*

A significant ore of nickel, garnierite was named after Jules Garnier, the French geologist who first discovered it at Nouméa on the Pacific island of New Caledonia.

NOT A MINERAL

Even though garnierite was first described in 1874, its precise nature has never been conclusively determined. Therefore it is not strictly a mineral, but is a general term applied to nickel-bearing hydrous silicates. The chemical formula generally ascribed to garnierite—$(Ni,Mg)_3Si_2O_5(OH)_4$—is not scientifically proven, it is merely speculation. This silicate may also be known as noumeite.

BRILLIANT GREEN

Garnierite conforms to the monoclinic system of symmetry and crystals usually form as lamellae (thin plates or scales), as crusts, or in massive habits. One of the most distinctive characteristics of this silicate is that it is often a vibrant, almost luminous green color. However, specimens may also be white, with an earthy (non-reflective) or waxy luster. The streak (the color it would be if it were reduced to powdered form) is light green—this may be tested by rubbing a specimen across a clean, white, porcelain tile.

Garnierite may contain between 14 and 40 percent by weight of nickel. Some specimens also feature between three and 30 percent of magnesium. It is not known whether or not the magnesium content is a result of atomic substitution of the nickel.

Left: Green is the characteristic color of garnierite, but this silicate may also be white.

GIBBSITE

Distinctive for the claylike smell it gives off when breathed on or rubbed, gibbsite often forms within the structure of other minerals.

*Most gibbsite is secondary in origin, having been formed through the alteration of primary aluminum-bearing rocks and minerals such as **feldspar**. Some specimens, however, are primary, having been deposited directly from hydrothermal fluids. Gibbsite often forms as layers within the structure of other minerals, particularly **kaolinite** and **montmorillonite**. It is also associated with **aurichalcite**, **azurite**, and **diaspore**.*

Main Sources: ◆ *Australia* ◆ *Brazil* ◆ *Canada* ◆ *France* ◆ *Germany* ◆ *Ghana* ◆ *Greece* ◆ *Guyana* ◆ *Hungary* ◆ *India* ◆ *Indonesia* ◆ *Italy* ◆ *Jamaica* ◆ *Madagascar* ◆ *Norway* ◆ *Russia* ◆ *Scotland* ◆ *Suriname* ◆ *Arizona, Arkansas, California, Massachusetts, New York, Pennsylvania, and Washington, United States*

An important ore of aluminum, gibbsite is one of the three main components of **bauxite**. It was confirmed as a distinct species in 1822 and named after Colonel George Gibbs (1776–1833), a mineralogist who helped to found the *American Journal of Science* and who later donated his entire collection of 12,000 rock and mineral specimens to Yale University. The type locality for gibbsite is Richmond, Berkshire County, Massachusetts.

This mineral is a hydroxide of aluminum with the chemical formula $Al(OH)_3$ and conforms to the monoclinic system of symmetry. It is polymorphous with three other minerals—bayerite, doyleite, and norstrandite. This means that all four species have exactly the same chemical formula but important physical differences.

PHYSICAL APPEARANCE

The external appearance, or habit, of gibbsite is usually massive, but rare crystals are found in flattened, tabular, pseudohexagonal shapes. When it occurs in bauxite, gibbsite often takes the form of pea-shaped aggregates known as pisoliths. The mineral may also be found as botryoidal (grapelike) encrustations, concretionary, stalactitic, and foliated masses. Most gibbsite is white, reddish white, or colorless with shades of gray, blue, and green and a pearly or vitreous luster.

SMELLS OF WET CLAY

The most important test for gibbsite is that it will give off a distinctive smell of wet clay when it is rubbed vigorously or breathed on. It is a soft mineral, measuring just 2½ to 3½ on the Mohs scale, and has perfect cleavage. It also has a low specific gravity, weighing only 2.4 times more than the equivalent volume of water at room temperature.

Above: A crust of white gibbsite on the surface of an aluminum-rich rock.

GLAUBERITE

This sulfate of sodium and calcium is named for the physician who discovered its benefits to health.

An evaporite mineral, glauberite forms in saline environments—dried-out seas, salt lakes, and lagoons. It also occurs around fumaroles (volcanic steam vents). As well as the pseudomorphs of this mineral (see below), it may be associated with **halite** *and* **thenardite**.

Main Sources: ◆ *Australia* ◆ *Austria* ◆ *Canada* ◆ *Chile* ◆ *China* ◆ *France* ◆ *Germany* ◆ *India* ◆ *Italy* ◆ *Kenya* ◆ *Russia* ◆ *Spain* ◆ *Arizona, California, New Jersey, New Mexico, Texas, and Utah, United States*

Above: Glauberite is a transparent to translucent mineral that tends to form in pyramidal shapes.

With the chemical formula $Na_2Ca(SO_4)_2$, glauberite is a sulfate of sodium and calcium. It is sometimes used as a laxative, known as Glauber's salt (*see* box, below), as a mordant (fixative) for dyes, and in the manufacture of glass (*see* photo, left) and glazes. The type locality of this mineral is Villa Rubia, Ocana in Toledo, Spain.

Crystals of glauberite conform to the monoclinic system of symmetry. Externally, they appear in steeply inclined wedge or tabular shapes with dipyramidal bases. Many glauberite crystals have striations (indented lines) along their faces.

Glauberite is often replaced by other minerals, which assume its shape in a process known as pseudomorphism. The most notable pseudomorphs of glauberite are **calcite**, **gypsum**, **opal**, and **quartz**. In addition, glauberite may itself sometimes replace quartz and **prehnite**. Pseudomorphism often causes identification problems that can be solved only by detailed analysis of both the chemistry and the physical properties of the specimens in which it occurs.

If left in the open air for long periods, the water in the atmosphere may alter glauberite to gypsum (hydrated calcium sulfate).

GLAUBER

Johann Rudolph Glauber (1604–70) was a German chemist and physician who discovered that the product of a reaction between common rock salt (the mineral halite) and sulfuric acid was safe for internal use and was effective as a purgative medicine. When a naturally occurring substance with the same chemical composition as Glauber's salt was positively identified in 1808, it was named glauberite in his memory. Nevertheless, most Glauber's salts are still manufactured rather than mined.

GLAUCOPHANE

An amphibole mineral, glaucophane is usually a gray or bluish-gray color, although green or red inclusions may occur within a specimen.

*Glaucophane is often found in crystalline **schist**, where it is associated with the minerals **aragonite**, almandine, **epidote**, and **garnet**.*

Main Sources: ◆ *France* ◆ *Greece* ◆ *Italy* ◆ *Japan* ◆ *Scotland* ◆ *Switzerland* ◆ *California, Colorado, and Washington, United States*

Glaucophane is an amphibole, one of a large group of silicates of aluminum, calcium, iron, magnesium, and/or sodium. Other members of this group include **actinolite**, **hornblende**, and **tremolite**.

Amphibole minerals such as glaucophane occur mainly in metamorphic rocks formed at low temperatures, under high pressure. Rocks that contain large amounts of these minerals are known as amphibolites.

In some deposits, the magnesium in glaucophane is gradually replaced by more iron to form ferro-glaucophane. As a result, these two minerals are the end members of a solid solution series.

The English name for glaucophane is derived from the Greek *glaukos*, meaning "bluish green," and *phainesthai*, meaning "to appear."

RUTILE IMPURITIES

Crystals of glaucophane conform to the monoclinic system. Externally, they may appear prismatic or acicular (needle-shaped). Some of the finest specimens have green or red acicular inclusions visible within them, due to the presence of impurities of **rutile**. Most commonly, however, glaucophane occurs as massive, fibrous, or granular aggregates.

Glaucophane often looks like, and may be mistaken for, **riebeckite**. One test for glaucophane is that when it is heated in an open flame, it melts at fairly low temperatures to form a green glass.

Above: Glaucophane often forms in fibrous aggregates typical of amphibole minerals.

CHEMICAL FORMULAE

Glaucophane:
$$Na_2(Mg,Fe^{2+})_3Al_2Si_8O_{22}(OH)_2$$
Ferro-glaucophane:
$$Na_2Fe^{2+}_3Al_2Si_8O_{22}(OH)_2$$

GNEISS

Formed from the high-grade metamorphism of any preexistent rock, gneiss comprises much of the Earth's deeper continental crust.

Gneiss is a product of high-grade regional metamorphism—it forms at temperatures of about 1,292° F (700° C) and under pressure of more than 6,000 atmospheres (6 kilobars).

Main Sources: *Gneiss is produced wherever granitic igneous rock or sedimentary rock have been subjected to intense heat and pressure.*

Gneiss is a medium- to coarse-grained, regional metamorphic rock. When applied to rocks, the term "regional" means "covering enormous areas." The most striking characteristic of this rock is the way it forms in alternating bands of dark and light colors. Some of the finest examples may be polished into ornamental slabs.

Gneiss is abundant on the surface of the Earth and is also believed to be one of the main components of the continental crust. Its English name comes from the Old Norse word *gneista*, meaning "to give off sparks."

ESSENTIAL COMPONENTS

The essential mineralogical components of gneiss are **feldspar**, **mica**, and **quartz**. In addition, it may contain a large number of accessory minerals including **apatite**, **epidote**, **garnet**, **hornblende**, **ilmenite**, **magnetite**, **monazite**, **pyrite**, and **pyrrhotite**. In banded gneisses, the light stripes are composed of feldspar and quartz, while the darker parts are made of hornblende, biotite, and **augite**, which contain either iron or magnesium.

There are many different forms of gneiss. Some varieties, such as **granite** gneiss, are named after the paragneisses (preexistent rocks) from which they were originally formed. Others are named after their main accessory mineral—staurolite gneiss, for example, is rich in **staurolite**.

In some deposits, the feldspar and quartz appear in small, round lenses that are scattered throughout the rock and are thought to resemble eyes. Such formations are known as augen gneiss, from the German *Augen*, meaning "eyes."

Left: Gneiss is characterized by clearly visible dark and light surface banding.

GOETHITE

An iron-bearing mineral, goethite occurs in many different shapes, including the needle-shaped crystals that gave it its original name.

Above: Goethite is usually black, but the presence of impurities may give it a reddish or yellowish-brown color.

*Goethite is an alteration product of **magnetite, pyrite,** and **siderite**. All four of these iron ores may occur together in weathered surface deposits known as gossan, or iron hat.*

Main Sources: ◆ *Brazil* ◆ *Cuba* ◆ *Chile* ◆ *Czech Republic* ◆ *England* ◆ *France* ◆ *Germany* ◆ *Italy* ◆ *Mexico* ◆ *Morocco* ◆ *Alabama, Arizona, Colorado, Georgia, Michigan, South Dakota, Tennessee, Texas, Utah, Virginia, and West Virginia, United States*

One of the Earth's most widely distributed and commonplace minerals, goethite is an ore of iron and is also used as an artist's brown pigment. It is named after Johann Wolfgang von Goethe (1749–1832), the great German writer, who was also an enthusiastic mineralogist. Before he was honored in this way, in 1806, the mineral had long been known as acicular iron, because it was often found as needle-shaped crystals.

The most extensive deposits of goethite are formed in fresh and saline water, especially calm, inland lagoons, where the mineral precipitates to become one of the main components of bog iron ore. Among the minerals with which goethite is most commonly associated are **hematite** and **limonite**— two more iron-bearing minerals—and also **quartz**. Goethite is polymorphous with **lepidocrocite** and with two other iron oxides, akaganéite and feroxyhyte. This means that it may take on the external form of these other minerals, which can make identification difficult.

MANY HABITS

Crystals of goethite conform to the orthorhombic system of symmetry and have a wide range of habits (external appearances). They may appear in acicular, prismatic, platy (flat, thin crystals), radiating, fibrous, reniform (kidney-shaped), botryoidal (resembling bunches of grapes), or stalactitic forms. Massive aggregates, with no definite shape, are also common.

In addition, some goethite forms in tiny egg-shaped grains known as oolites. Such deposits are known as minette ores.

Goethite is commonly black, but may take on other colors, such as brown, red, or yellow, depending on the impurities it contains, the other minerals with which it is associated, and whether or not partial alteration and replacement have taken place. Yellowness, for example, may be due to the presence of limonite in a specimen.

Although goethite is not magnetic under normal conditions, it can be made magnetic by heating. This is one of the key tests for the mineral.

GOLD

A rare and valuable metal, gold has been prized by humans for its beauty since the earliest civilizations.

Large quantities of this metal are found in ore deposits, and one third of all gold is obtained as a by-product of **copper**, *lead, and zinc production. It also occurs in* **quartz** *veins and in the gravel of river beds. Seawater contains gold, but it cannot be extracted economically.*

Main Sources: ◆ *Australia* ◆ *Brazil* ◆ *Canada* ◆ *Chile* ◆ *China* ◆ *England* ◆ *Hungary* ◆ *India* ◆ *Mexico* ◆ *Romania* ◆ *Russia* ◆ *Scotland* ◆ *South Africa* ◆ *Alaska, California, and South Dakota, United States* ◆ *Wales*

Above: A fine quartz prism with pyramidal terminations covered with flakes of gold.

Gold is very rare—the Earth's crust averages less than one seven thousandth of an ounce (0.004 g) per ton—but is widely distributed. It is a relatively unreactive metal so is found mainly in its elemental state. Indeed, there are few naturally occurring gold compounds. Those that do occur include calaverite, krennerite, nagyagite, and sylvanite, all of which also contain the non-metallic element tellurium.

PRIZED SINCE ANCIENT TIMES

Because of its poor chemical reactivity, gold was probably one of the first few metals, along with copper and silver, to be used by humans. This is because it could be used without first having to be refined. Even ancient societies that did not fully recognize its uses prized gold for its beauty.

Today the purity of gold used in jewelry (*see* photo, right) is measured in carats, with nine-carat gold containing at least 37.5 percent of the pure metal. The scale rises through 14, 18, and 22 carats; top of the scale is 24-carat gold (pure gold).

Gold has a very high specific gravity of 19.3, a melting point of 1,945° F (1,063° C), and a boiling point of 5,370° F (2,966° C). It is both the most malleable and the most ductile of all elements. This means that it can be hammered into gold leaf (extremely thin sheets) and drawn into fine wire. It is also an excellent conductor of electricity and heat, surpassed only by copper and **silver**. In addition, gold is highly resistant to any form of alteration or decomposition, so has been used and reused for centuries without deterioration or damage.

Although gold often forms in nuggets, these are rare because nearly all specimens of this metal are melted down to be turned into ingots.

GRANITE

Widespread and abundant, this coarse-grained igneous rock is often used as a building and an ornamental stone.

Most granites are formed by the cooling of magma (molten rock). They may later become exposed to the surface of the Earth by the erosion of less resistant overlying and surrounding rocks.

Main Sources: *Granites may be seen almost anywhere. One of the most spectacular formations is the West Coast Mountain Range, which extends along the shores of the Pacific Ocean through Alaska, Yukon, and British Columbia (Canada), Washington, Oregon, and California in the United States.*

A light-colored, acid igneous rock, granite is found throughout the land surface of the Earth. Its English name—which comes from the Latin word *granum*, meaning "grain"—alludes to the coarse-grained particles that are its most striking and consistent physical feature.

The essential components of granite are **feldspar**, **mica**, and between 10 and 40 percent **quartz**. Between them, these three minerals make up over 80 percent of the rock. The total silica content is more than 65 percent. Among the main accessory minerals in granite is **hornblende**.

ABUNDANT ROCKS

The rock has a mottled appearance and is usually white, gray, pinkish, or yellowish in color. Some altered forms of granite may be greenish.

Granites are the most abundant rocks in mountain belts and continental shield areas. They are plutonic in origin—in other words, they originated at great depth beneath the surface of the Earth. The rock is most commonly seen in exposed intrusions.

FOREIGN BODIES

Some granites contain fragments of unrelated metamorphic or sedimentary rocks. These features, which are known as xenoliths, are formed when pieces of older rock are incorporated into the magma from which granite is formed while it is still fluid and plastic.

These formations, which may extend for hundreds of square miles, are known as batholiths.

Granite may be used as a building and ornamental stone. In addition, many ore deposits—**copper**, lead, zinc, **gold**, and **silver**, for example—were produced by hydrothermal solutions created during the late stages of cooling of granite bodies.

Below: Granite is a coarse-grained igneous rock, with crystals measuring over $\frac{3}{16}$ in. (5 mm) in diameter.

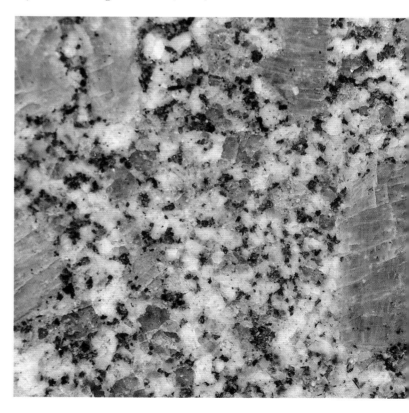

GRANODIORITE

Scientists think that there is more of this widespread and abundant rock than any other plutonic igneous formation.

Granodiorite is formed from cooling magma (molten rock) in deep zones of mountain belts.

Main Sources: *Seen all over the world, some of the finest granodiorite formations in the United States are in the Sierra Nevada of California and Nevada, where it often occurs in the form of batholiths (intrusions).*

Granodiorite is thought to be the most abundant igneous rock. It is also probably the most widely distributed and plentiful of all plutonic igneous rocks—rocks that form by the crystallization of magma deep beneath the Earth's surface.

SPECKLED ROCK

Granodiorite is a coarse-grained intermediate igneous rock composed mainly of **feldspar** and **quartz**. The plagioclase form of feldspar is generally more abundant in this rock than the orthoclase variety. In addition, **hornblende** and **mica** may constitute about 20 percent of the rock, together with small amounts of other accessory minerals. Dark forms of these minerals give the rock a speckled appearance. The total silica content in granodiorite is 55 to 65 percent.

PINK AND WHITE VARIETIES

There are two varieties of this rock—pink granodiorite and white granodiorite. The difference in color arises as a result of variations in the proportions of quartz and feldspar that the rock contains.

Above: Pink granodiorite often contains biotite, hornblende, and pyroxene.

COLOR INDEX

Geologists categorize igneous rocks according to the concentration of dark-colored minerals that they contain. Known as the Color Index, this categorization gives each rock a score of between 0 and 100. The higher the number, the darker the rock, each fitting broadly into four groups.

0 to 30: Very light in color; sometimes described as leucocratic, from the Greek *leukos*, meaning "white." Such formations are composed mainly of feldspar and quartz in felsic minerals; darker igneous formations have greater concentrations of mafic minerals, which contain magnesium and iron.

30 to 60: Mesotypes—neither very dark nor particularly light. The English word comes from the Greek *misos*, meaning "middle."

60 to 90: Melanocratic igneous rocks, from the Greek *melas*, meaning "black."

90 to 100: Hypermelanic igneous rocks—the darkest colored rocks. These tend to be ultrabasic formations such as **peridotite**.

GRANULITE

Tough and resistant to the elements, granulite may be used as a building stone, as well as to make ornamental slabs.

This rock is formed very deep in the Earth's crust at very high temperature and pressures, that is at about 1,652° F (900° C) and about 12,000 atmospheres (12 kilobars).

Main Sources: *There is abundant granulite in the Adirondack Mountains in New York, United States. Granulitic deposits around Madras, India, are sometimes known as charnockite.*

A regional metamorphic rock, granulite's grains, though coarse, are nevertheless finer than those of **granite**. This feature gives the rock its English name, which comes from the Latin *granulum*, meaning "small grain." Granulite's texture is generally equigranular (with equal-sized grains) and it may be banded. Yet some specimens may be interspersed with large, individual crystals of various minerals.

The essential mineralogical components of this rock are **feldspar**, **garnet**, pyroxenes such as **augite**, and **quartz**. It may also contain a number of accessory minerals including **corundum**, **enstatite**, **kyanite**, **magnetite**, **rutile**, and **spinel**.

HIGH-GRADE METAMORPHISM

Quartz is extremely resistant to physical change. Nonetheless, the quartz in granulite often looks as if it has been flattened. This is because of the high grade of metamorphism (alteration by heat, pressure, or chemical processes) to which the quartz was subjected when the granulite was formed.

Granulite almost never contains hydrous or hydrated minerals. Any moisture that may have been present when the rock formed was probably eradicated by the extreme subterranean conditions in which it originates.

Above: Granulite is composed of light, distinct crystals set in a fine-grained base (matrix).

The color of granulite is variable and determined by its exact components. Typically, however, it appears in dark or black masses of pyroxene interspersed with various lighter minerals, such as quartz.

The finest specimens have an attractive mosaic surface pattern and these are sometimes polished and used as ornamental slabs. In addition, granulite is an extremely tough and weather-resistant rock. As a result, where it occurs in large quantities it may be mined for use as a building stone, in particular to make building façades.

GRAPHITE

A black, shiny material that crumbles or flakes easily, graphite is used in pencils and, industrially, as a lubricant.

Graphite occurs naturally in metamorphic rocks (those that have been altered by heat and pressure). It is most likely to form in deposits of **slate** *(which occurs in sheets as graphite itself also does) and in* **schist**.

Main Sources: ◆ *Canada* ◆ *England* ◆ *Finland* ◆ *Germany* ◆ *Greenland* ◆ *Italy* ◆ *Madagascar* ◆ *Mexico* ◆ *North Korea* ◆ *Russia* ◆ *South Korea* ◆ *Sri Lanka* ◆ *Alabama, California, Montana, New Jersey, New Mexico, New York, North Carolina, Pennsylvania, South Dakota, and Washington, United States*

Below: Graphite looks and feels greasy—if it is rubbed on paper, it leaves a gray mark behind.

Although it is difficult to imagine two more different materials than graphite and **diamond**, they are both forms of the same element. While diamond is the hardest naturally occurring substance on Earth, and graphite is one of the softest, they are both allotropes (variant physical forms) of carbon.

When it is subjected to pressure, graphite will break up cleanly into sheetlike layers along its weakest structural planes. This tendency to cleave gives the mineral its distinctive greasy feel. Its most famous everyday use is in pencils (*see* photo, right). The substance known as "lead" in a pencil is in fact graphite.

The mineral is composed entirely of planes of carbon atoms joined in a honeycomb pattern to form sheets that slide smoothly over each other. This property gives graphite its main industrial use, as a lubricant. It is also chemically inert, so is widely used as a heat-resistant material and an electrical conductor.

In the 20th century, the demand for graphite so outstripped supply that it was manufactured artificially by heating coke and clay together. This treatment, the Acheson Process, is named for its inventor, Edward Goodrich Acheson (1856–1931).

FORMS OF CARBON		
	Diamond	**Graphite**
Chemical symbol	C	C
Specific gravity	3.52	2.1 to 2.3
Fracture	Conchoidal	Uneven
Hardness	10	1 to 2
Crystal shape	Cubic	Trigonal

GREENOCKITE

Although greenockite is an important ore of cadmium, it seldom occurs in economically viable formations.

Greenockite forms as a replacement and alteration product of **sphalerite** *in veins containing cadmium. Associated minerals include* **calcite, cassiterite, chalcopyrite, fluorite, marcasite, natrolite, prehnite, pyrite, quartz, smithsonite, sphalerite,** *and* **wavellite.**

Main Sources: ◆ *Australia* ◆ *Bolivia* ◆ *Czech Republic* ◆ *Italy* ◆ *Namibia* ◆ *Scotland* ◆ *Spain* ◆ *Arizona, Arkansas, California, Illinois, Kentucky, Missouri, Nevada, New Jersey, New Mexico, Pennsylvania, Utah, and Washington, United States*

Above: Greenockite on the surface of a cadmium-bearing rock that also contains sphalerite. Greenockite has a distinctively greasy (resinous) luster.

This rare mineral was confirmed as a distinct species in 1840 and was named after Lord Greenock (1783–1859), the British army officer who discovered it in Scotland.

A sulfide of cadmium, greenockite is the most important naturally occurring ore of this metal. However, it supplies only a small amount of the cadmium used in industry. Most cadmium is obtained during the processing of zinc ores—sphalerite contains 0.1 to 0.2 percent cadmium, while smithsonite contains up to 5 per cent cadmium.

CADMIUM AND ITS USES

About three quarters of all cadmium is used for plating easily corroded metals such as iron and steel. Because of its low melting point, cadmium is also used in special alloys such as aluminum solder (40 percent cadmium, 50 percent lead, 10 percent tin) and Wood's metal (50 percent **bismuth**, 25 percent lead, 15 percent cadmium, 10 percent tin), which has a melting point of 158° F (70° C). It is also alloyed with nickel to make rechargeable batteries.

Greenockite is closely related to hawleyite, another sulfide of cadmium with the same chemical formula but a different internal symmetry. Greenockite has hexagonal crystals, while those of hawleyite are cubic. The two minerals are dimorphous.

Some greenockite also has a hexagonal habit (appearance), but most specimens appear in prismatic or tabular form. Unusually, a few crystals of this mineral are hemimorphic. This means that one half appears in a different external shape from the other. Most deposits occur as yellow, powdery patinas (coatings) on the surface of zinc minerals, but there are some economically viable crystalline formations.

Greenockite is readily soluble in hydrochloric acid, giving off hydrogen sulfide, a gas with a smell like rotten eggs. This is one of the classic tests for establishing its identity.

GYPSUM

Commonly found with borax, calcite, halite, pyrite, and sulfur, gypsum is a mineral with a wide variety of forms and applications.

Gypsum is one of the more common minerals in sedimentary environments. It is a major rock-forming mineral that produces massive beds, usually through precipitation from highly saline waters.

Main Sources: ◆ *Austria* ◆ *Canada* ◆ *Chile* ◆ *England* ◆ *France* ◆ *Germany* ◆ *Italy* ◆ *Mexico* ◆ *Poland* ◆ *Russia* ◆ *California, Colorado, Iowa, Kansas, Michigan, New Mexico, New York, Oklahoma, South Dakota, and Utah, United States*

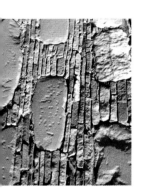

A hydrated sulfate of calcium with the chemical formula $CaSO_4.2H_2O$, this mineral's English name comes from the Greek *gypsos*, meaning "chalk."

About 75 percent of the gypsum extracted from the Earth is used to make plaster of Paris, the white cementing material used to set broken bones.

The mineral has numerous other applications—in plasterboard (*see* photo, left), some cements, fertilizer, ornamental stone, and as dressmakers' chalk. Also, because of the mineral's low thermal conductivity, it is widely used in drywall as an insulating filler.

Above: Magnificent crystals of selenite—the transparent variety of gypsum.

INTERESTING VARIETIES

There are several interesting and valuable varieties of gypsum. Colorless and transparent gypsum, for example, is known as selenite, a name derived from the Greek *selene*, meaning "the Moon." There is also a smooth, fibrous aggregate form known as satin spar, which is sometimes cut *en cabochon* and used as jewelry. Alabaster, meanwhile, is a fine-grained massive variety of gypsum that is used as an ornamental stone. Another form, desert rose, is a brown, flower-shaped variety of the mineral.

Crystals of gypsum conform to the monoclinic system of symmetry. Externally they often appear in tabular, bladed, or blocky crystals with slanted parallelogram outlines. Long, thin crystals may twist round into shapes known as ram's horn selenite.

Twinning is common with this mineral—it commonly forms butterfly twins, spearhead twins, swallowtail twins, and fishtail twins. It can also be massive, earthy, crusty, or granular in habit (external appearance). Some specimens of gypsum may be fluorescent and phosphorescent.

GYROLITE

A silicate of calcium, gyrolite is a white or colorless, glassy-looking mineral that has a chainlike bonding structure.

*Gyrolite is a secondary mineral formed through the alteration of preexistent calcium silicates and found mainly in crevices of **basalt**. Some of the finest formations may be seen in vesicles (solidified volcanic bubbles).*

Main Sources: ◆ *Brazil* ◆ *Canada* ◆ *Czech Republic* ◆ *Germany* ◆ *Greenland* ◆ *India* ◆ *Israel* ◆ *Japan* ◆ *Northern Ireland* ◆ *Scotland* ◆ *California, United States*

Gyrolite often forms in spherical concretions (rounded, nodular masses). It is from this habit that it gets its English name, which is derived from the Greek, *gyros*, meaning "round." The mineral was first described in 1851 and was confirmed as a distinct species four years later.

INOSILICATE

A hydrous hydrated silicate of calcium, gyrolite has the chemical formula $Ca_4(Si_6O_{15})(OH)_2.3H_2O$. It has a chainlike internal bonding structure whereby each molecule shares some of its oxygen atoms with those of adjacent molecules within the same mineral. This leads to the formation of molecular chains that are potentially infinite in length. Silicates of this type are known as inosilicates (*see* box, above).

Unlike other similar looking minerals—such as **prehnite** or **smithsonite**—gyrolite usually forms in individual nodules rather than in botryoidal (grape-like) or crustal growths. The largest spherules of gyrolite measure about 2 in. (5 cm) in diameter, while the biggest clusters may be 1 ft. (30 cm) across. Gyrolite is a white or colorless mineral with a vitreous (glassy) luster.

SILICATES

Silicate minerals have a variety of structural forms. Some, such as **garnet** and **olivine**, form in isolated silica tetrahedra. A few are made up of double silicate groups—the commonest, **epidote**, also has single tetrahedra—and a few of silicate rings. Among the latter, the best known is **beryl**. Among the inosilicates (chain silicates) are gyrolite and pyroxenes such as **augite**. Sheet silicates include **kaolinite**, **mica**, and **talc**.

Gyrolite aggregates are often accompanied by **apophyllite**, **quartz**, and zeolites such as **analcime**. They may associated with okenite, another hydrated calcium silicate, chemical formula $CaSi_2O_5.2H_2O$.

Below: White spherules of gyrolite on a basalt groundmass. The largest deposits of this type can measure up to 2 in. (5 cm) across.

HALITE

More commonly known as rock salt, halite is the mineral used all over the world as a food seasoning and preservative.

Above: Beautiful transparent crystals of halite. Specimens with concave faces are known as hopper crystals.

*Halite is found in bedrocks where large extinct salt lakes and seas have evaporated, leaving thick deposits of salt. It is frequently associated with **anhydrite**, **gypsum**, and **sylvine**.*

Main Sources: ◆ *Algeria* ◆ *Austria* ◆ *Canada* ◆ *Colombia* ◆ *England* ◆ *France* ◆ *Germany* ◆ *India* ◆ *Italy* ◆ *Peru* ◆ *Poland* ◆ *Russia* ◆ *Spain* ◆ *Switzerland* ◆ *Arizona, California, Kansas, Louisiana, Michigan, New York, Ohio, and Utah, United States*

Halite is sodium chloride, chemical formula $NaCl$. Its English name is derived from the Greek *hals*, meaning "salt." Around 80 percent of the material dissolved in seawater is salt.

This mineral is most famous as a food flavoring and as a preservative. It is also the main industrial source of chlorine, a gas with a wide range of uses, particularly as a component of the plastic polyvinyl chloride (PVC) (*see* photo, below). Chlorine is usually extracted from halite by the electrolysis of a solution of the mineral.

Halite is mined from evaporite deposits in many parts of the world. Some of the largest such deposits are those near Searles Lake (California) and Salt Lake City (Utah). The cities of Cleveland (Ohio) and Detroit (Michigan) are also built on huge halite deposits, parts of which are mined for spreading on roads. The presence of halite in water lowers the liquid's freezing point and so halite is spread on icy roads and sidewalks in winter.

Halite crystals conform to the cubic system and often have cubic habits, although massive and granular aggregates are more common. Halite is also characterized by fluorescence, and some crystals give off a green, orange, or red glow when placed under an ultraviolet lamp.

A MATTER OF TASTE

Halite can easily be distinguished by its taste. However, since it is potentially dangerous to put an unidentified substance in your mouth—many minerals are extremely poisonous, and some of them look like rock salt—mineralogists have a special method of tasting that minimizes the risk. They first lick one of their fingers, then rub it against the specimen, and then taste their finger, so limiting the amount of the mineral that actually gets into the mouth.

HARMOTOME

Known for the unusual shape of its crystals, the exact chemical formula of the mineral harmotome is still uncertain.

*Harmotome is often found with other members of the zeolite group such as **heulandite** and **stilbite** in vesicles (bubbles) in volcanic rock. It may also occur as lenses in **gneiss**. It is one of the only zeolites to be found in ore deposits, especially in veins of barium and manganese. It is also commonly associated with **barite**, **heulandite**, **pyrite**, **quartz**, and **stilbite**.*

Main Sources: ◆ *Canada* ◆ *Finland* ◆ *Germany* ◆ *Italy* ◆ *Norway* ◆ *Russia* ◆ *Scotland* ◆ *Arizona, Connecticut, New York, and Pennsylvania, United States* ◆ *Wales*

Above: Well-formed crystals of harmotome on a groundmass of igneous basalt.

Harmotome is one of the rarer zeolites—a group of minerals that includes **analcime**. Like all the zeolites, harmotome contains loosely held water that is expelled when the mineral is heated. The name harmotome is taken from the Greek *harmos* ("a joint") and *tome* ("a cut") and refers to its unusual crystal shapes. Its crystals conform to the monoclinic system of symmetry but often appear in table-top shapes that can be mistaken for orthorhombic forms.

MAGNIFICENT TWINS

Twinning is common and may be magnificent— some specimens appear to be composed of three prismatic crystals growing through each other at angles of nearly 90°. In scientific terms, these crystals are known as penetration twins.

Aggregates of harmotome can be radiating and columnar. Most harmotome is milky white, but many color variations are possible, especially yellowish or colorless. The appearance is further enhanced by a vitreous luster (glassy sheen).

In chemical terms, harmotome is a hydrated silicate of barium, potassium, and aluminum with the formula $(Ba,K)_{2-x}(Si,Al)_8O_{16}.6H_2O$. The "2-x" in the formula means that although each molecule contains at least two atoms of barium or potassium, the upper limit to the amount of these metals that may be present has not been determined. Matters have been further complicated by the discovery in Mohave County, Arizona, of harmotome that is rich in sodium—it is not clear whether this is an impurity or an integral part of the mineral. If it is the latter, the formula will need to be revised to include Na.

HAUSMANNITE

Hausmannite, named after an early 19th-century German professor of mineralogy, is a brownish-black mineral with a soft metallic sheen.

*Hausmannite is formed through the dehydration of manganese hydroxides in igneous rocks that have undergone contact metamorphism and in hydrothermal veins. It is most commonly associated with the mineral **pyrolusite**.*

Main Sources: ◆ *Belgium* ◆ *Brazil* ◆ *Bulgaria* ◆ *England* ◆ *Germany* ◆ *India* ◆ *Italy* ◆ *Morocco* ◆ *Russia* ◆ *Scotland* ◆ *South Africa* ◆ *Sweden* ◆ *Switzerland* ◆ *Arizona, Arkansas, California, New Jersey, and Washington, United States*

Confirmed as a distinct species in 1821, this mineral is named after its discoverer, Johann Hausmann (1782–1859), professor of mineralogy at the University of Göttingen, Germany.

Although not widespread or abundant enough to be a major ore of manganese, hausmannite is a minor industrial source of this metal. Most manganese is extracted from pyrolusite, which is often associated with hausmannite.

Hausmannite is an oxide of two forms of manganese—divalent and trivalent. Its chemical formula is $Mn^{2+}Mn^{3+}_2O_4$. In addition to its essential atoms, the mineral may contain impurities of up to seven percent iron oxide and eight percent zinc oxide.

THE SHAPE OF THE CRYSTALS

Hausmannite crystals conform to the tetragonal system of symmetry. The finest specimens have a slight metallic luster and form well-shaped tetragonal dipyramids—an eight-faced form. Twinning is common and extensive. If the crystals are heated to very high temperatures, they assume orthorhombic form. However, this takes place only with synthetic material; there is no evidence of it occurring in nature.

In addition to distinct crystals, hausmannite forms as granular masses and is always either a black or brownish color. The mineral is opaque in most cases except when it is in very slender pieces, which can then appear translucent.

Below: Close examination of these brown hausmannite crystals will reveal that many of the specimens are pyramidal and twinned.

HAÜYNE

Haüyne, first identified on the slopes of Mount Vesuvius in Italy, is also an ingredient of the vivid blue rock, lapis lazuli.

*Haüyne is found in silica-poor igneous rocks such as **trachyte** that have formed from volcanic lava deposits. The minerals with which haüyne is most commonly associated are **leucite**, **nepheline**, and **nosean**. All are members of the sodalite group, silicates of sodium and aluminum. Haüyne also features calcium, chlorine, **sulfur**, and sulfate ions.*

Main Sources: ◆ *Canada* ◆ *Canary Islands (Spain)* ◆ *Germany* ◆ *Italy* ◆ *Morocco* ◆ *Russia* ◆ *Tahiti* ◆ *Colorado, Montana, and South Dakota, United States*

Above: Externally, crystals of haüyne may appear in cubes or in eight- and 12-sided shapes.

Haüyne is one of the components of lapis lazuli, a precious blue rock that also contains **calcite**, **lazurite**, **pyrite**, and **sodalite**. Haüyne may be faceted on its own, but its perfect cleavage and its typical occurrence—as intergrowths with crystals of other minerals—make cutting so difficult that it is rarely attempted. Although cut haüyne gemstones do exist, they are almost always for display in mineral collections, rather than for use as jewelry.

The mineral is named after the Abbé René-Just Haüy (1743–1822), the eminent French geologist who is sometimes known as the father of crystallography. Haüyne was first identified on the slopes of the volcanic Mount Vesuvius near Naples, Italy and confirmed as a distinct species in 1807.

Nearly all haüyne is found in silica-poor igneous rocks formed from lava deposited on and around volcanoes. Some of these volcanoes are still active but many are long extinct. This may explain why Germany, for example, is one of the main sources of haüyne, although its volcanoes are no longer active.

Crystals of haüyne conform to the cubic system of symmetry. Externally, they appear in octahedral or dodecahedral forms and are often twinned (share a face or faces with one or more of their neighbors). Haüyne may also take the form of rounded grains. Its color can be white, yellow, green, blue, or red.

CHANGES IN HEAT AND ACID

Haüyne has a low sensitivity to heat—in other words, it melts only at high temperatures. When it does fuse, it turns into a bluish green glass. The mineral is soluble in acids, leaving behind a gel of silica.

CHEMICAL FORMULAE	
Haüyne:	$(Na,Ca)_{4-8}Al_6Si_6(O,S)_{24}(SO_4,Cl)_{1-2}$
Nosean:	$Na_8Al_6Si_6O_{24}(SO_4)$
Sodalite:	$Na_4Al_3Si_3O_{12}Cl$

HEDENBERGITE

Crystal combinations of this mineral and the closely related diopside are highly prized by collectors.

*Hedenbergite is a rock-forming mineral that is found in contact metamorphic rocks such as **skarn**. It may also occur in certain igneous rocks and ore bodies. The minerals with which hedenbergite is most commonly associated include **actinolite, calcite, galena, garnet, magnetite, rhodonite,** and **wollastonite.***

Main Sources: ◆ *Australia* ◆ *England* ◆ *Finland* ◆ *Greenland* ◆ *Italy* ◆ *Japan* ◆ *Kazakhstan* ◆ *Nigeria* ◆ *Norway* ◆ *Scotland* ◆ *Sweden* ◆ *Arizona, California, Colorado, New Jersey, New Mexico, New York, South Dakota, Utah, and Washington, United States*

This mineral was named by Swedish chemist Johan Jakob Berzelius (1779–1848) in memory of his collaborator, Ludvig Hedenberg.

Hedenbergite is a pyroxene that crystallizes in the monoclinic system and is therefore more specifically, categorized as a clinopyroxene. It is the iron-rich end member of the johannsenite series, a solid solution series that features another clinopyroxene, **diopside.**

AMOUNTS OF IRON AND CALCIUM

All hedenbergite contains iron, but it usually contains more calcium by weight. Some specimens, however, have been found to hold more iron than calcium—these are a variety known as ferrohedenbergite, which is a synonym for augite.

Crystals are rare, but most of those that do occur appear in short prisms with square cross-sections. A few are acicular; a small number are fibrous. Most hedenbergite forms in aggregates that may be compact, granular, lamellar, or massive.

The green and black colors of hedenbergite are broadly similar to those of diopside, but generally darker. Crystals with a good glassy or resinous sheen are particularly prized by mineral collectors.

Above: A mass of bladed crystals of hedenbergite. This specimen has a vitreous luster.

CHEMICAL FORMULAE

Johannsenite:	$Ca(Mn,Fe^{2+})Si_2O_6$
Diopside:	$MgCaSi_2O_6$
Hedenbergite:	$CaFe^{2+}Si_2O_6$

BERZELIUS

Johan Jakob Berzelius (1779–1848) was one of the 19th century's leading scientists. He wrote an important textbook, devised a system of chemical symbols, and compiled the first fairly accurate table of atomic weights. He introduced the use of filter paper into analytical chemistry and discovered several elements, including selenium (1818), silicon (about 1824), and thorium (1829).

HEMATITE

Named after the Greek word for "blood," hematite is often used in jewelry, cut *en cabochon*, carved, or polished to make beads.

*Hematite is both a primary and a secondary mineral. As a primary mineral, it occurs mainly as an accessory in igneous rocks and hydrothermal veins, and also sometimes in sedimentary rocks. As a secondary product, it is formed by the precipitation of iron-bearing fluids that alter or replace preexistent minerals. **Pyrite, quartz,** and **rutile** are just some of the many minerals with which hematite may be associated.*

Main Sources: ◆ *Australia* ◆ *Austria* ◆ *Brazil* ◆ *Canada* ◆ *Cuba* ◆ *Czech Republic* ◆ *England* ◆ *France* ◆ *Germany* ◆ *Italy* ◆ *Mexico* ◆ *Norway* ◆ *Romania* ◆ *Russia* ◆ *South Africa* ◆ *Sweden* ◆ *Switzerland* ◆ *Alabama, Michigan, Minnesota, Missouri, New York, Pennsylvania, South Dakota, Tennessee, Utah, Wisconsin, and Wyoming, United States* ◆ *Venezuela*

Hematite is an oxide of iron with the chemical formula Fe_2O_3. The metal is extracted by heating the mineral in a blast furnace until it melts. The liquid obtained, which is known as pig iron, is then poured into molds, where it is left to cool and resolidify into cast iron. The iron may then be further refined into wrought iron or alloyed with other metals and carbon to make steel.

Below: This hematite specimen shows two different forms of the mineral—crystalline and rounded, mamillated habits.

Hematite is one of the world's leading ores of iron. Its name is derived from the Greek *haema*, meaning "blood," in reference to its typical color. This mineral is often powdered for use as an artist's red pigment.

The mineral has several varieties. Iron rose is a circular arrangement of bladed hematite crystals that resemble the flower. Tiger iron is a sedimentary deposit more than two billion years old that consists of striped alternating layers of silver-gray hematite and red jasper (a form of chalcedony), **chert,** and quartz. Kidney ore is the reniform version. Oolitic hematite is a sedimentary formation composed of small rounded grains. Micaceous (flaky) deposits are sometimes used to make ornamental stones. This form of the mineral is known as specularite.

HEMIMORPHITE

Hemimorphite is one of the few minerals that is hemimorphic—when the end of one prism crystal is a different shape from the other.

Hemimorphite is a secondary mineral formed in parts of zinc-bearing ore veins that have been altered by oxidation. It is most commonly associated with **sphalerite,** *the main ore of zinc, and also with* **anglesite, aurichalcite, calcite, cerussite, galena, limonite,** *and* **smithsonite.**

Main Sources: ◆ *Algeria* ◆ *Australia* ◆ *Austria* ◆ *Belgium* ◆ *Brazil* ◆ *England* ◆ *France* ◆ *Greece* ◆ *Iran* ◆ *Italy* ◆ *Mexico* ◆ *Namibia* ◆ *Romania* ◆ *Russia* ◆ *Spain* ◆ *Arizona, California, Colorado, Missouri, Montana, Nevada, New Jersey, New Mexico, Pennsylvania, South Dakota, Virginia, and Washington, United States* ◆ *Zambia*

Above: Hemimorphite appears in a wide range of shapes and colors. These white crystals are tabular.

A widespread and commonplace mineral, hemimorphite is sometimes mined for its zinc. It may appear in a wide range of colors—blue, brown, gray, green, white, yellow—but it may also be colorless, like its streak.

Crystals conform to the orthorhombic system but they lack a center of symmetry and therefore appear in extraordinarily unconventional forms—one end of each prism has a different shape from the other. It is from this property that the mineral derives its name, which comes from the Greek *hemi* ("half") and *morphe* ("form"). Very few other minerals display hemimorphism; **tourmaline** is among those that do.

SHARING OXYGEN

Hemimorphite is a hydrous hydrated silicate of zinc, with the chemical formula $Zn_4Si_2O_7(OH)_2.H_2O$. Its silica molecules form in tetrahedra, each of which shares a common atom of oxygen with another tetrahedral molecule. Minerals of this type are known as sorosilicates.

Specimens of hemimorphite tend to appear in one of two main habits. Fan-shaped aggregates are composed of clear, thin, acicular (needle-shaped) crystals, often with many faces. Other deposits take the form of blue to blue-green grapelike (botryoidal) crusts, often with rough ridges or "cock's combs" on top of them.

Hemimorphite is strongly pyroelectric and piezo-electric. This means that it will conduct electricity when it is heated and when it is subjected to mechanical pressure.

HEULANDITE

Heulandite appears in various shapes, many environments, and in a range of colors from white to yellow, gray, pink, red, or brown.

CHEMICAL FORMULAE	
Heulandite:	$(Na,Ca)_{2-3}Al_3(Al,Si)_2Si_{13}O_{36}.12H_2O$
Clinoptilite:	$(Na,K,Ca)_6(Si,Al)_{36}O_{72}.20H_2O$

*Heulandite may form in a wide range of geological environments, but the largest crystals occur in the petrified bubbles (vesicles) of **basalts**. It is often found in association with **analcime, apophyllite, barite, calcite, chabazite, clinoptilite, natrolite, prehnite, pyrite, quartz, scolecite, stilbite,** and **tourmaline**.*

Main Sources: ◆ *Australia* ◆ *Austria* ◆ *Brazil* ◆ *Canada* ◆ *Germany* ◆ *Iceland* ◆ *India* ◆ *Iran* ◆ *Italy* ◆ *Japan* ◆ *New Zealand* ◆ *Russia* ◆ *Serbia* ◆ *Scotland* ◆ *Switzerland* ◆ *Alaska, Arizona, California, Colorado, Hawaii, Maryland, New Jersey, Oregon, Utah, Washington, and Wyoming, United States*

Heulandite is one of the most common members of the zeolite group (*see* analcime). It was confirmed as a distinct mineral in 1822 and, at the suggestion of Henry James Brooke (*see* **brookite**), it was named after the British mineral collector and dealer John Henry Heuland (1778–1856). Heulandite's structure is highly absorbent, and so it is sometimes used in industry as a chemical filter.

A MINERAL OF MANY HABITS

Crystals of heulandite conform to the monoclinic system of symmetry. They appear in a wide range of habits—they may be irregular, four-sided shapes (trapezoids), prisms with sloping ends that resemble rooftops, acicular (needle-shaped), or tabular.

VARIOUS IMPURITIES

Heulandite is a hydrated silicate of sodium, calcium, and aluminum. Some specimens also contain significant amounts of barium, magnesium, potassium, and strontium. However, these take the form of impurities and they therefore do not appear in the chemical formula for heulandite. Each molecule of heulandite shares all its oxygen molecules with its neighbors. This causes the mineral to form in sheets, and it is therefore classified as a tektosilicate.

The mineral clinoptilite, often found with heulandite, is so closely related that some geologists have questioned whether it is anything more than a potassium- and silica-rich variety of heulandite. For the time being, however, it is classified as a distinct species, but it may one day need to be reclassified.

Below: A lamellar (layered) aggregate of heulandite on a groundmass of basalt rock.

HORNBLENDE

Hornblende is a member of a large group called amphiboles, which are silicates of calcium, iron, magnesium, sodium, and aluminum.

*Hornblende is widely distributed in many types of igneous rock, including **diorite**, **gabbro**, **granodiorite**, and **syenite**. It may also occur in amphibolite, a metamorphic rock. It is associated with **augite**, **feldspar**, **magnetite**, **mica**, and **quartz**.*

Main Sources: ◆ *Australia* ◆ *Canada* ◆ *Czech Republic* ◆ *England* ◆ *Finland* ◆ *Italy* ◆ *Norway* ◆ *Scotland* ◆ *Sweden* ◆ *California and New York, United States* ◆ *Wales*

CHEMICAL FORMULAE

Hornblende:
$$Ca_2(Mg,Fe^{2+})_4AlSi_7AlO_{22}(OH)_2$$
Alumino-ferro-hornblende:
$$Ca_2Fe^{2+}_4Al_2Si_7O_{22}(OH)_2$$
Alumino-magnesio-hornblende:
$$Ca_2Mg_4Al_2Si_7O_{22}(OH)_2$$
Ferro-hornblende:
$$Ca_2Fe^{2+}_4Al_2Si_8O_{22}(OH)_2$$
Magnesio-hornblende:
$$Ca_2(Mg,Fe^{2+})_4Al(Si_7Al)O_{22}(OH,F)_2$$

This mineral's name comes from the German words *horn* ("horn") and *blenden* ("to deceive"). The first word alludes to the shape of some of its crystals and the second to the fact that, although it is found with iron ores, it has no commercial value.

Hornblende is an amphibole, one of a large group of silicates of calcium, iron, magnesium, potassium, sodium, and aluminum. Their exact composition is complicated and often difficult to determine because of the enormous amount of atomic substitution that takes place between them. Although usually categorized as a distinct species, some authorities see hornblende as a blanket term for a solid solution series that extends from an iron-rich end member known as ferro-hornblende to the magnesium-rich end member, magnesio-hornblende. Hornblende forms in chains of molecules, and is therefore categorized as an inosilicate.

Crystals of hornblende conform to the monoclinic system. Externally, they appear in short, stocky or long, thin prisms. Some have a hexagonal cross-section, although they are rarely symmetrical. The typical termination may resemble a dome, but is in fact two of the four faces of a prism. Hornblende is also found as granular, massive, and occasionally acicular aggregates. It has perfect cleavage and breaks in two directions, at 56° and 124°.

Left: A columnar aggregate of hornblende. When viewed under a microscope, each of the component crystals will reveal a hexagonal cross-section.

HORNFELS

Hornfels is formed at high temperatures near large igneous intrusions and often at great depths within the Earth's crust.

*Hornfels is a fine-grained metamorphic rock formed mainly from sedimentary rocks and volcanic **tuff** in zones of contact metamorphism surrounding igneous intrusions, especially granitic masses.*

Main Sources: *Hornfels is often visible in areas where preexistent clay rocks have been altered by heat. There are fine deposits in the mountains of the U.S. Pacific coast.*

A rock of even texture, hornfels is created at temperatures of 392 to 1,472 °F (200 to 800 °C) at depths of up to 6 miles (10 km) and under extremely high pressures (3 kilobars).

Above: A mass of gray hornfels, a metamorphic rock composed mainly of mica and quartz.

In many deposits of hornfels, there has been complete metamorphism. This means that there has been total recrystallization of the preexistent rocks from which it was originally formed. If, however, during the course of its formation the hornfels becomes foliated—pressed out into thin layers, like the pages of a book—it may still contain remnants of its sedimentary antecedents.

MAIN VARIETIES OF HORNFELS

There are a number of mineralogical varieties of this rock. These are indicated by prefixing the term "hornfels" with the names of its essential constituents. These are four of the main types of hornfels.

Chiastolite hornfels is gray or brown in color and contains **mica** and **quartz**, together with **andalusite** and **cordierite**. This variety takes its name from the thin-bladed crystals that stand out from the matrix (base). These crystals are chiastolite, which is the gem variety of andalusite.

The exact composition of cordierite hornfels is widely variable, and depends on the temperature at which it was formed. It is usually dark colored and contains cordierite, mica, and quartz, which develop during metamorphism. The cordierite appears as large crystals, often several inches in diameter, set in a fine-grained base. Formations of this type are known as porphyroblasts.

A third variety, garnet hornfels, is generally dark colored with reddish patches and crystals of **garnet** set in the matrix. It also contains mica and quartz together with **feldspar**.

The pyroxenes in pyroxene hornfels are also often porphyroblasts. The other essential components are mica and quartz. This rock forms in the higher temperature range and therefore contains no sedimentary structures.

HÜBNERITE

Hübnerite is a yellow to reddish brown mineral with perfect cleavage that forms prismatic and parallel crystals in hydrothermal ore veins.

*The mineral hübnerite is found in metal-bearing veins in **granite pegmatite** and in sedimentary placer deposits that have been transported from one location to another by ice or water. It is associated with **cassiterite, hematite, mica, pyrite, quartz,** and **tourmaline**.*

Main Sources: ◆ *Australia* ◆ *Bolivia* ◆ *China* ◆ *Czech Republic* ◆ *England* ◆ *France* ◆ *Myanmar (Burma)* ◆ *Peru* ◆ *Portugal* ◆ *Russia* ◆ *Spain* ◆ *Arizona, Colorado, Idaho Nevada, New Mexico, North Carolina, South Dakota, and Washington, United States*

Above: Hübnerite may be difficult to distinguish from wolframite, with which it is commonly associated.

This mineral was identified in 1865 and named after Adolph Hübner, a metallurgist from Freiburg, Germany. It contains manganese and tungsten (symbol W) and is a minor ore of tungsten.

FROM HÜBNERITE TO FERBERITE

Hübnerite is one end member of a solid solution series in which the manganese it contains is gradually replaced by iron. The process is known as continuous atomic substitution. Once the amount of manganese has fallen below 80 percent of the maximum possible within the compound, the mineral is reclassified as wolframite. Specimens containing 20 percent or less of manganese and 80 percent or more of iron are known as ferberite—the other end member.

Hübnerite is not common and ferberite is rare. Most of the molecules have an intermediate composition, and the continuum is therefore known as the wolframite series.

LIGHT IN COLOR AND WEIGHT

Hübnerite crystals conform to the monoclinic system; they are less dense and typically lighter in color and more transparent than those of other minerals in the series. Generally tabular in shape, hübnerite also forms in columnar aggregates and lamellar masses.

The type locality of hübnerite is in the Mammoth district of Nevada. It is always against a specimen from this area that any potential new finds are tested for authenticity.

CHEMICAL FORMULAE	
Ferberite:	$Fe^{2+}WO_4$
Wolframite:	$(Fe,Mn)WO_4$
Hübnerite:	$MnWO_4$

HUMITE

The mineral humite, named after an English mineralogist and art collector, also gives its name to a group with three other minerals.

HUMITE GROUP	
Chondrodite:	$(Mg,Fe^{2+})_5(SiO_4)_2(F,OH)_2$
Clinohumite:	$(Mg,Fe^{2+})_9(SiO_4)_4(F,OH)_2$
Humite:	$(Mg,Fe^{2+})_7(SiO_4)_3(F,OH)_2$
Norbergite:	$Mg_3SiO_4(F,OH)$

Humite is a fairly rare mineral that is found in hydrothermal veins and in contact and in regionally metamorphosed dolomitic limestones. It is often associated with **brucite** *and* **olivine**, *as well as* **calcite**, **diopside**, **magnetite**, *and* **spinel**.

Main Sources: ◆ *Finland* ◆ *Italy* ◆ *Spain* ◆ *Sweden* ◆ *New York, United States*

Confirmed as a distinct species in 1813, this mineral is a silicate of magnesium and iron. It is named after Sir Abraham Hume (1749–1838), an English mineralogist and art collector.

THE HUMITE GROUP

Humite is closely related to chondrodite, clino-humite, and norbergite. All four minerals are notable for the way their silicon and oxygen atoms form in layers. They contain varying amounts of their two metals, and norbergite has no iron at all. Collectively, they are known as the humite group.

Humite group minerals are very closely related to —and often associated with—brucite and olivine, the formulae of which are, respectively, $Mg(OH)_2$ and $(Mg,Fe)SiO_4$.

HOW TO DISTINGUISH HUMITE

Within humite are three consecutive layers of chemicals which, if they were free-standing, would be classified as olivine. These alternate between each layer of magnesium hydroxide, which is the chemical composition of brucite. The defining difference between humite and these two minerals is that humite also contains an atom of fluorine and a hydroxyl radical (chemical formula OH). One of the most common members of the humite group is chondrodite, which has only two olivine layers between each brucite layer.

CRYSTAL SHAPES

Crystals conform to the orthorhombic system of symmetry. Their habits include small prismatic to rounded crystals, but they appear most commonly in the form of tiny embedded grains.

Below: This granular aggregate of humite has been extracted from metamorphosed limestone.

ILMENITE

Ilmenite is the second most important ore of titanium, after rutile. It is also used as a flux in blast furnaces and as an abrasive.

Ilmenite forms in mafic igneous rocks through a process known as magmatic segregation. It also occurs in **pegmatites** *and in some metamorphic rocks, as well as in sedimentary rocks. It is also commonly associated with* **analcime, apatite, calcite, hematite, magnetite, monazite, nepheline, natrolite, olivine, pyrrhotite, quartz, rutile, spinel,** *and* **zircon.**

Main Sources: ◆ *Australia* ◆ *Brazil* ◆ *Canada* ◆ *China* ◆ *England* ◆ *Finland* ◆ *France* ◆ *Germany* ◆ *India* ◆ *Italy* ◆ *Malaysia* ◆ *Mexico* ◆ *Norway* ◆ *Pakistan* ◆ *Russia* ◆ *Sierra Leone* ◆ *South Africa* ◆ *Sri Lanka* ◆ *Sweden* ◆ *Switzerland* ◆ *Thailand* ◆ *Arizona, Arkansas, California, Colorado, Massachusetts, New York,* and *Wyoming, United States*

A primary mineral in mafic igneous rocks, ilmenite forms during a process called magmatic segregation. It crystallizes out of the magma at an early stage in the cooling process and its relatively heavy crystals—with a specific gravity of 4.72—sink to the bottom of the fluid and collect in layers. These crystals later make rich ore bodies for titanium miners. Ilmenite is named after its type locality, Lake Ilmen in the Ilmen Mountains, Miask, Russia.

BLACK ON BLACK

Ilmenite is generally iron black with a black to brownish red streak. At times it can form brightly lustered, intricately faceted crystals or in radial clusters arranged in rosettes. Platy hexagonal crystals with rhombohedral faces on the edges can appear very similar to hematite. Ilmenite can also form in compact, massive, granular, and lamellar shapes.

POOR COUSIN

Pure ilmenite is not a profitable ore of iron because the presence of titanium inhibits the smelting process. However, the mineral is often associated with magnetite, which is extracted in the same mining process for its iron content.

The iron in ilmenite may be substituted by magnesium to form geikielite—the two minerals are therefore the end members of a solid solution series.

CHEMICAL FORMULAE	
Geikielite:	$MgTiO_3$
Ilmenite:	$FeTiO_3$

Left: An ilmenite specimen with a metallic sheen. Specimens of this mineral often have a dull luster.

INESITE

The mineral inesite, named after the Greek word for "flesh-fiber," is renowned for its fleshy pink color.

Inesite is a secondary mineral formed in zones of metamorphism and by metasomatism—that is, by chemical alteration through the introduction of new materials from an external source. The other main minerals that are associated with inesite are **apophyllite, axinite, and rhodonite.**

Main Sources: ◆ *Australia* ◆ *Czech Republic* ◆ *Germany* ◆ *Japan* ◆ *Mexico* ◆ *South Africa* ◆ *Sweden* ◆ *California, Colorado, and Washington, United States*

A hydrous hydrated silicate of calcium, manganese, and iron, this mineral's English name is derived from the Greek word *ines*, meaning "flesh-fiber." This is a reference to inesite's threadlike shape and its

Above: This untarnished inesite specimen shows the long, needlelike shapes in which the crystals sometimes form.

pinkish, skinlike color. Inesite was confirmed as a distinct species in 1888.

Crystals of inesite conform to the triclinic system of symmetry. Externally, they are prismatic and commonly have slanted or chisel-shaped terminations. At first glance, some of the shorter of these crystals may be mistaken for rhombohedra, which have six equally slanted faces. But on closer examination, inesite turns out to have only one steeply slanted face, while the other faces are much less steeply inclined. This is an important aid to identification because **rhodochrosite**—another pink mineral with which inesite is commonly associated—also forms in rhombohedra.

Deposits of inesite may also be acicular (needle-like) or tabular, and the mineral often forms in massive aggregates.

A DISTINCT MINERAL OR A VARIETY?

In the 1940s, at least one geologist suggested that inesite may be merely a calcium-rich variety of rhodonite, but the consensus still regards inesite as a mineral in its own right.

PRETTY IN PINK

Although inesite is pink when first extracted from the Earth, it may tarnish on prolonged exposure to the air and turn brown.

The finest pink specimens of inesite are sometimes known alternatively as rhodotilite, from the Greek *rhodos* ("pink") and *tilos* ("fiber").

CHEMICAL FORMULAE	
Inesite:	$Ca_2(Mn,Fe)_7Si_{10}O_{28}(OH)_2.5H_2O$
Rhodonite:	$Mn^{2+}SiO_3$

IRONSTONE

Ironstone must contain at least 15 percent iron to live up to its name, but some of the most valuable specimens have up to 75 percent.

*Ironstone forms in igneous rocks through magmatic differentiation—dense, heavy minerals such as **magnetite** crystallize first and sink to the base of the still-molten magma to form a rich layer of iron. Sedimentary ironstone is found bedded among **limestone** or **sandstone**.*

Main Sources: *Some of the most famous sedimentary ironstones occur in England, especially in the Weald of Kent and Sussex, and in the coal seams of Staffordshire.*

Sedimentary ironstone is a black, brown, green, red, or yellow rock formation that may have a fine-, medium-, or coarse-grained texture, depending on its exact environment of formation.

The rock sometimes contains very small egg-shaped grains, between ⅕ and ⅒ in. (1 and 2 mm) in diameter. In scientific terms, deposits that have this texture are said to be oolitic.

Most ironstone appears in beds that have been deposited in marine environments. The beds themselves may be thick or thin, coarse or fine, in appearance and in composition.

WHAT'S IN A NAME?

To merit the name, ironstone must contain at least 15 percent iron, which usually appears in **chamosite**, **hematite**, **limonite**, magnetite, **pyrite**, and **siderite**. Detrital accessory minerals may also be present in ironstone, while the whole assemblage is cemented together by **calcite** and **dolomite**.

Ironstones are usually interbedded with **chert**, limestone, and sandstone, and the exact dividing line between these rocks is not always clearly defined. Rocks formations that are interbedded in this way are believed to be chemical deposits, formed when iron has been precipitated from solution.

Above: The red color commonly associated with iron is often visible in samples of ironstone.

Ironstone can also be igneous in origin. Oolitic deposits of this type are relatively poor in metal, containing only between about 30 and 40 percent of iron at most. By contrast, replacement deposits—where hematite has pervaded and replaced other rocks, especially limestones—are among the richest in iron, containing up to 75 percent of the metal. Such deposits are often mined extensively for their valuable ore.

JADE

Jade is the term used for green, polished gems and ornamental stone slabs that are made from two similar minerals.

Jade consists of two minerals—jadeite and nephrite. Jadeite is found in serpentinites from olivine rock or in cherts. Nephrite can be found in magnesium limestones and metamorphosed dolomites.

Main Sources: ◆ *Jadeite: China, Guatemala, Japan, Mexico, Myanmar (Burma), New Zealand, United States (California)* ◆ *Nephrite: Australia, Brazil, Myanmar (Burma), Canada, China, Germany, Italy, Mexico, New Zealand, Poland, Russia, Switzerland, Taiwan, Turkestan, United States (California), Zimbabwe*

Above: This rough version of jade shows the white translucence that is common in this hard gemstone.

For centuries, jade was thought to be a single material. It was not until 1863 that scientists discovered it was two minerals: jadeite and nephrite.

The more valuable of the two is jadeite. It is a silicate of sodium, aluminum, and iron, and a member of the pyroxene group. Rarely found in distinct crystals, it is made of microscopic interlocking aggregates that produce a very tough material.

Nephrite is not actually a mineral, but a variety of the mineral **actinolite**, which is characterized by fibrous crystals that are intertwinned to form tough, compact masses.

JADEITE STONES

Jadeite is sometimes sold as "kidney stones" and "loin stones"—names originating with the Spanish conquistadores, who thought the stones warded off hip and kidney complaints.

Jade's strength is remarkable. Tougher than many types of steel, it was used in early civilizations for axes, knives, and weapons. Today jade is valued for its beauty Jadeite jade is green, which is caused by impurities of chromium, but it can also be brown (with iron) or violet (with manganese). The finest specimens are marketed under the name imperial jade. Jadeite is often cut and polished to make jewelry (*see* photo, left).

SIMILARITIES AND DIFFERENCES

	Jadeite	Nephrite
Chemical Formula:	$Na(Al,Fe^{3+})Si_2O_6$	$Ca_2(Mg,Fe^{2+})_5Si_8O_{22}(OH)_2$
Specific Gravity:	3.3	2.9
Crystal System:	Monoclinic	Monoclinic
Hardness:	7	6.5

JAMESONITE

Jamesonite can be mistaken for minerals such as boulangerite and stibnite, but its best crystals are highly prized by mineral collectors.

Left: The metallic sheen of jamesonite's crystals can be seen in this specimen of the massive variety.

Confirmed as a distinct species in 1825, jamesonite is a sulfide of lead, iron, and **antimony**. It is named after the Scottish mineralogist Robert Jameson (1774–1854). The mineral may also be known as feather ore or gray antimony.

BEAUTIFUL CRYSTALS

Jamesonite is greatly sought after by mineral collectors because the finest specimens form beautiful acicular crystals up to 4 in. (11 cm) in length. Specimens can also be found as massive aggregates with a fibrous texture. The crystals are generally dark gray and opaque, with a silky or metallic luster and perfect cleavage. They conform to the monoclinic system of symmetry.

MISTAKEN FOR OTHER MINERALS

Jamesonite may be mistaken for **boulangerite**, a sulfide of lead and antimony that forms in similar acicular crystals. However, boulangerite has flexible crystals, whereas those of jamesonite are usually rigid. Large prismatic crystals of jamesonite may also be confused with stibnite, one of its associated minerals. However, jamesonite crystals have a higher specific gravity, tend to be more brittle than those of stibnite, and are less clearly defined. The crystals also lack stibnite's type of cleavage, which is parallel to the length of its crystals.

Jamesonite is dimorphous with parajamesonite, which has exactly the same chemical formula—$Pb_4FeSb_6S_{14}$—but conforms to the orthorhombic system of symmetry. The manganese analog of jamesonite is benavidesite, a mineral with the formula $Pb_4(Mn,Fe)Sb_6S_{14}$.

*Jamesonite is formed in hydrothermal veins, where it may be associated with a wide range of other minerals, including **arsenopyrite**, **calcite**, **dolomite**, **galena**, **pyrite**, **quartz**, **rhodochrosite**, **siderite**, **sphalerite**, and **stibnite**. It may also sometimes be found with the native elements **antimony** and **silver**, as well as with lead or zinc.*

Main Sources: ◆ *Argentina* ◆ *Australia* ◆ *Bolivia* ◆ *Canada* ◆ *China* ◆ *England* ◆ *Germany* ◆ *Italy* ◆ *Kosovo* ◆ *Mexico* ◆ *Romania* ◆ *Serbia* ◆ *Spain* ◆ *Arkansas, California, Colorado, Nevada, and South Dakota, United States*

JAROSITE

Jarosite's iron content can give it a reddish color and its crystals can appear externally in the shape of cubes that are called pseudocubes.

Jarosite is a secondary mineral found in iron-bearing rocks, particularly in association with decomposing **pyrite***, and in volcanic vents called fumaroles.*

Main Sources: ◆ *Australia* ◆ *Bolivia* ◆ *Chile* ◆ *Czech Republic* ◆ *France* ◆ *Germany* ◆ *Greece* ◆ *Italy* ◆ *Namibia* ◆ *Russia* ◆ *Spain* ◆ *Arizona, California, Colorado, Idaho, Nevada, South Dakota, Utah, and Virginia, United States*

This mineral is named after the locality in which it was discovered—Baranco Jaroso in the Sierra Alamagrera, a mountain range between Murcia and Almería in southern Spain. It was confirmed as a distinct species in 1852.

Jarosite is a hydrous sulfate of potassium and iron. In addition, some specimens may contain appreciable amounts of aluminum and **sulfur**, but these are seen as impurities and therefore do not appear in the chemical formula, which is $KFe^{3+}_3(SO_4)_2(OH)_6$.

Alunite has an almost identical composition to jarosite, except that it contains aluminum instead of iron. The two minerals form a solid solution series in which these metals are substituted for one another.

Other members of the alunite group are similar to jarosite but contain different elements instead of potassium. Niojarosite contains nitrogen and hydrogen (ammonia); natrojarosite has sodium; argentojaroiste has silver; plumbojarosite is the lead-bearing member. Minerals with the elements of plumbojarosite plus arsenic are reclassified as beudantite.

Jarosite crystals conform to the trigonal system. Externally they usually appear as pseudo-cubes with a distinctive vitreous luster, but some may have a resinous (waxy) appearance. If hit with a hammer or subjected to pressure, jarosite will split vertically along its length—this is known as basal cleavage.

Above: The color of jarosite can range from an earthy dark brown to a yellowish or reddish brown, as in this specimen.

PSEUDOCUBES

Although the Earth contains many cube-shaped crystals, the only ones that are described as cubic are those that come from minerals that conform to the cubic system of symmetry. To avoid any possible misunderstandings, other crystal formations that appear to have a cubic shape are said to be pseudocubic.

JET

Jet, popularized in the 19th century as a gemstone to wear to funerals, has been found in burial mounds from prehistoric times.

*Jet is a type of **coal** and is therefore classified as a sedimentary rock formation. It is formed from wood that has fallen into stagnant water and then been compacted and heated by pressure from subsequent layers of sediment that have formed on top of it.*

Main Sources: *The most famous source of jet is along the eastern coast of Yorkshire, England. In the United States, there are large deposits in Utah.*

Jet is an organic gemstone composed mainly of carbon. It is a type of coal, yet it is found in rocks of marine origin, whereas coal is formed from plant matter that has accumulated on land. Evidence of jet's origins include the large numbers of ammonite and bivalve shellfish fossils in the rocks that surround it. Jet is rarely found in extensive deposits, rather a little bit here and there. It has been used in jewelry since ancient times.

The word jet came into English from the French *jaiet*, which is in turn derived from the Greek *lithos gagates*, meaning "stone of Gagas," a town in Asia Minor (modern Turkey).

Jet is almost exclusively black or dark brown in color. However, some deposits contain impurities of **pyrite**, which give it a distinctive brassy yellow coloration and a sparkling metallic luster.

Jet may be tumbled to form beads, polished into cabochons, or cut into a range of other ornamental shapes. In the 19th century it was often made into jewelry, especially brooches and earrings. Queen Victoria took to wearing jet as a sign of mourning following the death of her husband, Prince Albert,

in 1861. She stayed in mourning until her own death in 1901. This set a trend that led to the stone being worn almost exclusively for funerals. However, fashions are now starting to change, and jet is once again acceptable as an accessory on less somber occasions.

Like **amber**, jet is piezoelectric and pyroelectric, meaning that it may generate static electricity when it is rubbed or heated.

The world's most famous historical source of jet is Whitby, England. It is known to have been extracted from this town in Yorkshire since the Roman occupation, before the time of Christ.

Below: These specimens of raw jet show the dimmer and more earthy luster of the stone before polishing.

KAINITE

Kainite is a sulfate mineral that is found only in combination with other salts in evaporite deposits.

*Most deposits of **kainite** appear as massive aggregates or in layers with other evaporites, especially **carnallite**, **gypsum**, **halite**, and **sylvine**. Although distinct crystals of kainite are rare, those that do form—mainly pressed together in rock cavities—may be several inches long.*

Main Sources: ◆ *Germany* ◆ *Italy* ◆ *Poland* ◆ *Russia* ◆ *Ukraine* ◆ *California, New Mexico, and Texas, United States*

The mineral kainite was the earliest commercial source of the fertilizer, potash. The English name of this mineral is derived from the Greek *kainos*, meaning "recent"—this is a reference to the fact that it is formed during a late stage of the evaporation of salt beds. It was first identified as a distnct mineral in 1865.

Kainite is a hydrated chlorosulfate of potassium and magnesium with the chemical formula $KMgSO_4Cl.3H_2O$. It conforms to the monoclinic system of symmetry. The mineral is soft, with a Mohs hardness of 3, and has a low specific gravity—it weighs only 2.1 to 2.2 times more than the equivalent volume of water at room temperature. Samples of kainite have a white streak.

Kainite dissolves easily in water. Specimens must therefore be kept in airtight containers, preferably with a small packet of silica gel to prevent them from deliquescing (dissolving away). They should be cleaned only with a soft brush or duster.

POTASH

Potash is made from potassium chloride. In the early part of the 20th century, most U.S. supplies of this agricultural fertilizer were extracted from kainite shipped from Europe. With the outbreak of World War I in 1914, however, the chemical was needed by Germany and Italy—the main producers—to make explosives, so new sources were sought in the United States. One of the most abundant deposits is in the brine of Searles Lake in California.

Left: A monoclinic prismatic crystal of kainite showing vitreous luster.

KAOLINITE

The clay mineral kaolinite has a variety of uses, from chinaware and porcelain to its use as a filler that adds weight and texture to paper.

Left: Kaolinite often forms in tiny hexagonal scales or plates. It is usually white or grayish in color.

Kaolinite is the main source of China clay, which is used to make chinaware and porcelain. Its name is derived from Kao-ling—literally "high ridge"—a hill near Jaucha Fa in Jianxi, China. Some of the first supplies of clay to reach Europe were extracted from this hill in about 1700. Kaolinite was confirmed as a distinct mineral in 1867.

Kaolinite is polymorphous with three of the kaolinite-serpentine group of minerals—it has the same chemical formula as dickite, halloysite, and nacrite, but its crystals are the only ones that conform to the triclinic system of symmetry, which is the defining difference.

Kaolinite forms on its own so rarely that its categorization as a mineral is more theoretical than real—kaolinite is practically a sedimentary rock formation.

In its pure form, kaolinite is a hydrous silicate of aluminum with the chemical formula $Al_2Si_2O_5(OH)_4$. But in reality it is seldom pure—it is nearly always found as part of a complex mixture with other closely related but significantly different clay minerals belonging to the kaolinite-serpentine group.

Main Sources: ◆ *Brazil* ◆ *Chile* ◆ *China* ◆ *Czech Republic* ◆ *England* ◆ *France* ◆ *Germany* ◆ *Italy* ◆ *Russia* ◆ *Arizona, Arkansas, California, Colorado, Delaware, Georgia, Montana, New Mexico, New York, Pennsylvania, South Dakota, Utah, Vermont, Virginia, and Washington, United States*

USES OF KAOLINITE

When kaolinite and minerals like it are mixed with 20 to 35 percent water, they become plastic (easy to mold under pressure) and retain their shape after that pressure has been removed and they have dried out. This property means that such minerals can be used to make pottery and ceramics. In addition, some 40 percent of the kaolinite mined each year is used as a filler that adds texture, color, and opacity to paper, making it able to take print without running or absorbing the ink. Kaolinite has a high resistance to heat and so it is also used to line the walls of kilns (*see* photo, above) and ovens.

KÖTTIGITE

Köttigite is a minor ore of zinc and is created as a result of the weathering of other zinc minerals.

*Köttigite is a weathering product of zinc minerals such as **sphalerite**. It is commonly associated with **adamite**, **goethite**, **limonite**, and **smithsonite**.*

Main Sources: ◆ *Bolivia* ◆ *Canada* ◆ *England* ◆ *Germany* ◆ *Greece* ◆ *Mexico* ◆ *Namibia* ◆ *Romania* ◆ *Russia* ◆ *Spain* ◆ *New Jersey and South Dakota, United States*

This minor ore of zinc is named after Otto Köttig, the chemist who first described a specimen found in the Daniel cobalt mine at Schneeburg, Saxony, Germany. It was confirmed as a distinct mineral in 1850.

The mineral is isostructural with **erythrite** and **annabergite** (a hydrated arsenate of nickel). This means that the minerals have the same structure but different chemistries. Annabergite, or nickel bloom, is bright green in color while erythrite, or cobalt bloom, is bright red-purple. Köttigite itself is dark red or brown.

Köttigite is a hydrated arsenate of zinc with the chemical formula $Zn_3(AsO_4)_2.8H_2O$. As its zinc is gradually replaced by iron, it forms a solid solution series with parasymplesite, another hydrated arsenate with the formula $Fe^{2+}_3(AsO_4)_2.8H_2O$. Both these minerals are members of the **vivianite** group.

Some köttigite has been found to contain significant quantities of magnesium. These may be impurities, but some scientists believe that the mineral may also form a solid solution series with hörnesite, an arsenate of magnesium with the formula $Mg_3(AsO_4)_2.8H_2O$.

RARE CRYSTALS

Köttigite conforms to the monoclinic system of symmetry. Its typical habits include striated blades and radiating acicular crystals, but crystals are rare. It is usually seen as crusts or earthy masses.

Freshly unearthed köttigite may be covered with brown rust-like stains of the iron oxides **goethite** and **limonite**—these may be removed by dabbing the specimen with cotton wool soaked in distilled water.

Left: This specimen from Mexico shows köttigite's characteristic dark red and brown coloration.

KUTNOHORITE

This rare carbonate mineral is named after its type locality of Kutna Hora, Bohemia, in the Czech Republic.

CHEMICAL FORMULAE	
Ankerite:	$Ca(Fe,Mg,Mn)(CO_3)_2$
Dolomite:	$CaMg(CO_3)_2$
Kutnohorite:	$Ca(Mn,Mg,Fe^{2+})(CO_3)_2$

Kutnohorite is greenish, gray, or pinkish in color. It scores 3½ to 4 on the Mohs Scale of Hardness and weighs 3.12 times more than the equivalent volume of water at room temperature. The mineral displays perfect cleavage—when it is hit with a hammer or subjected to pressure, it will break off cleanly along its weakest structural lines.

Kutnohorite forms in hydrothermal veins and in basic igneous rocks containing large amounts of magnesium.

Main Sources: ◆ *Australia* ◆ *Austria* ◆ *Canada* ◆ *Czech Republic* ◆ *Italy* ◆ *Japan* ◆ *Mexico* ◆ *Sweden* ◆ *Switzerland* ◆ *Colorado, New Jersey, North Carolina, and Pennsylvania, United States*

Below: This pink and gray specimen of kutnohorite has a pearly luster.

This mineral was confirmed as a distinct species in 1901 and named after the location where it was first discovered—Kutna Hora, Czech Republic.

Kutnohorite is closely related to **ankerite** and **dolomite**. All three minerals are carbonates of calcium and magnesium, but ankerite also contains iron, while kutnohorite is a carbonate of calcium, iron, and manganese. They form a solid solution series in which the iron, magnesium, and manganese replace each other in a process of continuous atomic substitution. The change is so gradual that the exact point at which one species ends and another begins may be difficult to pinpoint with scientific accuracy.

When analyzed, the first specimen of kutnohorite ever identified was found to contain two and a half times more manganese than magnesium—in geologists' notation, this ratio is written Mn:Mg = 5:2.

Ankerite has hexagonal crystals, while dolomite and kutnohorite conform to the closely related trigonal system of symmetry.

Externally, crystals of kutnohorite often share a face or faces with one or more of their neighbors, a phenomenon known as twinning. However, crystals of this mineral are rare—it usually appears in anhedral (shapeless) masses.

KYANITE

This mineral, named after the Greek word for "blue," has been used in spark plugs and polished into gemstones.

*Kyanite is formed in the metamorphic rocks **gneiss**, **granite**, **pegamatite**, and **schist**. It is often found in association with **garnet**, **quartz**, and **staurolite**.*

Main Sources: ◆ *Australia* ◆ *Austria* ◆ *Brazil* ◆ *Canada* ◆ *Czech Republic* ◆ *Democratic Republic of the Congo (formerly Zaire)* ◆ *France* ◆ *India* ◆ *Ireland* ◆ *Italy* ◆ *Kenya* ◆ *Myanmar (Burma)* ◆ *Romania* ◆ *Russia* ◆ *Scotland* ◆ *Serbia* ◆ *South Korea* ◆ *Sweden* ◆ *Switzerland* ◆ *Arizona, California, Colorado, Connecticut, Georgia, Idaho, Massachusetts, New York, North Carolina, South Dakota, Utah, Vermont, Virginia, and Washington, United States*

This widely distributed silicate of aluminum is named after the color of the finest specimens—the word kyanite is derived from the Greek word *kyanos*, meaning "blue." (The mineral may also be gray, green, white, or a combination of all these colors.) It is used in the manufacture of spark plugs and sometimes as a gemstone.

FORMED UNDER PRESSURE

Kyanite is polymorphous with two other minerals: **andalusite** and **sillimanite**. All three have the same chemical formula—Al_2SiO_5—but different crystal structures. Andalusite and sillimanite are orthorhombic, but kyanite conforms to the triclinic system of symmetry. Kyanite is formed under greater pressure than its polymorphs—it therefore has the highest specific gravity and the most tightly compacted internal structure of the trio.

Kyanite's most unusual property is that its hardness varies according to the direction in which it is scratched. It scores a 4 on the Mohs scale when it is scratched up and down its long axis, but is harder — Mohs scale 7½—when scratched across the grain.

Above: The darkest tints in kyanite are usually found at the interior of its crystals, or in patches or streaks.

Many kyanite crystals are blotchy—this detracts from their appearance and restricts their value. A few, however, have a consistent blue color throughout and may be as much as 2 in. (5 cm) in length. These crystals are sometimes faceted to enhance the mineral's weak pleochroism—a natural phenomenon that causes it to reveal different colors, depending on the angle from which it is viewed and the direction of the light that illuminates it. Kyanite is often fashioned into square and rectangular (baguette) shapes, which are known generically as step cuts.

LAZULITE

Named for its bluish coloration, this magnesium-rich phosphate mineral may be used as a gem or as an ornamental stone.

*Lazulite may be found in numerous geological environments, including quartz veins, granite **pegmatite**, and metamorphic rocks such as metaquartzite. Among the minerals with which it is associated are **andalusite**, **corundum**, **garnet**, **kyanite**, **pyrophyllite**, **quartz**, **rutile**, **siderite**, and **sillimanite**.*

Main Sources: ◆ *Angola* ◆ *Austria* ◆ *Bolivia* ◆ *Brazil* ◆ *Canada* ◆ *India* ◆ *Madagascar* ◆ *Rwanda* ◆ *Sweden* ◆ *Switzerland* ◆ *California and Georgia, United States*

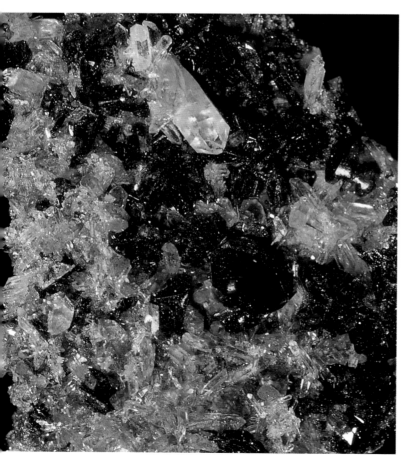

A relatively rare mineral that often looks like, and may easily be confused with, **lazurite**, lazulite is used as an ornamental stone and sometimes as a gem. Its name is derived from the Latin *lazulum*, which itself comes from the Arabic *lazaward*. Both words mean "blue" and refer to the typical colors of the mineral, which range from a rich azure to greenish blue or bluish green. Lazulite was first identified in 1795 by Martin Heinrich Klaproth (1743–1817), the German scientist who also discovered the elements cerium, uranium, and zirconium.

In chemical terms, lazulite is a hydrous phosphate of magnesium, iron, and aluminum. It forms a solid solution series with scorzalite, a mineral with an almost identical composition. The main difference between the two is that scorzalite always contains more iron than magnesium, while lazurite is richer in magnesium. Scorzalite is also denser and tends to be darker and less transparent than lazulite.

Crystals of lazulite are monoclinic, have dipyramidal or tabular habits, and are often twinned. Transparent examples display a strong pleochroism, changing color from blue to yellow to clear as they are rotated or looked at from different angles. However, such crystals are rare. Massive and granular forms are more common, and the most beautifully colored and sparkling aggregates may be polished into decorative "eggs," or tumbled to make beads.

CHEMICAL FORMULAE	
Lazulite:	$(Mg,Fe^{2+})Al_2(PO_4)_2(OH)_2$
Scorzalite:	$(Fe^{2+}, Mg)Al_2(PO_4)_2(OH)_2$

Left: A sparkling specimen of lazulite showing some of the rich azure blue that gives the mineral its name.

LAZURITE

Lazurite is famed for being the chief constituent of the precious stone, lapis lazuli. This blue gem material is found in Chile and Afghanistan.

Lazurite is a feldspathoid—it is similar to feldspar, but contains less silica. It is formed in limestone that has been metamorphosed (changed by heat). Deposits of lazurite are generally found in association with **pyrite**, **calcite**, *and—to a lesser degree—with* **haüyne** *and* **sodalite***. When these minerals are found together, they form lapis lazuli.*

Main Sources: ◆ *Afghanistan* ◆ *Canada* ◆ *Chile* ◆ *Italy* ◆ *Russia* ◆ *California and Colorado, United States*

Above: Lazurite on a groundmass of calcite. Lazurite comes in a range of hues, from deep blue to greenish blue.

This rare and complex mineral of the **sodalite** group is a major component of the precious rock formation lapis lazuli.

Lazurite is an aluminosilicate of sodium and calcium that also contains sulfur, chlorine, and a sulfate ion. Its formula is $(Na,Ca)_8(AlSiO_4)_6(S,SO_4,Cl)_{1-2}$.

Lazurite crystals conform to the cubic system of symmetry. Although dodecahedral (12-sided) shapes have been found, most deposits take the form of massive or compact masses.

LAPIS LAZULI

The rich blue color of the lazurite-rich rock, lapis lazuli, is caused by the sulfur the lazurite contains. The small crystals of pyrite that are always present in lapis help to distinguish it from sodalite rock, which lacks this naturally occurring iron sulfide. Another of lazurite's associate minerals, calcite, produces white streaks in the lapis. Too much of this will lower the value of the stone.

The best quality lapis lazuli comes from Kokcha, a remote valley in Afghanistan. It is thought to have been mined at this location for some 6,000 years.

Lapis lazuli is used in jewelry, for carvings, and as an ornamental stone. It was once ground into a powder for use as the artists' blue pigment, ultramarine. However, this is expensive, and most paints of this color are now manufactured synthetically.

PROTECTION

Lapis lazuli is believed to protect the wearer from evil. It may be imitated using stained jasper or paste with inclusions of copper.

LEADHILLITE

A transparent to translucent mineral, leadhillite appears in a number of colors including yellowish, pale green, pale blue, and white.

Leadhillite forms as a secondary mineral in the oxidation zones of lead deposits, where it is commonly associated with **anglesite, cerussite, chalcosite, dioptase, galena, linarite, malachite, silver, willemite,** *and* **wulfenite.**

Main Sources: ◆ *England* ◆ *France* ◆ *Greece* ◆ *Namibia* ◆ *Norway* ◆ *Scotland* ◆ *Arizona, California, Idaho, Massachusetts, Missouri, Utah, and Washington, United States*

Confirmed as a distinct species in 1832, this mineral is named after Leadhills in Lanarkshire, Scotland, where it was first discovered.

Leadhillite is a lead sulfate carbonate hydroxide with the chemical formula $Pb_4SO_4(CO_3)_2(OH)_2$. It is polymorphous with macphersonite and susannite, which means that the three minerals have exactly the same chemical composition and may be indistinguishable to the naked eye. However, detailed analysis will reveal important differences. For example, susannite has trigonal crystals, while leadhillite is monoclinic and macphersonite is orthorhombic.

From time to time, leadhillite may be completely replaced by cerussite, but the incoming mineral takes on the structure of the original leadhillite deposit. This phenomenon is known as pseudomorphism.

Externally, crystals of leadhillite may appear in prismatic shapes or as pseudohexagonal cyclic twins, but most deposits take the form of platy or tabular aggregates. Some specimens are fluorescent and give off a yellowy orange glow when placed under ultraviolet light. A rather heavy mineral, leadhillite has a specific gravity of 6.3 to 6.6. Cleavage is perfect in one direction (from the base) and poor in the others.

Some of the finest specimens of leadhillite come from the Mammoth Mine in Tiger, Arizona.

Above: Leadhillite, which crystallizes in the monoclinic system of symmetry, occurs in a wide range of colors.

LEPIDOCROCITE

Lepidocrocite is so similar to goethite that the two were once confused with each other and given the wrong names.

*Lepidocrocite is a secondary mineral that is generally found in association with **goethite** and other iron-bearing minerals, especially **hematite**, **ilmenite**, **limonite**, **magnetite**, **pyrite**, and **siderite**.*

Main Sources: ◆ *Australia* ◆ *Canada* ◆ *England* ◆ *France* ◆ *Germany* ◆ *India* ◆ *Japan* ◆ *Mexico* ◆ *Namibia* ◆ *Russia* ◆ *California, Pennsylvania, and South Dakota, United States*

When lepidocrocite occurs in large quantities in association with other iron–bearing minerals, it is mined as an ore of this metal.

Its English name is derived from the Greek *lepis*, meaning "scale," and *krokis*, meaning "fiber" or "thread." This is a reference to its habit, or external appearance. It may appear in flattened, scaly, or threadlike crystals, but actually occurs more often in fibrous or massive habits.

CONFUSED WITH GOETHITE

Lepidocrocite is very similar to goethite, the two minerals sharing the same chemical formula—$Fe^{3+}O(OH)$. Their crystals also conform to the same orthorhombic system of symmetry, and they both become magnetic when heated. Indeed, the two are so alike that an early 20th-century French geologist, Alfred Lacroix (1863–1948), wrote a learned paper in which he described one when he meant the other. His mistake caused great confusion, and the mineral now known as lepidocrocite was formerly known as goethite, while what 19th-century mineralogists called goethite is the modern lepidocrocite.

The key difference between the two minerals is their specific gravity (SG)—goethite has an SG of 3.3 to 3.4, while lepidocrocite is rather heavier, weighing

3.9 times more than the equivalent volume of water at room temperature. This difference is caused by the conditions that prevailed when they were formed. Lepidocrocite crystallized in a hotter and more pressurized environment than goethite, so is denser.

Lepidocrocite is also polymorphous with akaganéite, a tetragonal iron oxide, and feroxyhyte, which has hexagonal crystals.

Below: Lepidocrocite is usually found in massive or fibrous habits and has a submetallic luster.

LIBETHENITE

The finest specimens of this rare mineral occur as needle-shaped prisms with a deep green or an olive green coloration.

This rare secondary mineral is formed by metasomatism (the chemical alteration of preexistent material) in deeply weathered, highly concentrated copper sulfide ore bodies. Some of the finest specimens are found in what are known as druses—crystal-covered linings in rock cavities.

Main Sources: ◆ *Chile* ◆ *Democratic Republic of the Congo (formerly Zaire)* ◆ *England* ◆ *France* ◆ *Germany* ◆ *Romania* ◆ *Russia* ◆ *Slovakia* ◆ *Arizona, California, Nevada, New Mexico, Pennsylvania, and Utah, United States* ◆ *Zambia*

This mineral is named after the locality in which it was discovered—Libethen (now Lubietová) near Banská Bystrica, in Slovakia. It was confirmed as a distinct species in 1823. Libethenite, formed from a preexistent mineral or minerals, is commonly found in association with **adamite, brochantite, limonite, malachite, olivenite,** and **quartz**.

ISOSTRUCTURAL TRIO

Libethenite is isostructural with two other minerals, adamite and olivenite. The trio all conform to the orthorhombic system of symmetry and sometimes appear externally identical. Nonetheless, there are important chemical differences between the three. In particular, adamite and olivenite are hydrous arsenates of zinc and copper respectively, while libethenite is a hydrous phosphate of copper with the chemical formula Cu_2PO_4OH.

EXTERNAL APPEARANCE

Externally, crystals of libethenite sometimes appear in acicular (needle-shaped) prisms that terminate in pyramids. However, most deposits take the form of fibrous masses, nodules, or crusts on the surface of rocks or other minerals. The finest libethenite specimens are light to deep green or olive green in color. The mineral has a resinous (waxy) to vitreous (glassy) luster and displays good cleavage. This means that the crystals break off cleanly along their weakest structural lines when hit with a hammer or subjected to some other form of pressure.

Libethenite is a fairly soft mineral, measuring 4 on the Mohs Scale of Hardness, and has a specific gravity of between 3.6 and 3.9.

Left: Libethenite's rich color and bright luster make it popular with mineral collectors.

LIGNITE

Although it is of a lower grade than bituminous coal, this brown-colored coal is nonetheless widespread, abundant, and easily mined.

Lignite is formed from decayed and compressed vegetable matter—some of which may still be visible within it—so is a sedimentary formation.

Main Sources: *The main producers of this widely distributed rock are Australia, Canada, and Germany.*

Also known as brown coal, lignite is a form of **coal** of low rank, intermediate between peat and sub-bituminous coal. Its English name comes from the Latin *lignum*, meaning "wood."

Since the exact chemical composition of lignite is enormously variable, it is classified as a type of rock rather than as a mineral.

A typical lignite specimen may be expected to comprise about 60 to 75 percent carbon, 20 to 35 percent oxygen, five percent hydrogen, and one or two percent nitrogen. Raw specimens of brown lignite may contain as much as 60 percent water. Black lignite generally forms at higher temperatures and pressures than the brown variety.

INFERIOR TO COAL

Lignite is inferior to bituminous coal because it gives off less heat when burned. It is also friable (crumbles easily), and is thus difficult to transport. Another problem with lignite is that some of the impurities it contains are unstable in the Earth's atmosphere, and the rock is therefore liable to ignite spontaneously.

RELATED TO JET

Lignite is closely related to **jet**, a tightly compacted form of this low-grade coal. Jet itself is often used as a gem material.

Above: The lowest ranking form of coal, lignite still contains untransformed woody material.

Nonetheless, lignite is widely distributed and plentiful—some 45 percent of the world's coal reserves are thought to be of this type. In addition, many deposits lie close to the surface in beds about 100 ft. (30 m) deep; these can be extracted fairly easily and cheaply by opencast mining.

Lignite is found extensively across the United States. Vast woody deposits occur in Montana, North Dakota, and South Dakota. Earthy deposits are also found, especially in Arkansas and Texas.

LIMESTONE

Important reservoirs for petroleum, natural gas, and groundwater, limestones are composed mainly of calcite and fossil debris.

Limestones can form both organically or inorganically. Organic limestones include **chalk** *and other fossil-bearing materials. Examples of inorganic limestones include travertine, which is deposited by hot volcanic springs, and most oolites.*

Main Sources: *The limestones of Yellowstone National Park, Wyoming, were formed when hot solutions of calcium carbonate rose to the surface of a tropical lake.*

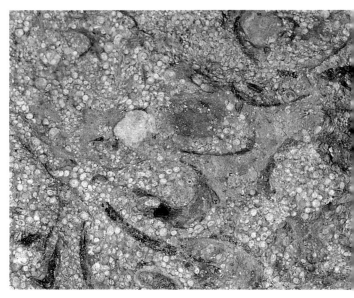

Above: This oolitic limestone from the Jurassic period shows small, rounded ooliths and many shell fragments.

Generally a light-colored sedimentary rock, limestone is composed of more than 50 percent by weight of calcium carbonate in the form of **calcite** and **aragonite**. **Dolomite**—a carbonate of calcium and magnesium—may also be present.

Limestones are a fine- to medium-grained mixture of calcium carbonate, clear crystalline calcite, and carbonate mud. It is believed that about 20 percent of all sedimentary rocks are limestones.

CHARACTERISTICS

Much limestone is rich in the fossils of creatures that once formed ancient shell banks or coral reefs. Some deposits have a clastic (fragmentary) texture; these are known as limestone breccia (*see* **breccia**).

Because of their high calcium carbonate content, limestones are often exposed to the surface. Acidic rainwater attacks the rock, producing calcium bicarbonate, which is soluble and carried away. Limestone terrains are often devoid of vegetation because water runs down joints in the rock enlarged by weathering.

Limestones differ greatly in texture and color, depending on the size of their component shells or crystals, and on the impurities they contain. Accessories include clay minerals such as **kaolinite**, together with **feldspar**, **pyrite**, and **quartz**.

Limestones are important reservoirs for petroleum and natural gas. They also store groundwater and contain ore deposits such as lead and zinc. The rock may be used for agricultural lime, cement, building stone, and concrete aggregate.

STROMATOLITES

Some limestones are made of fossil stromatolites, laminated structures in tidal flats. Stromatolites in Canada and South Africa are known to be about two billion years old and are among the oldest fossils.

OOLITIC LIMESTONE

Limestones composed of concentric layers of spheroidal or ellipsoidal calcite aggregates are said to be oolitic. The word is derived from the Greek *oon* ("egg") and *lithos* ("stone"). Each individual oolite is no more than about 1/12 in. (2 mm) in diameter.

LIMONITE

This yellowish brown mineral used to be an important source of iron but is now mainly used for its color in artists' pigments.

Limonite is a secondary product formed as a result of the oxidation of preexistent iron minerals. It is often found in laterite deposits, but the most extensive and widely seen form of limonite is rust.

Main Sources: ◆ *Angola* ◆ *Brazil* ◆ *Canada* ◆ *Cuba* ◆ *Democratic Republic of the Congo (formerly Zaire)* ◆ *England* ◆ *France* ◆ *India* ◆ *Italy*

COLLOIDS

A colloid is a substance that will not diffuse when it is passed through a membrane (a sheetlike tissue that functions as a sieve). Colloids differ from crystalloids, which will pass through a membrane, because they contain very small particles of matter. These particles, though invisible to the naked eye, are still much larger than molecules.

Colloids are usually classified according to their constituent parts. A solid dispersed in a liquid is known as a sol, while a solid or semisolid colloidal system is called a gel. An emulsion consists of one liquid dispersed in another, and an aerosol, such as smoke or mist, is a solid or liquid dispersed in a gas.

Not strictly a mineral, limonite is rather a mixture of several hydrated iron oxides. It is used for the artists' pigments ocher (a yellow, earthy color) and umber (brown). Its name comes from the Greek *leimon*, meaning "meadow," and refers to the marshes where the variety known as bog iron is found. Elsewhere, limonite is common in gossan, the weathered capping on the surface of iron sulfide deposits.

The principal minerals in limonite are **goethite**, **hematite**, and **lepidocrocite**. The mixture may also contain clays, oxides of manganese, and colloidal silica (*see* box, above right). It is amorphous (does not form in crystals) and often contains water. In some places, limonite may be a pseudomorph of **pyrite**. In such instances the limonite replaces pyrite but assumes the original mineral's shape.

Typical habits include yellowish, earthy coatings, brown to blackish, stalactitic or botryoidal (grapelike) aggregates, fibrous masses, and concretions. Limonite also appears in rocks that have an oolitic texture—egg-shaped spheroids and ellipsoids.

Limonite was once an important ore of iron, but it is seldom used for this purpose nowadays because it too often contains impurities of phosphorus.

Below: An earthy mass of limonite with a characteristic dull luster and rusty brown color.

LINARITE

A rare and colorful mineral, linarite is greatly sought after by collectors for its attractive crystals.

*Linarite is a secondary mineral formed in lead and copper veins that have been altered by the action of water and other circulating fluids. It is most often associated with **anglesite, brochantite, cerussite, chalcanthite, chalcopyrite, galena,** and **malachite.***

Main Sources: ◆ *Argentina* ◆ *Australia* ◆ *Canada* ◆ *Chile* ◆ *England* ◆ *Germany* ◆ *Italy* ◆ *Japan* ◆ *Namibia* ◆ *New Zealand* ◆ *Peru* ◆ *Russia* ◆ *Scotland* ◆ *Spain* ◆ *Arizona, California, Idaho, Montana, Nevada, New Mexico, and Utah, United States*

This rare but widely distributed mineral is named after the locality where it was discovered— Linares, a lead-mining city in Jáen province, Spain. It was confirmed as a distinct species in 1839.

Crystals of linarite conform to the monoclinic system of symmetry. Externally, they appear in tabular or prismatic shapes and twinning is common. The largest crystals may be up to 4 in. (10 cm) long, but most form as tiny encrustations on host rocks or in earthy masses.

Linarite is a hydrous sulfate of lead and copper with the chemical formula $PbCuSO_4(OH)_2$. In some deposits, the sulfur is replaced by selenium to form a different mineral, schmiederite. These two minerals are the end members of a solid solution series.

The deep blue color and the vitreous to sub-adamantine luster of linarite make it a collector's favorite. Its crystals are brittle and very soft (Mohs scale 2½) and have perfect cleavage. This means that they must be handled with great care to avoid scratching or breaking them.

As would be expected in a mineral containing lead, the specific gravity of linarite is fairly high—it weighs 5.3 times more than the equivalent volume of water at room temperature.

Above: Linarite forms crusts of small crystals with a deep blue color.

LITHARGE

A lead oxide, litharge was once used to prepare compounds for making rust-proof paint.

*Litharge and another mineral, massicot, often occur together, with crusts of litharge enveloping an inner core of massicot in a rock base (matrix). The two are commonly associated with **galena** and **magnetite** in the oxidation zones of mineral veins.*

Main Sources: ◆ *Australia* ◆ *Austria* ◆ *Bolivia* ◆ *Germany* ◆ *Greece* ◆ *Italy* ◆ *Namibia* ◆ *Sweden* ◆ *Arizona, California, Colorado, Idaho, Nevada, Virginia, and Washington, United States*

Litharge was made by humans long before it was discovered as a naturally occurring mineral. The first recorded usage of the Greek word *lithargyros*, meaning "rock silver," dates from about A.D. 50. At this time the word was applied to the material (lead oxide) that was obtained in the metallurgical process of separating silver from lead by roasting. Then, in 1917, the English form of the word was used to name an identical tetragonal lead oxide that had been found in Austria.

Litharge is said to be dimorphous with massicot. Both minerals have the same chemical formula (PbO) but different crystal structures and specific gravities. Litharge has tetragonal crystals and an SG of 9.3, while massicot conforms to the orthorhombic system and weighs 9.6 times more than the equivalent volume of water at room temperature.

USEFUL PROPERTIES

Both litharge and massicot are amphoteric minerals. In other words, they dissolve equally well in acids or alkalis. This unusual property made them useful in the preparation of lead salts (from reaction with acids) and plumbates (from reaction with alkalis). These compounds were widely used to make rust-resistant paints until the latter part of the 20th century, when they were replaced by titanium oxide and other less poisonous compounds.

The type locality of litharge is at Cuamongo Peak in San Bernardino County, California. It is against a specimen from here that all potential new finds are tested for authenticity.

Below: Litharge is a blood-red mineral that often forms, as here, on a mass of magnetite.

LÖLLINGITE

Silvery white or steel gray in color, löllingite often occurs on the surface of rocks and other minerals.

---

*Löllingite is found in veins where it was originally deposited at moderate temperatures in solution. It may also occur with **analcime, calcite, chalcopyrite, pyrrhotite, siderite, sodalite,** and **vesuvianite.***

Main Sources: ◆ *Austria* ◆ *Bolivia* ◆ *Brazil* ◆ *Canada* ◆ *Chile* ◆ *Czech Republic* ◆ *England* ◆ *Finland* ◆ *Germany* ◆ *Norway* ◆ *Poland* ◆ *Spain* ◆ *Sweden* ◆ *Arizona, California, Colorado, Connecticut, Maine, New Hampshire, New York, North Carolina, and South Dakota, United States*

Confirmed as a distinct species in 1845, this mineral is named after its discovery locality, Lölling, near Hüttenberg in Carinthia, Austria.

Löllingite often occurs in association with **arsenopyrite**, **orpiment**, and **realgar**. When these minerals are mined for their arsenic content, löllingite may be extracted with them and also used as a source of the metal. However, it is only a minor ore—it is neither abundant nor rich enough in arsenic to be a significant industrial source.

ARSENIC PARTIALLY REPLACED

Löllingite is notionally an arsenide of iron with the chemical formula $FeAs_2$. In reality, however, at least some of the arsenic is partially replaced by cobalt, nickel, or sulfur. Where this is the case with cobalt, the process of continuous atomic substitution may continue until a new mineral has been formed. This is known as safflorite, chemical formula $(Co,Fe)As_2$. Löllingite and safflorite are the two end members of a solid solution series.

Crystals of löllingite conform to the orthorhombic system of symmetry. Habits include prismatic to stubby crystals with chisel-like or domed terminations. When viewed in cross-section, many specimens

appear in diamond shapes with rounded angles. Twinning is common, and may cause the formation of star-shaped clusters. Most crystals have striations (grooves) and may be up to a foot (30 cm) long by 2 in. (5 cm) across. Compact and massive aggregates of löllingite are also found on the surface of rocks and other minerals, notably **quartz**. The largest such masses weigh more than 600 lb. (272 kg).

Below: Crystals of löllingite are silver white to gray with a metallic luster but tarnish to a darker color.

LUDWIGITE

A dark green or black mineral, ludwigite is often found with cassiterite and displays perfect cleavage.

*Ludwigite forms at high temperatures in contact zones of metamorphic rocks. It is found mainly in association with **cassiterite** and iron ores.*

Main Sources: ◆ *China* ◆ *Hungary* ◆ *Italy* ◆ *Japan* ◆ *Norway* ◆ *Romania* ◆ *South Korea* ◆ *Sweden* ◆ *California, Idaho, Montana, Nevada, Utah, and Washington, United States*

Above: A mass of ludwigite showing the characteristic grayish black color and silky luster.

This rare mineral is named after Ernst Ludwig (1842–1915), Professor of Chemistry at the University of Vienna, Austria, who first analyzed specimens extracted from Banat in what was then Romania but is now a part of Hungary.

Ludwigite is a borate of magnesium and ferric iron (chemical symbol Fe^{3+}). It is closely related to vonsenite, itself a borate of ferrous iron (Fe^{2+}) and ferric iron. The magnesium in ludwigite is replaced by the ferrous iron in vonsenite in a process of continuous atomic substitution. In between these two end members, the solid solution series contains an aluminum-bearing variety of ludwigite, known as alumoludwigite, and a second variety, titano-ludwigite, which features the metal titanium.

Ludwigite conforms to the orthorhombic system of symmetry, but distinct crystals are rare. Most deposits appear in fibrous, granular masses or aggregates of tiny, acicular (needle-shaped) crystals.

When ludwigite is hit with a hammer or subjected to pressure, it will split cleanly along its weakest structural planes. In scientific terms, then, it is said to display perfect cleavage. It has a Mohs scale hardness rating of 5 and a specific gravity of 3.9.

CHEMICAL FORMULAE

Ludwigite:	$Mg_2Fe^{3+}BO_5$
Vonsenite:	$Fe^{2+}_2Fe^{3+}BO_5$

NAMECHECK

In the early 20th century, a mineral unearthed in the United States was at first thought to be ilvaite, a hydrous silicate of calcium, ferrous iron, and ferric iron. However, more detailed tests failed to support this hypothesis and, in 1918, it was decided that it must be a new mineral. It was given the name collbranite. Then, in 1921, U.S. mineralogist E.V. Shannon proved that the specimen was in fact ludwigite, which had been established as a mineral since 1874. So the name collbranite was rendered obsolete.

MAGNESITE

Similar to chalk and calcite, magnesite has a wide range of applications including its use in medicine and in making cement.

*Magnesite commonly forms from the alteration of magnesium-rich igneous or metamorphic rocks during low-grade metamorphism while they are in contact with carbonate-rich solutions. It is also found as a sedimentary carbonate rock. It is commonly associated with **calcite**, **aragonite**, **dolomite**, and **strontianite**.*

Main Sources: ◆ *Algeria* ◆ *Austria* ◆ *Brazil* ◆ *China* ◆ *Democratic Republic of the Congo (formerly Zaire)* ◆ *Greece* ◆ *India* ◆ *North Korea* ◆ *Norway* ◆ *Poland* ◆ *South Africa* ◆ *California, Nevada, and Washington, United States*

Magnesite is used in the manufacture of bricks for furnace linings (*see* photo, right) and is a source of magnesia in chemicals and pharmaceuticals. Its English name is derived from the Greek *lithos magnetikos*, meaning "magnesian stone," an ore that originated either from Magnesia, the coastal

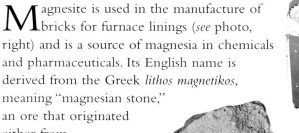

district of Thessaly, Greece, or from one of two locations in Asia Minor (modern Turkey): Soke or Manis.

A carbonate of magnesium, magnesite has the same molecular and crystal structure as calcite, hence its inclusion in the calcite mineral group.

Magnesite does not ordinarily form good crystals, but it can make up a substantial portion of some rock types. The finest magnesite crystals are found in hydrothermal seams and in **serpentinite**. Although these are sometimes faceted for display in mineral collections, cutting is rarely undertaken because of the great difficulties involved. Magnesite is soft (Mohs scale 3 to 4) and porous, so it cannot be cleaned with liquid. It is also very brittle and sensitive to heat and has many different directions of cleavage, so it may break off unexpectedly at various angles.

Pure magnesite contains up to 29 percent by weight of magnesium. In some deposits, however, this metal may be partially replaced by iron, which changes the mineral's appearance from translucent white to brown. When this substitution is complete, magnesite changes into **siderite**. In the middle of this solid solution series is gaspeite, a carbonate of magnesium, iron, and nickel (*see* box, below).

CHEMICAL FORMULAE	
Magnesite:	$MgCO_3$
Gaspeite:	$(Ni,Mg,Fe^{2+})CO_3$
Siderite:	$FeCO_3$

Left: Crystals of magnesite are rare. When they do occur, they take the form of rhombohedrons.

MAGNETITE

An important source of iron, the world's largest magnetite deposits are found in Norrbotten, Sweden.

Above: Magnetite is an opaque mineral with black crystals and a metallic luster.

Magnetite is found in a wide variety of rock types. It is a common accessory mineral in igneous rocks, where its fairly high specific gravity (5.2) often causes it to settle in economically significant deposits in a single location. It is also plentiful in contact and regionally metamorphosed rocks and in high-temperature mineral veins.

Main Sources: ◆ *Austria* ◆ *Brazil* ◆ *Canada* ◆ *Cuba* ◆ *England* ◆ *Germany* ◆ *Hungary* ◆ *Italy* ◆ *Mexico* ◆ *Norway* ◆ *Russia* ◆ *Scotland* ◆ *South Africa* ◆ *Sweden* ◆ *Switzerland* ◆ *Arizona, Arkansas, California, New Jersey, New Mexico, New York, North Carolina, South Dakota, Texas, Utah, Washington, and Wyoming, United States*

A major ore of iron, magnetite is also a strongly magnetic mineral—hence the name—and has been used for thousands of years in lodestones (the needles used in compasses).

The mineral may be associated with **corundum**, **hematite**, **pyrite**, and **talc**. It is an iron oxide, chemical formula Fe_3O_4, and a member of the **spinel** group.

Crystals of magnetite conform to the cubic system. They are typically octahedral in habit (external appearance) but may also be dodecahedral or take on other isometric forms; twinning is common. However, most deposits are massive or granular.

IRON AND ITS USES

Iron is extracted from magnetite in blast furnaces, where carbon monoxide and hydrogen gases are passed over the ore. This process reduces it to the pure metal, leaving carbon dioxide and water behind.

Iron has a vast range of uses because it is a good conductor of electricity and heat, and is both magnetic and easily magnetized. It may be melted and shaped in molds to make cast iron, purified to make wrought iron, or alloyed with carbon and other elements to make various forms of steel. Stainless steel, for example, which is used to make cooking utensils (*see* photo, above) is typically made up of iron together with 0.15 percent carbon, 18 percent chromium, and eight percent nickel.

MALACHITE

The distinctive, bright green banding of malachite results from the gradual formation of the mineral from hydrothermal fluids.

*Malachite is a commonplace secondary mineral formed through chemical reactions to preexistent copper-bearing minerals, notably **chalcopyrite**. It is also commonly found in association with **azurite, calcite, chrysocolla, cuprite,** and **limonite.***

Main Sources: ◆ *Australia* ◆ *Democratic Republic of Congo (formerly Zaire)* ◆ *England* ◆ *France* ◆ *Greece* ◆ *Mexico* ◆ *Namibia* ◆ *Russia* ◆ *Arizona, New Mexico, Pennsylvania, Tennessee, and Utah, United States* ◆ *Zambia*

Usually a brilliant green, the color of malachite resembles that of the mallow leaf. It is from the Greek name for this plant—*malache*—that the English word for this mineral is derived.

Malachite is a minor ore of **copper**, the principal industrial source of this metal being chalcopyrite. It is also used as a green pigment by artists. The finest aggregates are banded dark green and light green. These specimens are semiprecious and may be carved and polished for ornamental use—as decorative stones, for example, egg-shaped paperweights, ashtrays, trinket boxes, buttons, and beads.

The striking green of malachite is usually clearly visible on the surface of weathered zones of copper deposits, so it gives prospectors a good indication of the right place to locate this valuable metal.

Malachite is a hydrous carbonate of copper with the chemical formula $Cu_2CO_3(OH)_2$. Its crystals conform to the monoclinic system of symmetry, and are acicular (needle-shaped) or fibrous in habit, although distinct individual formations are very rare. Most malachite deposits appear in botryoidal (grape-like), stalactitic, or globular masses of microcrystals.

BEAUTIFUL COMBINATIONS

Some of the most attractive specimens of malachite contain special combinations with other minerals. For example, a deposit may be combined with the blues of azurite and chrysocolla, or with the rusty red of limonite. Masses of malachite weighing up to 50 tons (51 tonnes) have been found in the Ural Mountains of Russia.

The internal banding of malachite often follows the external shape of the specimen.

Left: Botryoidal mass of malachite. Ancient Egyptian women used finely ground malachite powder as eye makeup.

MANGANITE

Sometimes used as an ore of manganese, manganite frequently occurs in bundles of prismatic crystals.

*Manganite is formed through the action of water on manganese oxide at low temperatures in hydrothermal veins, shallow seas, and in fresh water. As well as **pyrolusite**, manganite may be associated with **calcite**, **barite**, **garnet**, **limonite**, and **siderite**.*

Main Sources: ◆ *Canada* ◆ *China* ◆ *England* ◆ *France* ◆ *Germany* ◆ *Romania* ◆ *Scotland* ◆ *South Africa* ◆ *Sweden* ◆ *Ukraine* ◆ *Arizona, California, Colorado, Georgia, Michigan, Minnesota, New Jersey, New Mexico, South Dakota, Utah, and Virginia, United States*

Above: Crystals of manganite are grouped into bundles. The mineral has a reddish to brownish-black streak.

As its name suggests, this mineral is an ore of the metallic element, manganese. Manganite contains a very high concentration of this metal— 62.5 percent by weight.

"GRAY MANGANESE ORE"

However, manganite is not as important as pyrolusite as an industrial source of manganese because it is less abundant in the Earth. The two minerals have a similar chemical composition and are often closely associated in ore veins. As a result, it was not until 1827 that scientists realized that they were in fact two distinct species. Prior to this, manganite and pyrolusite had been lumped together under the blanket term "gray manganese ore."

CRYSTAL BUNDLES

Manganite crystallizes in the monoclinic system of symmetry. Externally, the crystals typically appear in short, prismatic forms with pseudo-orthorhombic shapes. The terminations are generally blunted with domes and minor pyramid faces. The crystals are striated (scored) lengthwise and are usually grouped in tight bundles, some of which may radiate out from a

central point. Penetration and contact twinning sometimes occur. Columnar, massive, granular, concretionary, and fibrous aggregates are also found.

Manganite is a hydrous oxide of manganese with the chemical formula $MnO(OH)$. A dark steel-gray to black, opaque mineral with a submetallic luster, it has the same external appearance as feitknechtite and groutite. However, there are important chemical differences between them, and in scientific terms the three minerals are said to be isomorphous.

MARBLE

This beautiful, calcite-rich metamorphic rock has been used for building and ornamental purposes for centuries.

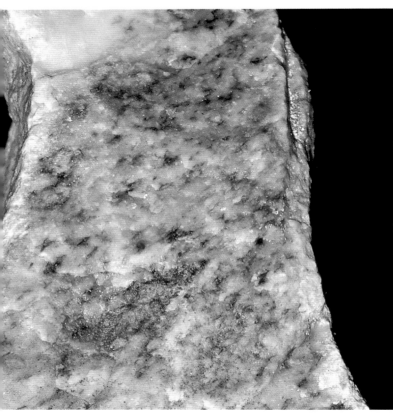

Above: The natural beauty of marble is enhanced by impurities, which give the rock an array of colors.

*A crystalline carbonate rock, marble is formed through the metamorphism of **limestone** or **dolostone**, sedimentary rock formations composed principally of **calcite** or **dolomite**. It may occur in the roots of mountain chains and is exposed to the surface by weathering or folding.*

Main Sources: *Marble is widespread all over the world. In North America commercial marble comes from the Appalachians and the Rocky Mountains. New York and Quebec have well-known marble quarries, as do Proctor, Vermont, and Sylacauga, Alabama.*

The English name for this rock is derived from the Greek, *marmairein*, meaning "to gleam." Marble may contain up to 95 percent calcite, and tends to be coarser-grained than the rocks from which it is derived. Calcite marbles have a mosaic texture, while dolomite varieties are granular. During metamorphism, impurities such as **clays** and **quartz** in the original rock react with calcite and dolomite to form minerals such as **garnet** and **olivine**.

Marble may be a uniform gray or white, or it may have streaks of other colors. These colors are determined by the quantity and nature of the accessory minerals the rock contains. Iron oxides such as **goethite** and **hematite** produce red marble, while epidote-rich marbles are green. Deposits with large amounts of **graphite** are grayish blue.

Because of its beautiful appearance, abundance, and strength, marble has long been used in architecture (*see* photo, right) and statuary. The Greeks quarried marble on the island of Paros and on Mounts Pentelicus and Hymettos. The Parthenon (447–432 B.C.) in Athens is built of marble. One of the world's most famous quarries, at Carrara in the Italian Apennines, supplies a creamy form of the rock that was used in the construction of the Vatican Museum, the Arch of Constantine, and the Theater of Marcellus in Rome, Italy. It was also the stone chosen by Michelangelo for his great sculpture, *La Pietá.*

MARCASITE

A pale bronze-yellow to white, metallic-looking mineral, marcasite commonly occurs in twinned formations known as cockscombs.

*Marcasite forms in some of the coolest hydrothermals, at temperatures lower than 842° F (450° C). In addition to **pyrite**, it is commonly associated with **bornite**, **calcite**, **chalcosite**, **dolomite**, **fluorite**, **galena**, **goethite**, **pyrrhotite**, **quartz**, and **sphalerite**. It also occurs in sedimentary rocks such as **coal**, **shale**, **clay**, **chalk**, and **limestone**.*

Main Sources: ◆ *Bolivia* ◆ *China* ◆ *Czech Republic* ◆ *England* ◆ *France* ◆ *Germany* ◆ *Italy* ◆ *Mexico* ◆ *Peru* ◆ *Russia* ◆ *Arizona, Illinois, Iowa, Kansas, Missouri, New York, Oklahoma, Utah, and Wisconsin, United States*

Below: Rounded clusters of marcasite with a characteristic metallic luster.

Often found in close association with pyrite, marcasite may sometimes be mistaken for this mineral. Indeed, its English name is derived from *marqashita*, the Arabic word for pyrite.

Chemically, marcasite and pyrite are identical—they are both sulfides of iron with the formula FeS_2. They are therefore described as being dimorphous. Structurally, however, there are important differences between the two. Marcasite conforms to the othorhombic system of symmetry, while crystals of pyrite are classified in the cubic system. In addition, their specific gravities are slightly, but significantly, different—pyrite weighs five times more than the equivalent volume of water at room temperature, while marcasite has a specific gravity of 4.85 to 4.90.

COCKSCOMB APPEARANCE

Marcasite crystals appear in many shapes, including tabular and pyramidal. The most famous habits are twinned formations known as cockscombs, although stellate, stalactitic, and reniform habits also occur.

Marcasite may form pseudomorphs with other minerals, notably fluorite, goethite, **gypsum**, and pyrite. It may also replace fossils.

The name marcasite is sometimes applied to small polished and faceted stones that are inlaid in sterling **silver**. However, X-ray analysis has shown that the iron sulfide found in Illinois coal mines that is used for this purpose in stones known as "marcasite suns" or "marcasite dollars" is, in fact, mostly pyrite.

Collectors find marcasite very difficult to keep. This is because, when exposed to the air for long periods in mineral collections, the mineral will oxidize, freeing **sulfur** and forming sulfuric acid. The acid then attacks the paper label and even the box holding the specimen. Over a period of decades, most marcasite will disintegrate into dust.

MENDIPITE

A rare mineral, found in a small number of locations, mendipite has a high density but scores low on the Mohs Scale of Hardness.

*Mendipite is formed around fumaroles (volcanic vents) and in hydrothermal veins. It is most commonly found in association with **calcite, cerussite, malachite, manganite, pyrolusite,** and **pyromorphite.***

Main Sources: ◆ *England* ◆ *Germany* ◆ *Russia* ◆ *Sweden*

This mineral is named after its discovery locality: the Mendip Hills in Somerset, England. It was confirmed as a distinct mineral species in 1839.

Mendipite is a halide of lead with the chemical formula $Pb_3Cl_2O_2$. There are currently just over 20 mineral halides of this metal. All are rare and most are localized in only a small number of deposits.

HIGH SPECIFIC GRAVITY

As would be expected in any mineral containing lead, the specific gravity is quite high—mendipite weighs between 7.2 and 7.4 times more than the equivalent volume of water at room temperature. It is usually white, gray, or colorless. The streak is white, as revealed when a specimen is rubbed across a piece of unglazed porcelain.

COLUMNAR OR FIBROUS HABITS

Crystals of mendipite conform to the orthorhombic system of symmetry, but distinct formations are rare. Most deposits take the form of columnar or fibrous masses, often with radiating external shapes. When freshly extracted from the Earth, mendipite has an adamantine luster (a diamondlike sparkle), but this fades on exposure to the atmosphere and the mineral develops a pearly or silky sheen.

Mendipite is a soft mineral, scoring only 2½ on the Mohs Scale of Hardness, and may be scratched with the edge of a coin. Another of its properties is that, when hit with a hammer or subjected to some other form of pressure, it will break off cleanly along its weakest structural planes. In scientific terms, then, it is said to display perfect cleavage.

Left: Specimens of mendipite can be white, gray, or colorless and can appear with tinges of blue or yellow. The green area here is composed of crystals of malachite.

MESOLITE

As a zeolite mineral, mesolite may be used as a chemical sieve, but it is also popular with collectors because of its clear sprays of crystals.

*Mesolite forms from high-temperature hydrothermals in cavities of basaltic rock. In addition to **natrolite** and **scolecite**, it is commonly associated with **apophyllite**, **heulandite**, **quartz**, and **stilbite**.*

Main Sources: ◆ *Australia* ◆ *Canada* ◆ *Faroe Islands* ◆ *Greenland* ◆ *Iceland* ◆ *India* ◆ *Italy* ◆ *Northern Ireland* ◆ *Scotland* ◆ *California, Colorado, New Jersey, Oregon, Pennsylvania, and Washington, United States*

Below: Mesolite is a white mineral that forms in tufts or compact masses. Crystals are always twinned.

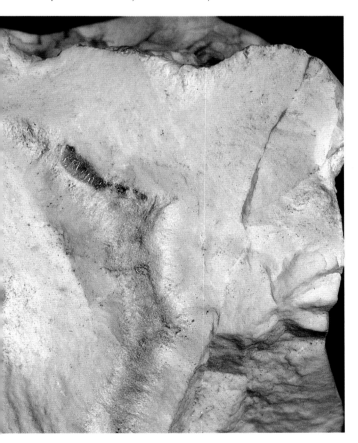

Mesolite is a zeolite mineral (*see* **analcime**) that often appears in radiating sprays of ice-clear or white crystals. The finest specimens are very popular with mineral collectors.

The chemical composition of mesolite is halfway between that of natrolite and scolecite. Natrolite is a hydrated silicate of sodium and aluminum, while scolecite is a hydrated silicate of calcium. Mesolite itself is a hydrated silicate of all three metals. This explains its name, which is derived from the Greek *mesos*, meaning "middle." It was confirmed as a distinct species in 1816.

The three minerals are sometimes found together and are very difficult to distinguish without detailed analysis. However, mesolite's fiberlike crystals tend to be more slender than those of natrolite and scolecite.

CAT'S EYE EFFECT

Crystals of mesolite conform to the monoclinic system of symmetry, although they may appear to be orthorhombic when twinned with scolecite. Externally, the crystals often take on acicular (needle-like) shapes with slanted terminations. Alternatively they may form as nodular masses or earthy, fibrous aggregates, and the crystals sometimes display a cat's eye effect known as chatoyancy. Mesolite's cleavage is perfect but seldom visible, owing to the smallness of most crystals.

The internal structure of mesolite has a typical zeolite openness that allows large ions and molecules to reside and move around inside the overall framework of the mineral. This structure contains open channels that allow water and large ions to travel into and out of the crystal framework. The size of these channels controls the size of the molecules or ions that can move around. Because of this property, mesolite is sometimes used as a chemical sieve.

METAQUARTZITE

Composed almost entirely of quartz, metaquartzite is formed under fairly low pressure, but at very high temperatures.

Metaquartzite is formed by contact metamorphism of **sandstone** *near large igneous intrusions. It is also formed by regional metamorphism, which occurs over very wide areas where sedimentary rocks may be dragged deep into the Earth's crust and subjected to high pressure and temperature during periods of mountain building.*

Main Sources: *Metaquartzite is found all over the world, wherever sandstone has been altered by heat and pressure. It is often recognizable by its even-textured, granular appearance.*

Above: This specimen shows a mass of fused quartz with no remaining sign of the original sandstone grains.

Metaquartzite is a metamorphosed sandstone, in which the grains of silica have melted (fused) together to form a hard, massive rock.

The pale, sugary appearance of metaquartzite is due to the large amount of **quartz** it contains. More than 90 percent of this metamorphic rock is made of quartz, and often its other mineralogical components become visible only when it is examined under a microscope. Typical accessories include **feldspar**, **mica**, and iron oxides such as **goethite** and **limonite**.

FORMED AT HIGH TEMPERATURES

Metaquartzite is a fine- to medium-grained rock. Its texture is very even because the quartz crystals, of which it is composed, were fused together at high temperatures. Although the rock formed under great heat, the pressure under which it was created was relatively low.

The resulting rock is very tough and crystalline, with interlocking grains. These properties are quite unlike those of the arenaceous (sandy) sediment from which it was metamorphosed, which would have been loosely compacted with pore spaces between the grains. In metaquartzite, most traces of the original sediments have been erased.

TIGHT BONDING

One of the most important differences between metaquartzite and sandstone is the tightness with which its components are bound together. Sandstone can sometimes be rubbed apart in the hand, while metaquartzite has been tightly bonded by metamorphism.

METEORITE

Meteorites not only provide scientists with information about the solar system, they may also be the origin of life on Earth.

Meteorites originate in space. Most formed shortly after the birth of the solar system, around 4,550 million years ago, though some Martian meteorites may be as young as 180 million years old.

Main Sources: *Meteorites may hit the Earth anywhere, at any time, but most fall unnoticed. The best places to look for them are in Antarctica and the Sahara Desert, where they are not hidden by vegetation and lie in plain view on the surface.*

Every year, the Earth is hit by an estimated 19,000 meteorite fragments weighing in excess of 4 oz. (113 g). Most of the material they contain is mineralogical, but it is possible—just possible—that one or more of them brought life to our planet.

THREE VARIETIES

There are three main types of meteorite—irons (also known as siderites), stones (known as aerolites), and stony irons (or siderolites).

Iron meteorites are extremely dense and contain about 90 percent iron and 10 percent nickel. Stone meteorites consist mainly of silicates and have only about 10 percent nickel and iron combined. Stony iron meteorites, which are rare, are composed of iron and silicates in roughly equal proportions.

Stone meteorites are further subdivided into chondrites and achondrites. Chondrites contain chondrules (small, spherical particles composed of up to 50 minerals including **olivine**, pyroxenes, and orthopyroxenes). Achondrites are stone meteorites without chondrules; they contain mainly pyroxene and plagioclase **feldspar** with little or no nickel or iron.

Iron meteorites are the type most often found, because of their unusual appearance. Stone meteorites are actually more numerous, but since

they resemble ordinary rocks, they are not often found unless a fall is actually observed. Of all observed meteorite falls, 85 percent are chondrites.

Carbonaceous chondrites consist largely of the mineral serpentine and contain amino acids and other organic compounds believed to be of extraterrestrial origin. Most of the evidence suggests that these compounds are nonbiological, but it is nevertheless possible that primitive life might arise from them. Some people believe that meteorites may be the origin of life on Earth. Carbonaceous chondrites are dark in color and extremely rare, constituting only about two percent of all impacts.

Below: Meteorites partly melt as they enter the atmosphere. When they land, they resolidify into dark, glassy forms.

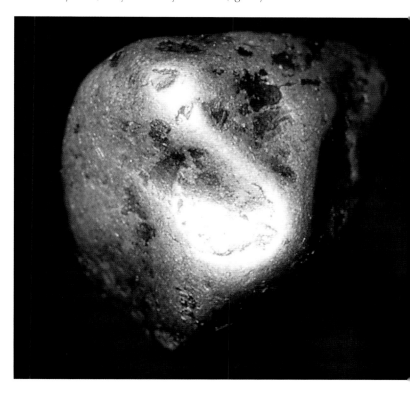

MICA

A large group of minerals with a distinctive sheetlike formation, micas have a wide range of industrial applications.

*Micas are closely associated with **clay** minerals such as **gibbsite** and **kaolinite**, and the two groups may be found in alternating layers.*

Main Sources: ◆*Australia* ◆ *Austria* ◆ *Brazil* ◆ *Canada* ◆ *Finland* ◆ *Germany* ◆ *Greece* ◆ *Greenland* ◆ *India* ◆ *Italy* ◆ *Japan* ◆ *Norway* ◆ *Russia* ◆ *Sweden* ◆ *Switzerland* ◆ *California, Colorado, North Carolina, and South Dakota, United States*

Above: The sheetlike internal structure of mica minerals is often reflected in their external appearance. This specimen shows many individual sheets of mica.

A group of rock-forming minerals that are highly resistant to electricity and heat, micas are widely used as insulators. They are also phyllosilicates that form in continuous chains; those with layered structures can be used without alteration to make sheet glass. In addition, micas are added to paint and wallpaper to give them a silky luster.

The English name mica is the same as the Latin word for "crumb," but this may be misleading because the most striking physical characteristic of these minerals is their sheetlike formation—the ratio of diameter to thickness may be as much as 25 to one, greater than that of any other mineral.

There are more than 30 mica minerals, the most common being biotite, lepidolite, and muscovite. The group also contains glauconite, paragonite, phlogopite, and zinnwaldite. Members of the group usually contain potassium and aluminum or iron.

The relative quantities of aluminum and iron affect the coloration—micas with a high aluminum content are known as light mica, while iron-rich specimens are described as dark mica.

Although many micas appear in six-sided crystals, these are in fact pseudohexagons. All micas conform to the monoclinic system of symmetry.

GENERAL FORMULA

The general formula of micas is AB_{2-3} $(X,Si)_4O_{10}(O,F,OH)_2$. A is usually potassium but may also be sodium, calcium, barium, cesium, and/or ammonia. B can be either aluminum, lithium, iron, zinc, chromium, vanadium, titanium, manganese, and/or magnesium. X is usually aluminum but can also be beryllium, boron, and/or ferric iron (Fe^{3+}).

MIGMATITE

A mixture of two intermingled rocks, migmatite is often banded green or black with white or lighter stripes, mainly of granite.

*Migmatites are found in layers or veins in the contact areas of large **granite** intrusions (granite formations that invade older rock).*

Main Sources: *Some of the best migmatite forms in parts of continental shields that have been exposed to the surface by erosional forces. There are outstanding deposits in North Cascades National Park, Washington.*

Migmatite is a regional metamorphic rock composed of two preexistent formations that have combined but may remain distinguishable. Its English name is taken from the Greek word, *migma,* meaning "mixture."

A medium- to coarse-grained rock, migmatite forms in distinctive stripes or bands of different colors—mainly greens or blacks. In each deposit, the darker areas are parts of the host rock (rocks that were in place before the metamorphism occurred). These host rocks are typically **basalt**, while the lighter areas are principally granite.

The banding is formed when the rock is plastic, at which point it may flow until it cools and solidifies. The heat and pressure that cause this plasticity are sometimes so great that all traces of the original structure—the so-called fabric of the rock— are completely obliterated.

NEBULITE AND ANATEXTITE FORMS

When some evidence of the antecedent, or original, rocks remains, the migmatite may be known by an alternative name, nebulite. On the other hand, when all traces of these rocks have been expunged, the migmatite may be called anatextite.

The essential mineralogical components of migmatite are **feldspar**, **mica** (biotite variety),

pyroxenes such as **augite**, **quartz**, and small quantities of **hornblende**. Among the possible accessory minerals are **apatite**, **magnetite**, and **zircon**. Within some migmatites there may also be isolated masses of **marble** or quartz. These materials have a low sensitivity to heat, so are resistant to metamorphism.

Below: Migmatite is a mixture of dark-colored rock (the basic component) and lighter-colored rock (the acid component) that may become folded.

MILARITE

This confusingly named mineral is of interest for the large number of metals it contains and the double-ring arrangement of its silica ions.

Milarite forms as a primary mineral in granitic pegmatite and syenite, in hydrothermal veins, and in alpine clefts. It is associated with **quartz, hornblende, feldspar,** *and* **mica.**

Main Sources: ◆ *Brazil* ◆ *Canada* ◆ *Czech Republic* ◆ *Germany* ◆ *Italy* ◆ *Mexico* ◆ *Namibia* ◆ *Norway* ◆ *Russia* ◆ *Switzerland*

This rare mineral was first identified in 1873 and named after the Val Milar in Switzerland, where it was thought to have originated. Four years later, however, milarite's type locality was shown to be the nearby Val Guif. Scientists proposed the new name guiffite, but this was not accepted, and the original, slightly misleading, name remains.

MANY METALS

Milarite is a hydrated silicate of potassium, calcium, aluminum, and beryllium with the chemical formula $K_2Ca_4Al_2Be_4Si_{24}O_{60} \cdot H_2O$. It is a member of the osumilite group, a closely related collection of cyclosilicates. Osumilite itself is a hydrated silicate of potassium, sodium, ferrous iron (Fe^{2+}), magnesium, aluminum, and ferric iron (Fe^{3+}). The other important member of the group is sugilite, a silicate of potassium, sodium, ferrous iron, manganese, aluminum, and lithium.

Osumilite group minerals are of great scientific interest both for the large number of metals they contain and for the unusual arrangement of their silica ions. These ions form in double rings with the formula $Si_{12}O_{30}$ and share an atom of oxygen with their neighboring molecules.

Crystals of milarite are hexagonal and often have six-sided, prismatic shapes. The crystals are generally small, but can make excellent micromounted

Above: Twinned crystals of translucent milarite showing prismatic habit.

specimens. They are often colored green or yellow, and some milarite crystals are fluorescent.

Another property of this mineral is that it is brittle and has no cleavage. This means that when it is hit with a hammer or breaks up under pressure it does so along no discernible lines of structure. In addition, milarite scores 5½ to 6 on the Mohs Scale of Hardness and has a specific gravity of 2.5—it weighs 2.5 times more than the equivalent volume of water at room temperature.

MIMETITE

Closely related to, and resembling, pyromorphite, mimetite may be yellow, orange, brown, green, or white, in color.

*Mimetite is formed from hydrothermal fluids in the oxidation areas of lead deposits, especially those that also contain **arsenic**. In addition to its close relative, **pyromorphite**, mimetite may be associated with **barite**, **calcite**, **galena**, **limonite**, and **wulfenite**.*

Main Sources: ◆ *Algeria* ◆ *Australia* ◆ *Czech Republic* ◆ *England* ◆ *France* ◆ *Germany* ◆ *Mexico* ◆ *Namibia* ◆ *Russia* ◆ *Scotland* ◆ *Sweden* ◆ *Arizona, California, Colorado, Nevada, Pennsylvania, South Dakota, and Utah, United States*

Mimetite is closely related to pyromorphite and resembles this mineral so strongly that its English name is derived from the Greek word, *mimetes*, meaning "imitator." While pyromorphite was confirmed as a distinct mineral in 1813, mimetite was not identified until 1832. Both species belong to the **apatite** group—mimetite is an arsenochloride of lead, while pyromorphite is a lead chlorophosphate. The two related minerals form a solid solution series in which the arsenic of the former may be gradually replaced by phosphorus until the latter is formed. The same process of continuous atomic substitution may also occur in reverse.

HARD TO DISTINGUISH

Without analyzing specimens to determine their chemical composition, it can be very difficult to tell mimetite and pyromorphite apart. This is especially true when specimens are green or yellow. The best clue is that mimetite seldom forms in distinct crystals, most deposits being botryoidal (grapelike) crusts, spherical masses, or acicular (needlelike) aggregates.

TESTING BY SMELL

When mimetite is held in an open flame, it melts (fuses) easily, and gives off a strong odor that is reminiscent of garlic. Pyromorphite does not have the same reaction when tested in this way because the smell is produced by arsenic.

Nevertheless, large crystals of mimetite have been found. One outstanding example, from the mines in Tsumeb, Namibia, measures 2½ in. (6.4 cm) in length, an inch (2.5 cm) in diameter and weighs about 6 oz. (170 g). It now forms part of the Keith Proctor Private Collection in Colorado Springs. The basic structure of mimetite crystals is hexagonal. Externally, they appear in barrel-shaped, six-sided prisms with hexagonal pyramids as terminations.

Below: Barrel-shaped mimetite with pyromorphite—the two minerals are indistinguishable without analysis.

MOLYBDENITE

A gray, metallic-looking mineral, molybdenite is an important source of molybdenum, a metal used as an alloy in steel.

*Molybdenite is formed by hydrothermals in sulfide ore bodies, and also in recrystallized granitic rocks such as **marble**, **granite**, and **pegmatite**. It is frequently found in association with **chalcopyrite**, **fluorite**, **pyrite**, **quartz**, **scheelite**, and **wolframite**.*

Main Sources: ◆ *Australia* ◆ *Canada* ◆ *China* ◆ *Czech Republic* ◆ *England* ◆ *Germany* ◆ *Japan* ◆ *Mexico* ◆ *Morocco* ◆ *Norway* ◆ *Peru* ◆ *Portugal* ◆ *Russia* ◆ *Sweden* ◆ *Alaska, Arizona, Colorado, Maine, New Mexico, and Utah, United States*

With **wulfenite** and powellite, this mineral is one of the most important ores of the silver-white metallic element, molybdenum. Molybdenite was identified in 1778 by Carl Wilhelm Scheele (1742–86), the Swedish chemist who also first described the metal it contains.

ALLOYED WITH STEEL

Molybdenum has a very high melting point—4,743° F (2,617° C)—so is used as an alloy in almost all high-strength steels. It is an important component of hastelloys, nickel-based steels that are highly resistant to heat and corrosion. Molybdenum wire is used to make filaments in electron tubes. In addition, the metal is used in the electrodes of electrically heated glass furnaces. Molybdenite itself is widely employed as a high-temperature lubricant.

Molybdenite is a sulfide of molybdenum, formula MoS_2. It is a very soft mineral, Mohs Scale 1 to 1½, so may be confused with **graphite**. However, molybdenite has a higher specific gravity of 4.6 to 4.8. The crystals conform to the hexagonal system. Externally, they appear in thin and platy six-sided shapes with tapering six-sided pyramidal terminations. Other deposits are massive, lamellar (sheetlike), or granular.

Above: Scaly gray crystals of molybdenite on a groundmass of granite rock.

VARIANT FORMS

Some molybdenite conforms to the trigonal system of symmetry and contains impurities of rhenium (chemical symbol Re), a metal used with molybdenum and tungsten to make thermocouples (electronic devices for measuring temperature). This variant form of the mineral is known as molybdenite-3R.

MONAZITE

This slightly radioactive mineral may be the source of any one of four valuable elements, each with a range of industrial applications.

Above: Monazite sand is a river sediment containing monazite (a placer deposit).

*Monazite is found in **pegmatites**, metamorphic rocks, and in veins. It is fairly common in placer deposits, especially in the sands of rivers and beaches. The largest crystals of this mineral weigh several pounds.*

Main Sources: ◆ *Australia* ◆ *Austria* ◆ *Bolivia* ◆ *Brazil* ◆ *Finland* ◆ *India* ◆ *Italy* ◆ *Madagascar* ◆ *Malaysia* ◆ *Nigeria* ◆ *Norway* ◆ *Sri Lanka* ◆ *Switzerland* ◆ *Colorado, Florida, Idaho, Montana, New Mexico, North Carolina, South Carolina, Virginia, and Wyoming, United States*

An important industrial mineral, monazite is used in a wide range of products, from nuclear reactors to cigarette lighters.

When monazite was first discovered at the beginning of the 19th century it was classified as a rare mineral. Indeed, its name comes from the Greek meaning "to be solitary." However, it was not long before scientists realized that the huge loads of heavy black sand ballast that were being shipped regularly from Brazil to India at that time actually contained rich concentrations of the mineral.

Monazite is a phosphate with a wide range of industrial uses. It is mildly radioactive but, more importantly, may contain any one of four unusual and valuable earth elements. When written down, each one of the four varieties of monazite is distinguished by placing the chemical symbol of the element it mainly contains in brackets after the word "monazite."

SOURCE OF RARE ELEMENTS

One variety, monazite (Ce), is an important source of cerium. This element is used to make an alloy known as misch metal, which is widely used in the flints of cigarette lighters (*see* photo, right).

Monazite (Th), on the other hand, contains thorium, a radioactive element used as a nuclear fuel in breeder reactors. The compound thorium dioxide is used to make gas mantles and furnace linings.

Neodymium, the rare earth element contained in monazite (Nd), is used to color glass violet-purple so as to make it show two different colors, depending on the angle from which it is viewed. This optical phenomenon is known as dichroism.

Finally, monazite (La) contains lanthanum, an element used mainly as a catalyst for cracking crude petroleum and as a phosphor in fluorescent lamps.

MONTMORILLONITE

Montmorillonite may be used industrially as a drilling mud or in agriculture to prevent water loss on farmland.

*Montmorillonite is found in many sedimentary rocks, especially bentonite (of which it is the main component), and in some metamorphic rocks. It is formed mainly through the alteration of preexistent **feldspar** in rocks that are poor in silica. It may also occur in volcanic glass and **tuff**, where it is deposited by hydrothermals. In addition to clay minerals, feldspar, and **quartz**, montmorillonite may be associated with **garnet**.*

Main Sources: ◆ *Brazil* ◆ *Czech Republic* ◆ *France* ◆ *Germany* ◆ *Italy* ◆ *Japan* ◆ *Romania* ◆ *Alabama, Arizona, California, Connecticut, Georgia, Florida, Maine, Mississippi, New Mexico, South Dakota, Utah, Washington, and Wyoming, United States*

This mineral was discovered at Montmorillon, about 50 miles (80 km) northwest of Limoges, France. It was named for this location and confirmed as a distinct species in 1847.

USED AS A DRILLING MUD

Montmorillonite is a form of clay that occurs with other minerals of the same type, such as **kaolinite**. Its main industrial use is in the petroleum industry where it is used as a drilling mud, a substance that forms caked layers around bore holes and keeps oil in and groundwater out. The mud also helps to keep the drill bit cool and lubricated. Montmorillonite is also used to plug old drill holes to prevent leakage of toxic fluids into aquifers used for drinking water. The mineral is also used agriculturally, scattered on farmland to slow down water loss from soil during extended dry periods.

Chemically, montmorillonite is a hydrous hydrated silicate of sodium, calcium, aluminum, and magnesium. The amount of attached water of crystallization is variable, and this is reflected in the formula—

Above: A compact aggregate of montmorillonite, which is usually white but may be colored by impurities.

$(Na, Ca)(Al, Mg)_6(Si_4O_{10})_3(OH)_6.nH_2O$—in which n is any large number. The mineral is a phyllosilicate, that is one that forms in molecular chains.

Montmorillonite conforms to the monoclinic system of symmetry but almost never appears in distinct crystals. Instead, most deposits are compact or lamellar masses. It is sometimes seen as fibrous or powdery inclusions in quartz.

MOTTRAMITE

A vanadate mineral, mottramite usually occurs as green to black, vitreous (glassy) crusts on other minerals or rocks.

*Mottramite is found in areas where metal-bearing deposits have been oxidized by the action of air and/or water. It is most commonly associated with **descloizite**, and may also be found with **calcite, cerussite, malachite, mimetite, pyromorphite,** and **vanadinite**.*

Main Sources: ◆ *Bolivia* ◆ *Chile* ◆ *England* ◆ *France* ◆ *Germany* ◆ *Italy* ◆ *Namibia* ◆ *Arizona, California, and New Mexico, United States* ◆ *Zambia*

Positively identified in 1876, this mineral is named after its discovery locality, Mottram St. Andrew near Manchester, England. It is sometimes used as a minor ore of lead and copper, but only when it is mined with other, more valuable, sources of these metals—mottramite is never extracted industrially on its own account.

The mineral is a hydrous vanadate of lead, copper, and zinc (*see* box, above right). It is the copper-rich end member of a solid solution series that it forms with zinc-rich descloizite. Both mottramite and descloizite usually contain significant percentages of copper and zinc and are rarely pure.

SPARKLING CRUSTS

Mottramite crystals conform to the orthorhombic system of symmetry. Large, distinct formations are rare, however. Most deposits occur as sparkling crusts and radiating or stalactitic masses of microcrystals.

The mineral is fairly soft, Mohs scale hardness of 3 to 3½, and it can be scratched with the edge of a coin. It weighs 5.9 times more than the equivalent volume of water at room temperature. Mottramite

---

VANADATES

There are currently known to be about 100 vanadate minerals—naturally occurring compounds containing vanadium and oxygen in the form of vanadate ions (chemical formula VO_4). Industrially, the most important of these is vanadinite. Some vanadate minerals form solid solution series with arsenate minerals, exchanging vanadium for arsenic in a process of continuous atomic substitution.

---

displays no cleavage—when it is hit with a hammer or subjected to pressure it will fragment, rather than break off cleanly along internal lines of structure.

Below: A dark and sparkling mass of tiny mottramite crystals on a rocky groundmass.

MYLONITE

The exact mineralogical composition of mylonite is governed by the preexistent rocks from which it is metamorphosed.

Mylonite occurs almost exclusively in thrust faults, where rocks are forced up from depth to rest on top of geological material that is stratigraphically younger. Thrust faults form at very acute angles, typically less than 10°. The rock is associated particularly with areas of mountain-building (orogeny)—deep-lying regions of the Earth's crust where the lower side of a fault plane has been forced downward by compression.

Main Sources: *Mylonite may be seen in mountain ranges such as the Alps of Europe, the Andes of South America, and the Himalayas of Asia.*

This metamorphic rock is created when preexistent rocks are crushed, ground, or rolled into new formations along major thrust faults. The English name for mylonite is derived from the Greek word *mulon*, meaning "mill."

Although mylonite is sometimes described as a product of pressure, rather than of heat, this distinction is not scientifically accurate. All pressure generates heat, and this rock is formed at temperatures of up to about 572° F (300° C). In geological terms, however, this is not hot at all, and it is almost insignificant beside the enormous pressure of 10 kilobars—about 10,000 times greater than atmospheric pressure—in which the rock originates.

Often, the greater the pressure under which a rock is formed, the smaller its grains will be. The smallest fragments of mylonite are powdery and known as rock flour; these were formed at the height of metamorphism. As the pressure abates during the latter part of the process, the component grains become larger, and when metamorphism is finally complete, distinct crystals may appear.

NO MINERALS

Mylonite is a cataclastic formation. This means that it is a rock that has been broken down from preexistent materials during bouts of crushing and shearing deep beneath the surface of the Earth. It has no essential minerals of its own and may contain any of the components of the rocks from which it was formed, more or less unaltered chemically. Deposits of mylonite are always cohesive (tightly packed). In this deposits differ from **breccia**, which is loosely formed.

Left: During movement along a thrust fault, mylonite rock is ground to dust and streaked out into bands.

NATROLITE

The mineral natrolite is a commonly occurring sodium zeolite and derives its name from its Na (sodium) content.

Natrolite is most often found in cavities (vesicles) in **basalt**. *It is formed through the alteration of plagioclase* **feldspar**, **nepheline**, *or* **sodalite**. *Among a host of other minerals, natrolite often occurs with* **apophyllite**, **benitoite**, **heulandite**, **quartz**, *and* **stilbite**.

Main Sources: ◆ *Canada* ◆ *Czech Republic* ◆ *Faroe Islands* ◆ *France* ◆ *Germany* ◆ *Greenland* ◆ *Iceland* ◆ *India* ◆ *Italy* ◆ *Northern Ireland* ◆ *Norway* ◆ *Scotland* ◆ *California, Colorado, Montana, New Jersey, Oregon, Pennsylvania, and Washington, United States*

THE NAME GAME

The name natrolite was originally proposed by Martin Heinrich Klaproth (1743–1817), the great German scientist who discovered the metallic elements cerium, uranium, and zirconium. It was accepted by geologists in 1803, the year in which the mineral was confirmed as a distinct species.

Natrolite is one of the most widely occurring zeolite minerals (*see* **analcime**). The name reflects its sodium content—*natrium* is the Latin for this metal, which has the chemical symbol Na.

A sodium zeolite, natrolite is often found along with **scolecite**, a calcium zeolite, and **mesolite**, a calcium and sodium zeolite. All three look superficially similar, especially when scolecite and mesolite are twinned and appear in pseudo-orthorhombic structures. Of the three, natrolite is the only one that conforms to the real orthorhombic system of symmetry—the others have monoclinic crystals.

Natrolite tends to form in sprays of acicular crystals with pyramidal terminations. It also appears in nodules and in fibrous and massive crusts. Crystals have perfect cleavage and many have vertical striations along their faces. Its crystals are usually very small, but specimens up to 3 ft. (90 cm) long and 4 in. (10 cm) across have been found at an asbestos mine in Quebec, Canada.

The chemical formula of natrolite is $Na_2Al_2Si_3O_{10}.2H_2O$. Each molecule shares its oxygen atoms with four of its neighbors. The mineral is therefore classified as a tektosilicate.

Left: Usually white or gray in color, natrolite crystals conform to the orthorhombic system of symmetry.

NEPHELINE

Named after the Greek word for "cloud" because it forms a nebulous white gel when placed in acid, nepheline is used to make glassware.

*Nepheline is formed mainly in **pegmatite** associated with nepheline **syenite**, but may also occur in **gneiss** and **schist**. In addition to feldspars and other feldspathoids, nepheline may be found in association with **calcite, cancrinite, hornblende,** and **sodalite**.*

Main Sources: ◆ *Cameroon* ◆ *Canada* ◆ *Democratic Republic of Congo (formerly Zaire)* ◆ *Finland* ◆ *Greenland* ◆ *Italy* ◆ *Kenya* ◆ *Myanmar (Burma)* ◆ *New Zealand* ◆ *Norway* ◆ *Portugal* ◆ *Romania* ◆ *Russia* ◆ *Scotland* ◆ *South Africa* ◆ *South Korea* ◆ *Arizona, Arkansas, Colorado, Maine, Massachusetts, Montana, New Hampshire, South Dakota, Texas, and Washington, United States*

Above: Frequently occurring in compact or massive (shapeless) habits, nepheline is usually colorless, white, or gray.

Confirmed as a distinct species in 1801, this mineral is a silicate of sodium, potassium, and aluminum with the chemical formula $(Na,K)AlSiO_4$. It seldom occurs in large quantities, but when it does it may be mined as a raw material for special forms of glass and ceramic ware.

FELDSPATHOID GROUP

Nepheline is a feldspathoid, one of a group of minerals that are similar to **feldspar**, but contain less silica and more sodium and potassium. Other members of the feldspathoid group include **analcime** and **leucite**.

NEPHELINE SYENITES

Nepheline is the main mineral component of some plutonic igneous rocks, and these are named to reflect their composition—so, for example, we may encounter formations that are known as nepheline syenites.

Crystals of nepheline conform to the hexagonal system of symmetry. Most deposits are massive or granular, but some prismatic or columnar crystals are found with six-sided cross-sections.

THE ACID TEST

Scientists trying to identify nepheline may place part of an unidentified specimen in a strong acid, such as hydrochloric or nitric acid. If it turns to an opaque, white gel, it may be nepheline. It is from this reaction that nepheline derives its English name, which is taken from the Greek *nephele*, meaning "cloud."

NEPTUNITE

Named after the Roman god of the sea, the best specimens of this mineral have prismatic jet-black crystals with streaks of red.

*Neptunite occurs in **pegmatites** or in intermediate igneous rocks such as **nepheline syenite**, and often in association with **aegirine**. It may also be found in plutonic **serpentinite** rocks with **benitoite** and **natrolite**.*

Main Sources: ◆ *Australia* ◆ *Canada* ◆ *Greenland* ◆ *Russia* ◆ *California and New Mexico, United States*

Confirmed as a distinct species in 1893, this mineral is named after Neptune, the Roman god of the sea, because it is found in association with aegirine, which was named after the equivalent Norse deity. Neptunite is a silicate of sodium, potassium, lithium, iron, manganese, and titanium. More precisely, it is an inosilicate—in other words its molecules are linked together in chain formations. It forms a solid solution series with mangan-neptunite, a similar mineral that is composed of all the same elements, but contains more manganese than iron.

Neptunite's crystals conform to the monoclinic system of symmetry. Many are well formed and clearly defined, and they are often nearly square in cross-section. Perfect crystals measuring up to 2½ in. (6 cm) in length have been found in San Benito County, California. The terminations are slanted dome faces. The mineral is also found in massive aggregates and disseminated grains.

THE FINEST CRYSTAL SPECIMENS

Most specimens are jet black, but some show flashes of red that appear to emanate from the stone's center. The finest crystals come from the Benitoite Gem Mine in San Benito County where the serpentinite rock contains beautiful assemblages with veins of pure white natrolite and blue benitoite. Neptunite displays perfect cleavage in two directions.

Above: An accessory mineral, black neptunite crystals form in intermediate rocks and pegmatites.

CHEMICAL FORMULAE	
Mangan-neptunite:	$Na_2KLi(Mn^{2+},Fe^{2+})_2Ti_2Si_8O_{24}$
Neptunite:	$Na_2KLi(Fe,Mn)_2Ti_2(SiO_3)_8$

NICKELINE

Nickeline's metallic luster led to it being mistaken for copper by German miners, who called it *Kupfernickel*—"devil's copper."

Nickeline is found mainly in gabbro. It is commonly associated with annabergite, arsenopyrite, barite, chalcopyrite, cobaltite, pentlandite, pyrrhotite, and silver.

Main Sources: ◆ *Australia* ◆ *Austria* ◆ *Canada* ◆ *Czech Republic* ◆ *England* ◆ *France* ◆ *Germany* ◆ *Iran* ◆ *Japan* ◆ *Mexico* ◆ *Morocco* ◆ *Russia* ◆ *California, Colorado, and New Jersey, United States*

NICKELINE GROUP

Nickeline is also the name of a group of minerals with hexagonal symmetry and the general formula *AX*. *A* may be cobalt, palladium, platinum, nickel, and/or iron; *X* may be arsenic, selenium, bismuth, tellurium, and/or antimony, with some members also having sulfur.

Nickeline—also known as niccolite, especially in Europe—is an arsenide of nickel with the chemical formula NiAs.

Although it was confirmed as a distinct mineral comparatively recently, in 1832, nickeline had been well known for centuries. In the Middle Ages, miners had extracted it in the belief that it contained copper. When it proved impossible to extract the metal from the compound, the Germans called the mineral *Kupfernickel* ("devil's copper"), a name that is still sometimes used in English today.

It was not until 1751 that nickeline's true composition was discovered by Swedish chemist Baron Axel F. Cronstedt (1722–65). Nickeline soon acquired the name "nickel," a contraction of the German for the mineral in which it had been identified. However, nickeline is not an important ore of nickel—the major industrial sources of this metal are **garnierite** and **pentlandite**.

RARE CRYSTALS

Distinct crystals of nickeline are rare, but those that do occur have pyramidal or tabular shapes and may be twinned (share a face or faces with their neighbors) and striated. Habits are mainly massive and granular, although columnar and reniform (kidney-shaped) structures are also seen.

Below: A copper-red, metallic looking mineral, nickeline commonly forms in massive or reniform habits.

NOSEAN

Named after the German mineralogist who first described it, nosean is found in materials ejected by volcanoes.

Nosean is found in extrusive igneous rocks, especially in alkali-rich, silica-poor lavas, and in phonolite. It may also be formed from fragments of rock that have been ejected by explosions from volcanoes.

Main Sources: ◆ *Bolivia* ◆ *Brazil* ◆ *Canada* ◆ *Cape Verde* ◆ *China* ◆ *Czech Republic* ◆ *England* ◆ *Germany* ◆ *Greenland* ◆ *Italy* ◆ *Romania* ◆ *Russia* ◆ *Arkansas, Colorado, Maine, South Dakota, and Utah, United States*

Confirmed as a distinct species in 1815, nosean was named after the German mineralogist Karl Wilhelm Nose (1753–1835), who first described it.

A sodium aluminum silicate sulfate with the chemical formula $Na_8Al_6Si_6O_{24}(SO_4)$, nosean is a member of the **sodalite** group, which also contains **haüyne** and **lazurite**.

Nosean crystals conform to the cubic system of symmetry. Externally, they may appear dodecahedral (12-sided), but more commonly take the form of granular masses. Fairly large crystals of nosean may sometimes be found set in a base composed mainly of smaller crystals of alkali **feldspar** and **nepheline**. Rocks with this composition—distinct crystals in a fine-grained groundmass—are said to have a porphyritic texture. The biggest crystals, which in the case of nosean may measure up to ¼ in. (6 mm) in length, are known as phenocrysts.

HARD BUT LIGHT

Nosean is moderately hard, scoring 5 to 5½ on the Mohs scale. It has a low specific gravity, weighing between 2.3 and 2.4 times more than the equivalent volume of water at room temperature.

The type locality of nosean is along the shores of the Laacher See in Germany—it is against specimens from here that potential new discoveries are tested for authenticity.

Below: Forming mainly in silica-poor lavas, nosean crystals have a vitreous (glassy) luster.

OBSIDIAN

Obsidian has been known and used as a natural form of glass since prehistoric times, but today it features largely as a gemstone.

*Obsidian is an extrusive igneous rock that is composed mainly of the minerals **feldspar**, and **quartz**. The principal accessory minerals are **ilmenite** and **magnetite**.*

Main Sources: *Most obsidian forms in small outcrops, but large expanses sometimes occur, as in the Valles Caldera, New Mexico, and the Glass Buttes, Oregon.*

Used by people in ancient times as a cutting tool and a weapon, the finest specimens of obsidian are today used as gems or ornamental stones.

The English name "obsidian" is derived from the Latin *obsianus lapis*—a stone that, according to the Roman historian Pliny, was discovered by someone named Obsius in Ethiopia.

Obsidian forms either from viscous lava—hot fluid made sticky by the fact that it contains only about one percent water—or from lava that has come into contact with water in a lake or sea so suddenly that it has cooled and resolidified too quickly for crystals to form. Its crystals have no discernible structure and it is therefore described as amorphous.

Internally, obsidian is composed of tiny, tightly packed, embryonic crystals (crystallites) that disperse incident light in such a way as to make the rock appear predominantly black (although some specimens are green in color). It can contain small air bubbles, trapped by the sudden cooling process, that can cause interesting optical effects such as the golden play of light in sheen obsidian and the iridescence of rainbow obsidian.

The rock may also contain small, white, radially clustered crystals of **cristobalite**, which create snowflake obsidian. This is one of the forms most widely used in decoration.

Yet not all the matter found in obsidian is microscopic—the largest inclusions may measure more than 3 ft. (90 cm) in diameter.

Fragments of obsidian that have been smoothed and rounded by the action of wind and water are known as Apache tears.

Left: Usually black, this natural glass is occasionally red and may show spots or banding across its surface.

OLIVENITE

Named for the olive green color of some of its best crystals, copper-rich olivenite is sometimes mined for its metal content.

Left: This rare secondary mineral also has an olive-green streak, the color it would be if it were reduced to powder.

The name of this popular collector's mineral is derived from the distinctive green color of the finest specimens—some deposits, however, may be brown or yellow. It is a hydrous arsenate of copper with the chemical formula $Cu_2AsO_4(OH)$. When olivenite occurs in large quantities with ores such as **chalcopyrite**, it may be mined for its metal content. It was confirmed as a distinct species in 1820.

UNIDENTICAL TRIPLETS

Olivenite is isostructural with **adamite** and **libethenite**. All three of these minerals conform to the orthorhombic system of symmetry and sometimes appear identical. Yet there are important chemical differences between them—adamite contains zinc instead of copper, while libethenite is a phosphate rather than an arsenate.

Olivenite may also form with euchroite, a mineral that is almost identical apart from the fact that it has attached water of crystallization—its formula is $Cu_2AsO_4OH.3H_2O$.

Crystals of olivenite appear in long, acicular prisms. It may also occur in fibrous, globular, or reniform (kidney-shaped) masses, in tiny crystalline druses (crystal-lined rock cavities), nodules, or crusts.

The mineral weighs 4.4 times more than the equivalent volume of water at room temperature and scores 3 on the Mohs Scale of Hardness—it can be marked quite easily with a penknife. It is brittle and has an indistinct, rather difficult cleavage.

*Olivenite is a secondary mineral found in deeply weathered, highly concentrated **copper sulfide** ore bodies. Among the other minerals with which olivenite is commonly associated are **azurite, calcite, dioptase, goethite, limonite, malachite, quartz,** and **scorodite.***

Main Sources: ◆ *Bulgaria* ◆ *Chile* ◆ *England* ◆ *France* ◆ *Germany* ◆ *Greece* ◆ *Hungary* ◆ *Italy* ◆ *Namibia* ◆ *Arizona, Nevada, and Utah, United States*

OLIVINE

The name of a mineral group rather than a single species, olivine's resistance to heat makes it useful in the manufacture of abrasives.

*Olivine is found mainly in ultramafic igneous rocks. It also occurs in **marble** formed from metamorphosed impure **limestone**. Associated minerals include **augite**, **chromite**, **diopside**, **plagioclase**, **feldspar**, **hornblende**, and **spinel**.*

Main Sources: *◆ Australia ◆ Brazil ◆ Egypt ◆ England ◆ Ethiopia ◆ Finland ◆ France ◆ Germany ◆ Greenland ◆ Italy ◆ Mexico ◆ Myanmar (Burma) ◆ Norway ◆ Pakistan ◆ Russia ◆ South Africa ◆ Sweden ◆ Arizona, Colorado, Hawaii, Massachusetts, New Mexico, North Carolina, South Dakota, Washington, and Wyoming, United States*

Above: Olivine minerals, named for their olive-green coloration, often form as granular aggregates.

Like **olivenite**, olivine is named after its characteristic green color. Unlike it, however, olivine is a mineral group rather than a single species.

The term "olivine" is used for a solid solution series of silicate minerals that contain varying amounts of iron and magnesium. The two end members are fayalite, the iron-rich species with the formula Fe_2SiO_4, and forsterite, the magnesium variety with the formula Mg_2SiO_4.

Yet these formulae are mostly theoretical—nearly all fayalite contains some magnesium, and forsterite is practically never iron-free. As a result, it is almost impossible to determine the point in the series at which one of these minerals ends and the other begins—hence the blanket term olivine.

Olivine minerals are hard and highly resistant to heat. They are therefore used as abrasives and refractory sands and some are mined for their magnesium.

Olivines are among the first minerals to crystallize from mafic magma. Conforming to the orthorhombic system of symmetry, good crystals are tabular or box-shaped, but these are rare. The minerals are often found as grains in alluvial gravels and basaltic lavas.

PERIDOT

The most valuable gem-quality olivine is known as peridot. Most peridot is magnesium-rich forsterite; its color is caused by the presence of up to fifteen percent by volume of iron, together with nickel and chromium as trace elements.

OPAL

Opals come in many types and colors, but the best crystals are treasured for the extraordinary play of light across their features.

Opal forms at low temperatures and may fill cavities in sedimentary rocks or veins in igneous rocks. It also forms in stalactites or stalagmites and sometimes replaces fossilized bones, shells, or wood. It is commonly associated with **chert***.*

Main Sources: ◆ *Australia* ◆ *Brazil* ◆ *Czech Republic* ◆ *England* ◆ *Honduras* ◆ *Hungary* ◆ *Iceland* ◆ *Italy* ◆ *Mexico* ◆ *New Zealand* ◆ *Romania* ◆ *South Africa* ◆ *Arizona, California, Colorado, Georgia, Idaho, Nebraska, Nevada, New Mexico, Oregon, South Dakota, Utah, Washington, and Wyoming, United States*

Opal is a form of silicon dioxide that is hydrated by a theoretically indefinite number of molecules of water of crystallization. Its chemical formula is $SiO_2.nH_2O$. In practice, the stone normally contains between five and ten percent water. Because of the water it contains, it will change color when heated, even when held in the palm of the hand. Yet if its water is allowed to dry out, the opal will crack.

OPALESCENCE

Precious opals are used in jewelry (*see* photo, above right) and appear in a wide range of colors—fire opals, for example, are red or orange, boulder opal is brown, and black opal, despite its name, is multicolored with a dark background. Many show a play of colors across their surfaces—an effect known as opalescence. Hyalite, a glasslike form of opal, is basically colorless, yet incident light is broken up into all the colors of the rainbow, which appear to be suspended inside the stone.

Opal does not conform to any of the seven systems of crystal symmetry, so is often classified as an amorphous product. However, its internal structure is not entirely random. This is particularly true of the finest specimens, which contain tightly packed, regular pockets of tiny spheres. The gaps between them are thought to have a direct bearing on the external coloration of the gem. Often the color's intensity varies according to the angle from which the opal is viewed.

Some opals are fluorescent—when they are placed under an ultraviolet lamp, they may give off a green or yellow light of their own. Non-precious varieties, which are known as potch opals, are opaque and display no iridescence.

Below: Amorphous in structure, the colors of opal often change and become more brilliant if it is warmed.

ORPIMENT

One of the most important sources of industrial arsenic, the mineral orpiment was used in ancient times as a paint or tanning pigment.

Orpiment is a secondary mineral that is usually formed at low temperatures through the alteration of preexistent arsenic minerals and some silver minerals. It may also be found in hot spring deposits. It is almost always found in association with realgar, and often with **barite,** *calcite,* **gypsum,** *and* **stibnite.**

Main Sources: ◆ *Australia* ◆ *China* ◆ *France* ◆ *Georgia* ◆ *Germany* ◆ *Greece* ◆ *Hungary* ◆ *Iran* ◆ *Italy* ◆ *Japan* ◆ *Kurdistan* ◆ *Pakistan* ◆ *Peru* ◆ *Romania* ◆ *Serbia* ◆ *Switzerland* ◆ *Turkey* ◆ *California, Nevada, Utah, and Wyoming, United States*

The geological name of this mineral is derived from the Latin *auripigmentum* ("golden pigment"). It is commonly known as yellow arsenic.

Orpiment is one of the three main industrial sources of arsenic—the others are **arsenopyrite** and realgar.

ANCIENT USES

Although orpiment was not confirmed as a distinct mineral until 1771, it has been known since ancient times and was used for tanning animal hides, as a cosmetic hair remover, and—most commonly—to give paint a golden yellow color.

However, orpiment has severe practical limitations. It is unstable when exposed to light for long periods, and over time crumbles into powder. These characteristics reduce its effectiveness as a pigment. It is dangerous to apply it to the body because it is a sulfide of highly poisonous arsenic. As a result, these functions are performed today by artificial products.

Orpiment is a sulfide of arsenic with the chemical formula As_2S_3. Each molecule contains 61 percent of arsenic and 39 percent sulfur.

Crystals of orpiment conform to the monoclinic system. Small, prismatic, and tabular formations do occur, but these are rare—most deposits take the form of thin, leaflike (dendritic) foliated masses or long columnar structures. Orpiment can show a pearly luster along its cleavage surfaces.

Below: As a mineral rich in arsenic, orpiment gives off a strong smell of garlic when heated.

ALL THAT GLISTERS ...

Alchemists were scientists, or pseudo-scientists, who searched—or claimed to be searching—for a method of turning base metal into gold. We know that this is impossible, but some medieval people were tricked into paying for "gold," which was in fact copper coated with orpiment paint.

PEARL

Pearl is a precious organic gemstone that is created by certain shellfish as a protective device.

Pearls form inside the shells of pearl oysters (Pinctada) and pearl mussels—two forms of bivalve molluscs. Pearl oysters are found in marine environments while pearl mussels occur in freshwater. Both are found at depths of 48 to 120 ft. (14.5 to 36 m).

Main Sources: *The largest natural pearl center is the Persian Gulf, which also produces the finest saltwater pearls. Other important sources are the coasts of Australia, China, India, Japan, various Pacific islands, and Venezuela, and the rivers of Europe and North America.*

Pearls are formed in oysters and mussels as a response to irritation caused by parasites or grains of sand that have become lodged inside their shells. Many freshwater and marine shellfish produce this reaction, but only certain species of saltwater oysters and freshwater mussels produce gem-quality pearls. Pearls from other molluscs tend to be red or white and have a porcelainlike texture.

Below: Pearls occur in marine and freshwater bivalve molluscs. This pearl mussel is from a river in Scotland.

The commercial value of these other pearls is limited by their lack of iridescence. This rainbowlike luster, which plays across the surface of the true pearl, is caused by the reflection and refraction of light from the pearl's translucent overlapping layers—the thinner and more numerous these layers, the finer the effect, and the more valuable the gemstone.

Pearls may be round, pear-shaped, button-shaped, or irregular (baroque) and are valued in that order. Those found attached to the inner surface of a shell are known as blister pearls. The finest quality pearls are usually white, sometimes with a creamy or pinkish tinge, but they may be tinted yellow, green, blue, brown, or black. Because they are so rare, black pearls are often highly valued.

Pearls are very soft and sensitive to acids, heat, and humidity. As a result, they are not cut or polished like other gems. However, holes may be drilled in specimens intended for beads, earrings (*see* photo, above) necklaces, or ornamental settings.

Pearls may be cultured, with humans introducing irritants into the shells of molluscs to induce them to form pearls. Another artificial variety, the nucleated pearl, is "grown" by placing a small mother-of-pearl bead inside the shell. The oysters are then placed in cages suspended in sheltered bays for periods of up to four years while the gem forms around the bead.

PEAT

Peat, formed when deposits of plant matter are saturated in marshland water and compacted, is used as both a fuel and fertilizer.

Peat is a loosely consolidated sedimentary rock that is widely extensive in many parts of northern Europe and North America. It is formed from plant material that falls into bogs or marshes and decomposes, eventually becoming hard and compact.

Main Sources: *Peat is found worldwide, especially in Denmark, Germany, Ireland, Poland, and Scotland.*

Peat is a cheap, low-grade fuel made of partially decomposed plant remains that have been saturated with water and compacted. Although not a form of **coal**, it represents an early stage in the reconstitution of vegetable matter into this fossil fuel.

Peat is formed in temperate or subarctic climates when plants fall into bogs and marshes, where there is little chance for them to be contaminated by detrital minerals. After saturation they are compressed by subsequent deposits, which leads to the formation of carbon, the element that makes peat suitable for burning. The richest forms may contain as much as 60 percent by volume of carbon.

DANGEROUSLY VOLATILE

A big disadvantage of peat is that it contains volatile material, which can cause it to burst spontaneously into flames. Among the most dangerous substances that may lurk inside peat are simonellite (a solid hydrocarbon with a chemical formula of $C_{19}H_{24}$) and ammonia gas (NH_3).

In many peat deposits, branches and leaves may still be visible. The main genera are the mosses *Hypnum* and *Spnagnum*, along with heathers, rushes, and sedges.

Peat may form in layers many feet thick on the Earth's surface. These are cut into blocks and left to dry out before being sold as fuel. Peat is also used as a plant fertilizer (*see* photo, right).

Some peat also accumulates in lakes bayous, and estuaries, but in such areas mineral contamination is likely to be greater, and deposits may contain **amber**, **calcite**, and **quartz**.

If the water table is lowered or drained, any peaty accumulations already in place will be degraded by fungi, eaten away by small insects, and finally oxidized—the end product of this process is humus.

Left: Although peat is a type of rock, its organic origins are clearly visible.

PECTOLITE

Pectolite is a brittle mineral that is sharp to the touch and is often found in the cavities of petrified basaltic lava.

*This mineral is formed in cavities in basaltic lava, often with zeolites such as **heulandite** and **natrolite**. These cavities are usually vesicles of petrified lava, which were once bubbles of gas. Vesicles that have been filled with crystals are known as amygdales. Pectolite may be associated with **calcite** and **prehnite**.*

Main Sources: ◆ *Bahamas* ◆ *Dominican Republic* ◆ *Greenland* ◆ *Italy* ◆ *Morocco* ◆ *South Africa* ◆ *Sweden* ◆ *California, Kansas, and New Jersey, United States*

CHEMICAL FORMULAE	
Pectolite:	$NaCa_2Si_3O_8(OH)$
Serandite:	$Na(Mn,Ca)_2Si_3O_8(OH)$

Below: Radiating aggregates of acicular (needle-shaped) pectolite crystals.

The English name of this mineral is derived from the Greek *pektos*, meaning "well put together," and refers to its compact structure. It was first identified in the Italian Tyrol and confirmed as a distinct species in 1828.

Pectolite is a hydrous silicate of sodium and calcium. In some deposits, the calcium may gradually be replaced by manganese. When this process of continuous atomic substitution goes beyond the point at which there is more manganese than calcium, the mineral is reclassified as serandite—the two species are thus the end members of a solid solution series.

Pectolite conforms to the triclinic system of symmetry. White, colorless, or gray individual crystals do occur, but most deposits are fibrous tufts, radiating acicular clusters, and compact or botryoidal masses.

Splinters of pectolite are brittle and sharp, so may puncture the skin if not handled properly. Some specimens give off flashes of light when scraped with metal—the scientific term for luminescence caused by friction is triboluminescence. Another mineral that displays this unusual property is **corundum**.

The finest specimens of pectolite come from the Bahamas and the Dominican Republic. They have a sky-blue tinge and are sometimes marketed as semiprecious gemstones under the trade name Lorimar.

PEGMATITE

This plutonic igneous rock can contain large crystals of such precious gemstones as emerald, garnet, and topaz.

Pegmatite is usually a plutonic rock, although it may occur in hypabyssal (intermediate) environments. It is never formed by volcanic activity. Pegmatite is found in intrusions such as dikes and sills.

Main Sources: *Fine deposits of this rock occur at Mesa Grande, California, South Glastonbury, Connecticut, Oxford County, Maine, and Baringer Hill, Texas.*

Above: This pegmatite specimen shows very large crystals of feldspar and quartz.

Pegmatite is a coarse-grained igneous rock. Its smallest crystals are typically just over 1 in. (2.5 cm) in diameter, but the most spectacular pegmatites contain extraordinarily large crystals—some are over 30 ft. (9 m) long.

Rocks of this type may be composed of any type of plutonic material, including **granite** pegmatite, **gabbro** pegmatite, and **syenite** pegmatite. Its English name is derived from the Greek *pegma*, meaning "something joined together."

Many pegmatites are of acidic composition—that is, they are composed of more than 65 percent total silica. They also contain much **feldspar** and **quartz**.

Complex pegmatites may be composed of a wide range of accessory mineral ores in large enough quantities to make them suitable for commercial mining. These include **beryl, bismuthinite, borax, cassiterite, columbite, spodumene, molybdenite, tantalite, uraninite,** and **wolframite**.

Many large gemstone crystals are found in pegmatites. The most valuable are **emerald** (a precious form of beryl); **garnet, topaz, tourmaline,** and **zircon** may also be present. These have been formed mainly through the action of hot gases during igneous activity—a hydrothermal process known as pneumatolysis.

Pegmatites are thought to have formed during late-stage crystallization of plutonic complexes. They were probably rich in volatile materials such as chlorine, fluorine, phosphorus, **sulfur**, and water. This highly fluid, aqueous melt provided an environment for the concentration of atoms that were too big to fit into the crystalline lattices of the major rock-forming minerals.

PENTLANDITE

The most important industrial source of nickel, pentlandite is made up of crystals so tiny that they are rarely visible to the naked eye.

*Pentlandite forms in basic igneous rocks such as **diabase** and **gabbro** through magmatic segregation—as hot liquid magma cools, crystals of high-density minerals such as metal sulfides sink to the bottom of the magma chamber, which later becomes a rich source of ores for miners. Pentlandite is thus commonly associated with other sulfides such as **chalcopyrite**, **pyrite**, and **pyrrhotite**.*

Main Sources: *◆ Australia ◆ Canada ◆ Norway ◆ South Africa ◆ Alaska, California, Colorado, Montana, Nevada, and Washington, United States*

Pentlandite is the main industrial ore of nickel—the second most important source of this metal is **garnierite**. Pentlandite is also a minor source of iron.

The mineral was confirmed as a distinct species in 1856 and named after Joseph Barclay Pentland (1797–1873), the Irish-born scientist who first found it in nickel ores at Sudbury, Ontario, Canada.

Pentlandite is a sulfide of iron and nickel with the formula $(Fe,Ni)_9S_8$. It forms a solid solution series with cobalt pentlandite, in which both metals are replaced by cobalt.

PENTLANDITE GROUP

Pentlandite may also be associated with some rare sulfides with a closely related structure. They have the general formula $AB_8(S,Se)_8$ in which A may be silver, manganese, cadmium, or lead, and B may be copper. Metals such as iron, nickel, and cobalt can occupy either the A or B positions.

Argentopentlandite:	$Ag(Fe,Ni)_8S_8$
Cobalt pentlandite:	$(Co,Fe,Ni)_9S_8$

Above: This massive aggregate of pentlandite was extracted from a basic igneous rock formation. Note the metallic luster and the signs of uneven fracture.

Crystals of pentlandite conform to the cubic system of symmetry, but they are very small and often invisible to the naked eye. Instead, the mineral almost always appears in massive or granular aggregates. It is usually bronze-yellow in color.

NICKEL'S USE AS AN ALLOY

The Earth's crust contains 0.018 percent by weight of nickel, although the core is believed to be much richer. Nickel is used mainly in alloys to improve their strength and resistance to corrosion. Stainless steel, an alloy of iron and chromium, may contain up to 35 percent nickel. Special nickel alloys such as alnico, cunife, and cunico are used as permanent magnets, while nichrome is used as a heating element in many household electrical appliances. The U.S. coin known as the nickel is composed of 75 percent **copper** and 25 percent nickel.

PERIDOTITE

Formed from within the Earth's mantle and brought to the surface by mountain building, peridotite can sometimes contain diamond ores.

*This intrusive igneous rock is thought to be one of the major components of the Earth's mantle. It is also found in parts of the crust into which it has been intruded to form inclusions in **basalt** and kimberlite. Elsewhere, **peridotite** may be dragged up during tectonic plate movement or volcanic activity.*

Main Sources: *Peridotite often forms in batholiths, large rounded bodies of cooled molten rock with exposed surface areas of more than about 60 sq.miles (100 sq.km).*

A plutonic rock composed mainly of coarse grains of **olivine**, peridotite derives its name from a variety of olivine called peridot. Peridotites may also contain substantial amounts of **hornblende**, **mica**, and pyroxenes such as **augite**. Some formations include small but valuable quantities of **garnet** and **spinel** gemstones.

Among the other accessories that may be present in this rock are **apatite**, **chromite**, garnet, **magnetite**, and **pyrrhotite**. Because of the predominance of minerals containing magnesium and iron, peridotite is classified as an ultramafic formation.

MOTTLED COMPLEXION

Although peridotite typically has a medium-grained texture, its component olivine minerals are sometimes completely enclosed within larger crystals. This gives the rock a mottled appearance that is described as poikilitic (the word means "variegated").

Peridotite is also used as a blanket term for a rock containing more than 40 percent olivine. When subjected to more detailed analysis, it is subdivided into four more specific rock types. In decreasing order of olivine content, these are dunite (including over 90 percent olivine), harzburgite, lherzolite, and wehrlite.

Above: Perodotite is generally dark colored and formed from dense, heavy minerals.

Peridotites can be partially altered to become **serpentinite**. Some specimens of peridotite are valuable, providing ores of chromium, asbestos, and **diamond**. They occur at the bases of layered igneous rock, probably as the result of gravitational settling of dense crystals of early formation.

PHARMACOSIDERITE

Bright green, olive, or brownish in color, pharmacosiderite is an oxidation product of various primary, arsenic-bearing minerals.

*Pharmacosiderite is a secondary mineral formed through the oxidation of preexistent arsenic-bearing minerals such as **arsenopyrite**. It is also commonly found in association with **goethite, pyrite, realgar**, and **scorodite**.*

Main Sources: ◆ *Algeria* ◆ *Australia* ◆ *Brazil* ◆ *Chile* ◆ *Czech Republic* ◆ *England* ◆ *France* ◆ *Germany* ◆ *Greece* ◆ *Italy* ◆ *Peru* ◆ *Nevada, New Jersey, South Dakota, and Utah, United States*

Left: A crust of pharmacosiderite crystals on a rock matrix from the mineral's type locality in Cornwall, England.

The English name of this mineral is derived from the Greek *pharmakon*, meaning "drug" (a reference to its **arsenic** content) and *sideros*, meaning "iron." Pharmacosiderite was confirmed as a distinct species in 1813.

EXCHANGEABLE BASE

Chemically, pharmacosiderite is a hydrous hydrated arsenate of potassium and ferric iron (Fe^{3+}). However, although potassium is an essential component of the mineral in its pure form, this metal is not present in all specimens. In scientific terms, then, the potassium is said to be an exchangeable base.

In some deposits, the potassium may be completely substituted by one of three other metals—aluminum, barium, or sodium. The resulting products—respectively, alumopharmacosiderite, barium-pharmacosiderite, and sodiumpharmacosiderite—are all classified as distinct minerals.

Pharmacosiderite itself is sometimes mined fortuitously during the commercial extraction of iron ore. If the mineral is then smelted during the purification process, its potassium may be substituted by ammonia, which, in its isolated form, is a gas. The artificial product that results can often be found discarded on slag heaps near steel works.

Crystals of pharmacosiderite conform to the cubic system of symmetry and often appear as cubes. Their faces often show diagonal striations (surface grooves). The mineral is usually brownish, olive green, or bright emerald green in color and it has a greasy or adamantine (very bright, shiny) luster. The type locality of pharmacosiderite is at the Pednandrea mine in Cornwall, England.

PIEMONTITE

Named after its type locality in the Italian Piedmont, some of the finest specimens of piemontite are sold as gemstones.

*Piemontite is a rare mineral that is found in metasomatic manganese ore deposits in **andesite**, **rhyolite**, and low-grade **schist**. It may also occur in **pegmatite**, but rarely.*

Main Sources: ◆ *Belarus* ◆ *Egypt* ◆ *France* ◆ *Italy* ◆ *Japan* ◆ *New Zealand* ◆ *Poland* ◆ *Scotland* ◆ *Sweden* ◆ *Arizona, California, Colorado, Missouri, and Pennsylvania, United States*

Confirmed as a distinct mineral in 1853, piemontite—also known as piedmontite—was originally discovered in New Zealand. Its name, however, was taken from its type locality at the Pavorna mine in St. Marcel, near Aosta in the Piedmont region of northern Italy.

This mineral is essentially a hydrous silicate of calcium, aluminum, and ferric iron with the chemical formula $Ca_2(Al,Fe^{3+})_3Si_3O_{12}OH$. In addition, it usually contains at least five percent and sometimes as much as 20 percent by volume of manganese oxide (Mn_2O_3). It is the presence of this metallic impurity that gives the mineral its distinctive reddish brown color.

ONLY SEMIPRECIOUS

Piemontite conforms to the monoclinic crystal system. Most deposits take the form of coarse-grained masses, but good-sized crystals do occur. These appear as acicular prisms. Some of the finest examples are smoothed and polished into domed cabochons and sold as gemstones. They are virtually never faceted, because they display perfect cleavage. This makes them difficult to cut, and the effort would not be adequately rewarded by the market price—the finest piemontite is considered to be only semiprecious.

The specific gravity of piemontite is 3.4 to 3.5 and it scores 6 on the Mohs scale. Its streak is red and it has a vitreous luster.

Piemontite is a member of the **epidote** group—one of several minerals composed of calcium, aluminum and/or iron, silicon, and a hydroxyl radical (formula OH).

Left: Dark crystals of piemontite set in rock from a pegmatite formation.

PITCHSTONE

Pitchstone is a dark, glassy igneous rock that contains more water than any other formation of this type.

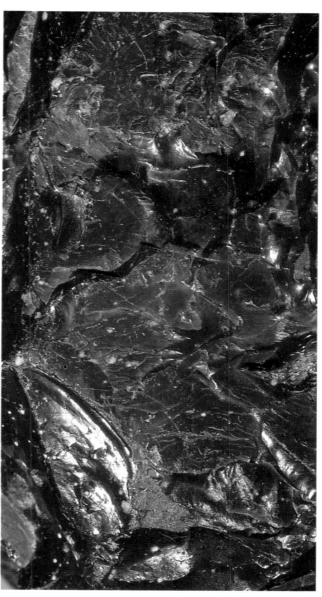

An extrusive igneous rock, pitchstone is a naturally occurring glass produced by the rapid cooling of lava.

Main Sources: *Worldwide, but particularly in Yellowstone Park, Wyoming, United States.*

Pitchstone is very dark and usually black, brown, green, or gray in color. Its essential components are **feldspar** and **quartz**.

Glass is formed when fluids cool so quickly that they have insufficient time to crystallize into well-formed minerals. Pitchstone generally contains more water than any other glassy rock—typically between four and 10 percent of the total body weight. Most of this liquid is thought to have come from the seawater or wet sediment into which the lava first erupted.

A CLOSE RELATIVE

Pitchstone is closely related to **obsidian**. The two rocks have a very similar chemical composition and reflect light in much the same way. However, pitchstone is usually less shiny than obsidian because it has cooled more slowly and contains fewer sparkling microscopic crystals (crystallites). In scientific terms, pitchstone is said to show signs of devitrification.

PHENOCRYSTS

Some pitchstones—notably those that form along the margins of igneous intrusions such as sills and dikes—feature large, individual crystals (phenocrysts) in a vitreous groundmass. The phenocrysts in pitchstone are often composed of the minerals **hornblende**, **olivine**, and pyroxenes such as **augite**.

Above: Pitchstone is mainly dark and glassy in appearance. Some may contain distinct individual crystals.

If there are large numbers of these phenocrysts, the rock may be classified as porphyritic pitchstone.

If exposed to the open air for long periods, pitchstone will decompose and crumble into a powdery aggregate of fine-grained crystals. This is caused by the water evaporating within the body of the rock.

PLATTNERITE

A member of the rutile group, plattnerite is generally black and heavy with a bright metallic luster.

*Plattnerite is a secondary mineral formed through the alteration of primary lead-bearing minerals and the oxidation of lead itself. It is commonly associated with other lead oxides, such as **litharge** and **massicot**, and with **aurichalcite**, **hemimorphite**, and **limonite**.*

Main Sources: ◆ *Mexico* ◆ *Namibia* ◆ *Scotland* ◆ *Idaho, New Mexico, and South Dakota, United States*

Confirmed as a distinct mineral in 1845, plattnerite is named after K.F. Plattner (1800–58), professor of metallurgy and assaying (mineral testing) at the University of Freiburg, Germany, who is most famous for his pioneering work in the field of blowpipe analysis.

Plattnerite is an oxide of lead with the chemical formula PbO_2. It is a member of the **rutile** group. Although plattnerite is sometimes mined, this is only when it occurs with extensive deposits of **galena**, the main ore of lead.

MASSIVELY HEAVY

Plattnerite is mainly black with a brilliant metallic luster and a chestnut brown streak. Crystals conform to the tetragonal system and may appear in eight-sided prisms and blocky crystals with blunt four-sided or complex pyramidal terminations. Large crystals are rare and massive forms are common: some found in Idaho weigh as much as 200 lbs. (90 kg). Other habits include botryoidal, fibrous, and nodular. The mineral also occurs as drusy crusts with tiny sparkling crystals.

As would be expected of a lead-bearing mineral, plattnerite has a high specific gravity—it weighs 9.4 times more than the equivalent volume of water at room temperature.

Above: The metallic gray appearance of plattnerite may cause it to be confused with associated galena.

Plattnerite is closely related to scrutinyite, which has exactly the same formula but conforms to the orthorhombic system of symmetry. The two minerals are dimorphous and so alike that the latter was identified only in 1988.

PLUMBOGUMMITE

Plumbogummite is a brightly colored and widely distributed mineral with a high lead content.

*Plumbogummite is a secondary mineral formed mainly in the oxidation zones of lead ores. It may also sometimes occur as rolled fragments in alluvial deposits that contain diamond. Among the minerals with which plumbogummite is most commonly associated are **calcite**, **limonite**, **marcasite**, **mimetite**, **pyromorphite**, and **quartz**.*

Main Sources: ◆ *Brazil* ◆ *England* ◆ *France* ◆ *Arizona, California, Colorado, Georgia, and Missouri, United States*

The name of this mineral is derived from the Latin *plumbum* ("lead") and *gummi* ("gum")—references to its main metal and its resinous luster. It was confirmed as a distinct species in 1819.

Plumbogummite is a hydrous hydrated phosphate of lead and aluminum with the chemical formula $PbAl_3(PO_4)_2(OH)_5.H_2O$. It is typically white but can be gray, yellow, greenish blue, or reddish brown.

Plumbogummite crystals conform to the trigonal system of symmetry. Externally, they often take the form of minute prisms with hexagonal outlines. Elsewhere the mineral may appear in botryoidal (grape-shaped) clusters with circular internal structures or in microcrystalline crusts on the surface of other minerals and rocks. Plumbogummite may also appear in stalactitic formations.

The mineral is also found with the closely related crandallite. In its pure form, crandallite is a hydrous hydrated phosphate, which contains calcium instead of plumbogummite's lead. But crandallite is seldom pure—some of its phosphate ions (PO_4) may be replaced by hydroxyl ions (OH), and it may also contain impurities of barium, iron, or strontium.

Plumbogummite scores 4½ to 5 on the Mohs Scale of Hardness and has a specific gravity of 4, which is fairly low for a lead-bearing mineral.

Below: Plumbogummite from a mineral vein showing typical blue coloring.

PREHNITE

Discovered at the Cape of Good Hope in South Africa, prehnite may be cut into gemstones.

Left: Stalactitic prehnite with botryoidal (grape-shaped) clusters—formations like this are popular with collectors.

This mineral is named after Colonel Hendrick von Prehn (1733-85), a Boer who discovered it at the Cape of Good Hope in South Africa and who first introduced it into Europe. It was confirmed as a distinct species in 1788.

A hydrous silicate of calcium and aluminum with the chemical formula $Ca_2Al_2Si_3O_{10}(OH)_2$, prehnite is more particularly a phyllosilicate—a silicate that forms in continuous molecular chains.

Prehnite conforms to the orthorhombic system of symmetry. Externally, most deposits appear as compact granular masses, nodules, concretions, crusts, or stalactites. Botryoidal and reniform habits are also seen. Individual crystals are rare, but some nodular specimens show tabular crystal protrusions.

CAT'S EYE

The surface of the finest prehnite may reveal a play of light that resembles the narrow pupil of a cat's eye. This effect is known as chatoyancy. In addition, some crystals are pleochroic—their colors may appear to alter, depending on the direction of the light source and the angle from which they are viewed.

Prehnite crystals that display these characteristics are polished or cut into ornamental stones. The mineral is quite hard (Mohs scale 6) and fibrous and is therefore suitable for fashioning in a wide range of styles. The most widely employed is the cabochon, but step cuts are also made. Gem varieties are sometimes marketed under the name Cape emerald.

The mineral bears a close resemblance to **jade** and **vesuvianite**, but prehnite is the only member of the trio that will give off water when heated in a closed test tube.

*Prehnite is formed mainly in the veins and cavities of igneous **basalt**. It may also occur in some metamorphic rocks such as **diorite** and **gneiss**. It is associated with the minerals **apophyllite**, **calcite**, **copper**, **epidote**, **quartz**, and **stilbite**.*

Main Sources: ◆ *Australia* ◆ *Austria* ◆ *Canada* ◆ *Czech Republic* ◆ *France* ◆ *Germany* ◆ *India* ◆ *Italy* ◆ *New Zealand* ◆ *Pakistan* ◆ *Russia* ◆ *Scotland* ◆ *South Africa* ◆ *Switzerland* ◆ *California, Colorado, Connecticut, Massachusetts, Michigan, New Jersey, North Carolina, Pennsylvania, and Virginia, United States*

PSEUDOMALACHITE

Named for its superficial resemblance to malachite, pseudomalachite is a favorite with collectors.

Malachite and pseudomalachite occur together in the oxidation zones of copper ore deposits. Among the other minerals that are associated with pseudomalachite are **atacamite, brochantite, chalcedony, chrysocolla, cornetite, jarosite, lepidocrocite, libethenite, limonite,** *and* **quartz.**

Main Sources: ◆ *Australia* ◆ *Belgium* ◆ *Canada* ◆ *Chile* ◆ *Democratic Republic of the Congo (formerly Zaire)* ◆ *Czech Republic* ◆ *England* ◆ *France* ◆ *Germany* ◆ *Portugal* ◆ *Romania* ◆ *Russia* ◆ *Slovakia* ◆ *Arizona, United States* ◆ *Zambia*

This attractive green mineral is named for its superficial resemblance to **malachite**. Both contain copper, but malachite is a hydrous carbonate, while pseudomalachite is a hydrous hydrated phosphate. But pseudomalachite is much rarer and lacks the characteristic light and dark green banding of malachite. It is also slightly harder (Mohs scale 4½ to 5) and denser (specific gravity 4.3) than malachite. Even when the two minerals appear indistinguishable, a simple test will quickly establish the difference between them—only malachite will effervesce when placed in warm hydrochloric acid.

Pseudomalachite is trimorphous with the minerals ludjibaite and reichenbachite. A trimorph is any one of three minerals that all have the same chemistry but different structures.

GRAPELIKE OR KIDNEY-SHAPED

Crystals of pseudomalachite conform to the monoclinic system of symmetry. Externally, although they may appear in distinct prismatic shapes, they more often take the form of tiny botryoidal or reniform masses. Some deposits appear to be composed of crystals arranged almost in parallel.

When hit with a hammer or subjected to pressure, pseudomalachite will break off cleanly along its weakest structural lines, giving it perfect cleavage.

The type locality of this mineral is at Virneberg near Rheinbreitbach in Germany. It was there that it was first discovered. Pseudomalachite was confirmed as a distinct mineral in 1813.

Below: Clusters of greenish pseudomalachite on the surface of a copper-bearing ore.

PUMICE

A volcanic igneous rock, pumice is well known for its many uses as a scourer, abrasive, polisher, and in soundproofing tiles.

*Given the right conditions, pumice may appear in any type of lava, but it is more often found in **rhyolite** and **trachyte** than in **basalt**.*

Main Sources: *Pumice is particularly abundant on the volcanic islands of Santorini, Greece; Lipari, Italy; and Hawaii, United States.*

Pumice is a pyroclastic igneous rock. "Pyroclastic" means that it is a fiery fragment, yet it cools so quickly that it has no time to crystallize or to form glass, like **obsidian**. Pumice is full of pock marks (vesicles)—solidified remnants of bubbles that were in the molten lava from which the rock originated.

SCORIA

Scoria is a volcanic rock that is similar to pumice but denser and contains fewer vesicles, or gas cavities. It is often found in basaltic lava flows.

Despite its overall amorphous form, pumice may contain tiny crystals of accessory minerals. These can include **augite**, **hornblende**, zeolite minerals such as **analcime**, and **zircon**.

Pumice is less dense than water and it is porous. It will float until it becomes saturated. Some fragments have been found floating as many as 4,000 miles (6,400 km) from their original source.

In its massive form, pumice is used as a scourer for removing hardened skin, and in dental pastes. Powdered pumice (*see* photo, above right) is an abrasive in cleaning and polishing. The rock is also used as ballast beneath railroad sleepers, in precast masonry, in plaster, and in the manufacture of concrete and soundproofing tiles.

HEAT TREATMENT

Obsidian is what pumice would be if it were formed at higher temperatures and under greater pressure. If pumice is heated artificially until it melts, it may turn into obsidian.

Left: The small hollows characteristic of pumice are spaces where gas bubbles formed in the original lava.

PYRITE

Used in jewelry for thousands of years, pyrite is also known as "fool's gold" because of its metallic yellow coloration.

*Pyrite is one of the Earth's most common minerals and forms from hydrothermals in all three main rock types—igneous, metamorphic, and sedimentary. It is frequently associated with **calcite**, **fluorite**, **galena**, **gold**, **quartz**, and **sphalerite**.*

Main Sources: ◆ *Australia* ◆ *Canada* ◆ *Chile* ◆ *Czech Republic* ◆ *England* ◆ *France* ◆ *Germany* ◆ *India* ◆ *Ireland* ◆ *Italy* ◆ *Japan* ◆ *Mexico* ◆ *Norway* ◆ *Peru* ◆ *Russia* ◆ *Scotland* ◆ *South Africa* ◆ *Spain* ◆ *Sweden* ◆ *Illinois and Missouri, United States* ◆ *Wales*

Above: Twinned crystals of pyrite. Magnificent aggregates like this are fairly common.

The shiny yellow color of much pyrite gives rise to its common name of "fool's gold." Its mineralogical name comes from the Greek *pyr*, meaning "fire"—this is a reference to the fact that it gives off sparks when struck with steel.

Pyrite is dimorphous with **marcasite**. In other words, they are chemically identical—both are sulfides of iron with the formula FeS_2—but structurally discrete: they conform to different crystal systems, have different specific gravities, and marcasite is of a paler yellow color than pyrite.

In some deposits, the iron in pyrite may be replaced by cobalt to form cattierite—the two minerals are therefore the end members of a solid solution series. Cattierite then forms another series with vaesite, in which cobalt is substituted by nickel. Also closely related is bravoite, an iron sulfide that contains up to 20 percent nickel.

CUBES AND GROOVES

Crystals of pyrite are of the cubic system. They often form in cubes, as well as in octahedral and dodeca-hedral shapes. Twinning is common and many of the crystal faces have grooves (striations). Deposits may also be massive, granular, nodular, botryoidal, reniform or stalactitic. The mineral has a metallic luster and a greenish black streak.

USED DURING THE WAR

Although in general pyrite has few industrial uses, it was mined in the United States during World War II (1939–1945) for its sulfur, which was used in the production of sulfuric acid. The most productive mine was at Ducktown, Tennessee. In peacetime, however, most sulfuric acid is made from hydrogen sulfide gas that is recovered from natural gas wells.

PYROLUSITE

Pyrolusite provides much of the manganese used to make alloys in the steel industry.

Pyrolusite forms in manganese deposits that have reacted with air and water. It is widely distributed in bogs, shallow marine sediments, and at the bottom of the sea. It is also sometimes found in veins of **quartz**. *Among the other minerals with which it is commonly associated are* **hematite**, **limonite**, *and* **manganite**.

Main Sources: ◆ *Australia* ◆ *Brazil* ◆ *Canada* ◆ *China* ◆ *Democratic Republic of the Congo (formerly Zaire)* ◆ *Czech Republic* ◆ *England* ◆ *Gabon* ◆ *Georgia* ◆ *Germany* ◆ *India* ◆ *Italy* ◆ *South Africa* ◆ *Ukraine* ◆ *California, Minnesota, Michigan, Montana, and New Mexico, United States*

Above: A radiating coating of pyrolusite seen on the surface of a rock.

P yrolusite is the most important mineral ore of manganese, a metal that occurs in 850 parts per million of the Earth's crust.

The English name of this mineral is derived from the Greek *pyr* ("fire") and *louein* ("to wash")—this refers to pyrolusite's use as an additive in glassmaking to remove unwanted brown and green tints.

Confirmed as a distinct species in 1827, pyrolusite is an oxide with the chemical formula MnO_2. It is a member of the **rutile** group. Crystals conform to the tetragonal system of symmetry. They may appear in prismatic forms, but these are very rare. Most pyrolusite takes the form of columnar, dendritic, fibrous or granular masses, concretions, or wads.

USES OF MANGANESE

Some 95 percent of the world's annual production of manganese is used in the steel industry to purify iron and make alloys. Manganese is added to iron because it reduces iron oxide to form manganese oxide, which dissolves well in molten slag and is easily separated from the iron. The metal also increases steel's resistance to corrosion, making it more malleable.

Manganese steel, which contains 11 to 14 percent manganese and 1 to 1.5 percent carbon, is more resistant to corrosion than ordinary steel and is used in grinding machinery and wrecking equipment.

Among the many manganese alloys that do not contain iron are the Heusler alloys (containing 18 to 25 percent manganese plus copper and aluminum or zinc), which are the strongest of the nonferrous metals, and manganese copper (about 75 percent copper and 25 percent manganese), which has great electrical resistance.

PYROMORPHITE

Formerly known as "green lead," pyromorphite's new name comes from its unusual reaction when it is melted and resolidifies.

*Pyromorphite forms through the alteration of the primary minerals **anglesite** and **galena** in the oxidation zones of lead veins. It is associated with **cerussite** and **limonite**.*

Main Sources: ◆ *Australia* ◆ *Canada* ◆ *Czech Republic* ◆ *England* ◆ *Germany* ◆ *Mexico* ◆ *Myanmar (Burma)* ◆ *Russia* ◆ *Scotland* ◆ *California, Colorado, Idaho, New Mexico, Pennsylvania, South Dakota, and Utah, United States*

When pyromorphite is melted, it will form globules that resolidify on cooling in the form of crystals. It is from this unusual reaction that the mineral gets its modern scientific name, which comes from the Greek *pyr* ("fire") and *morphe* ("form").

ARSENIC SUBSTITUTION

Pyromorphite is a chlorophosphate of lead with the chemical formula $Pb_5(PO_4)_3Cl$. In some deposits, its phosphorus may be substituted by **arsenic** until **mimetite** is formed and the two compounds therefore form a solid solution series. Up to 15 percent of pyromorphite's lead may also be replaced by calcium. Pyromorphite forms another series with vanadinite, a chlorovanadate of lead.

Crystals of pyromorphite conform to the hexagonal system of symmetry. The most attractive specimens appear in six-sided barrel-shaped prisms with pyramidal terminations. Some crystalline clusters of pyromorphite appear in green, branchlike formations, which are said to have an arborescent habit. The mineral may also appear in granular encrustations or in reniform or massive aggregates.

Pyromorphite has a specific gravity of 6.5 to 7.1 and scores 3½ to 4 on the Mohs Scale of Hardness. With ill-defined structural lines, it has poor cleavage.

Although pyromorphite and mimetite are often confusingly similar in appearance, the two can be easily differentiated without quantitative analysis. The test involves placing any unidentified specimens in acid; it will be found that mimetite is soluble in hydrochloric acid, while pyromorphite will dissolve only in nitric acid.

Below: An attractive aggregate of prismatic, green pyromorphite crystals.

PYROPHYLLITE

Named after the way it reacts when heated, pyrophyllite has a number of uses—from a paint filler to carved ornamental stones.

*Pyrophyllite is formed in aluminum-rich **schist**, which is a metamorphic rock. When found in schist, it is most commonly associated with **andalusite**, **barite**, **epidote**, **graphite**, **gypsum**, **kyanite**, **lazulite**, **sillimanite**, and **talc**. Pyrophyllite is also found with **mica** and **quartz** in hydrothermal veins.*

Main Sources: ◆ *Belgium* ◆ *Brazil* ◆ *China* ◆ *England* ◆ *Finland* ◆ *Italy* ◆ *Japan* ◆ *Mexico* ◆ *Russia* ◆ *Scotland* ◆ *South Africa* ◆ *South Korea* ◆ *Spain* ◆ *Sweden* ◆ *Switzerland* ◆ *Arizona, California, Georgia, North Carolina, Pennsylvania, and South Carolina, United States*

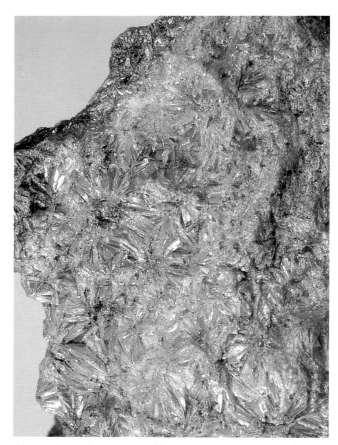

Above: Radiating masses of brown pyrophyllite crystals with a vitreous luster.

Pyrophyllite has a wide variety of uses: as a refractory mineral, as a filler for rubber, paints, and insecticides (*see* photo, below), and as an ingredient in ceramics. The massive form, sometimes known as agalmatolite, is used as an ornamental stone and may be carved, especially in China.

The English name of this mineral is derived from the Greek *pyr* ("fire") and *phyllon* ("a leaf"), referring to the fact that, when it is heated to temperatures of over about 1,470° F (800° C), it does not melt, as would normally be expected, but splits into thin flakes and spreads out in leaflike formations many times its original size. The scientific term for reactions of this type is exfoliation.

A hydrous silicate of aluminum with the formula $Al_2Si_4O_{10}(OH)_2$, pyrophyllite forms in continuous chains so is defined as a phyllosilicate. Crystals of pyrophyllite may conform to either the monoclinic or the triclinic system of symmetry, depending on the conditions in which they were

formed. Distinct individuals are rare, but those that do occur tend to appear in elongated or deformed tabular shapes. The mineral more commonly appears in foliated, radiating, fibrous, or layered masses. The radiating stellate aggregates from Mariposa County, California, are of the greatest interest to collectors.

Pyrophyllite is sometimes isomorphous with talc. In other words, the two minerals have the same crystal shapes and may appear externally identical, even though they have different chemistries.

PYROXENITE

Pyroxenite is an intrusive igneous plutonic rock that is made up almost completely of pyroxene minerals.

Pyroxenite is found in small, independent intrusions that are usually associated with basic rocks such as gabbro.

Main Sources: *Although rock formations of this type originate deep inside the Earth, they are often propeled closer—or even on—to the surface by subsequent geological activity.*

An intrusive igneous rock, pyroxenite contains large quantities of iron- and magnesium-bearing minerals. In scientific terms, therefore, it is classified as an ultramafic formation. Pyroxenite originates very deep in the Earth's crust and is therefore plutonic. It contains less than 45 percent total silica, and is thus described as ultrabasic. As its name suggests, it is composed almost entirely of pyroxene minerals. Some biotite—a form of **mica**—and iron oxides may also be present, together with **horn-blende** and **olivine**. The light-colored crystals in some pyroxenite are **feldspar**.

Pyroxenite is a medium- to coarse-grained rock. It has a granular texture, with well-formed crystals that sometimes occur in layers.

PYROXENES

Pyroxene minerals are chain silicates (inosilicates) with the general formula $X_2Si_2O_6$, in which X may be aluminum, calcium, iron, lithium, magnesium, manganese, sodium, or titanium.

The pyroxenes are common rock-forming minerals which are found in most igneous and many metamorphic rocks. Their presence in a rock indicates that it crystallized at a high temperature.

The term "pyroxene" is derived from the Greek *pyr* ("fire") and *xenos* ("stranger")—this is because rocks of this type were once erroneously believed to have been incorporated into lava by chance.

Below: The coarse grains of pyroxenite are readily visible to the naked eye.

PYROXENE MINERALS

Aegirine:	$NaFeSi_2O_6$
Diopside:	$MgCaSi_2O_6$
Enstatite:	$Mg_2Si_2O_6$
Hedenbergite:	$CaFe^{2+}Si_2O_6$
Jadeite (*see* Jade):	$NaAlSi_2O_6$
Spodumene:	$LiAlSi_2O_6$

PYRRHOTITE

Pyrrhotite is an iron sulfide that can display two symmetries within a single crystal and may be magnetic.

*Most deposits of pyrrotite are found with other sulfides in massive rock-forming beds, especially of igneous rocks such as **gabbro** and **peridotite**. It is a product of magmatic segregation, during which minerals precipitate out of the fluid in order of heaviness—the densest congregate first at the bottom of a deposit, the lightest form last at the top. Pyrrhotite is commonly associated with **ankerite**, **pentlandite**, **pyrite**, and **quartz**.*

Main Sources: ◆ *Austria* ◆ *Bolivia* ◆ *Brazil* ◆ *Canada* ◆ *Germany* ◆ *India* ◆ *Italy* ◆ *Japan* ◆ *Mexico* ◆ *Norway* ◆ *Romania* ◆ *Serbia* ◆ *Sweden* ◆ *Maine, Pennsylvania, Tennessee, and South Dakota, United States*

A minor ore of iron and **sulfur**, pyrrhotite gets its name from the Greek *pyrros*, meaning "red colored." It was confirmed as a distinct mineral in 1835.

Pyrrhotite is an iron sulfide. Its formula is usually given as FeS, but this is something of a simplification—the mineral is often deficient in iron, and may in fact have a composition closer to $Fe_{0.8}S$. This affects the proportion of sulfur, which may vary within a range of plus or minus 20 percent.

TWO SHAPES IN ONE

Because of its unusual chemistry, pyrrhotite has two symmetries—when it is low in sulfur and the formula is close to FeS, the structure is hexagonal. But when it is rich in sulfur, the structure is monoclinic. In normal circumstances, it would be expected that these varieties would be classified as different minerals. But in pyrrhotite, both forms may appear within a single crystal.

Pyrrhotite may be weakly magnetic. It is the second most common magnetic mineral after **magnetite**. Although not all specimens of pyrrhotite will

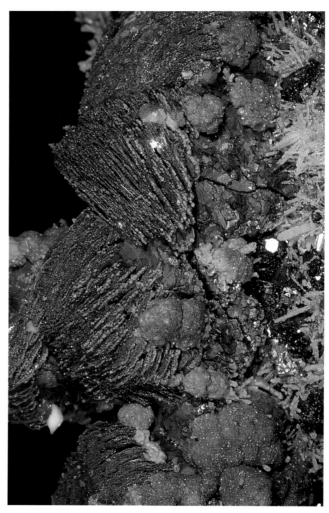

Above: Masses of platy brownish pyrrhotite crystals from a mineral vein.

show great evidence of magnetism if any, some will attract a paperclip or needle suspended from a string or move the needle of a compass. Pyrrhotite in massive habits is common, and magnetism is sometimes the only way to distinguish it from other brassy colored sulfide minerals.

QUARTZ

The second most abundant rock-forming mineral, quartz has a large number of polymorphs and different varieties.

Above: Amethyst, a purple form of quartz that may be colored by impurities of manganese.

Quartz is one of the most common minerals on the face of the Earth. It is found in nearly every geological environment and is at least a component of almost every rock type.

Main Sources: ◆ *Amethyst: Brazil; Canada; Mexico; Russia; Uruguay* ◆ *Smoky quartz: Brazil; Scotland; Switzerland; Colorado, United States* ◆ *Rose quartz: Brazil* ◆ *Rock crystal: Brazil; Arkansas, United States* ◆ *Agate: Brazil; Germany; Mexico; Michigan and Montana, United States*

Chemically, quartz is a form of silicon dioxide with the formula SiO_2. It has a wide range of uses—as silica for glass, in electrical components such as clocks and radios (*see* photo, right), as optical lenses, abrasives, and ornamental and building stones.

Quartz has been known since prehistory, though the origin of its name is uncertain. It may come from the Greek, *krustallos*, meaning "ice," the West Slav, *kwardy*, meaning "hard," or the Old English *querklufterz* ("cross-vein ore").

There are many varieties of quartz (*see* box, below) due to its different colors and forms. The color of aventurine quartz may vary according to the impurities—for example, inclusions of fuchsite **mica** give a green stone, **pyrite** makes it appear brown, and **goethite** gives a greenish brown effect.

COMMON VARIETIES OF QUARTZ

Name	Color	Comments
Agate	Various	Forms in curved bands of different colors
Amethyst	Purple	Birthstone for February
Carnelian	Reddish orange	Colored by iron oxides
Chalcedony	Various	All agates are varieties of this form of quartz
Chrysoprase	Apple green	Colored by inclusions of nickel
Jasper	Reddish brown	Colored by iron oxide; believed to cure blindness
Onyx	Various	Like agate, but bands are straight, not curved
Plasma	Reddish brown	Colored by iron oxides; may sometimes be green
Rock crystal	Clear	Fortune tellers' crystal balls are made of this
Rose quartz	Pink	Colored by impurities of titanium
Sardonyx	Various	Like agate, but bands are straight, not curved
Smoky quartz	Brown to gray	Colored by inclusions of **rutile**; also known as Cairngorm

QUARTZITE

White, gray, brownish, or pink in color, this widespread and abundant rock may occur as sedimentary quartzite or metaquartzite.

Sedimentary quartzite (orthoquartzite) forms from very pure sand on the beds of shallow seas. **Metaquartzite** *occurs as a result of sedimentary quartzite being changed by heat.*

Main Sources: *Quartzite is abundant and widely distributed throughout the world. Some of the most striking formations may be seen in Minas Gerais in Brazil, the Deccan Plateau in India, Ireland's County Galway, the Highlands of Scotland, and in North and South Carolina, the United States.*

There are two forms of quartzite: metaquartzite (*see* box, right), and sedimentary quartzite (also known as orthoquartzite). This latter form is a hard rock that contains a high percentage of **quartz**—many deposits contain more than 90 percent of this mineral. Deposits display many typical sedimentary features such as stratification, crossbedding, and ripple marks. A few contain fossilized worm casts.

METAQUARTZITE

Metaquartzite is formed when sedimentary quartzite is metamorphosed by heat. It acquires a new texture as grains of quartz become interlocked. As the degree of metamorphism increases, sedimentary structures—bedding planes, crossbedding, ripple arks, and desiccation cracks, for example—will tend to be obliterated.

Some metamorphic quartzite, however, is of great interest to geologists because it retains the bedding, grains, and other textural features of the pre-existent sandstone or chert from which it was originally formed.

In addition to quartz, sedimentary quartzite may also contain the accessories **apatite**, **feldspar**, **ilmenite**, **magnetite**, **mica**, **pyrite**, and **zircon**. Among the fortuitous (accidental) minerals that may sometimes be present in quartzite are **calcite**, **garnet**, and **graphite**.

Sedimentary quartzite has a wide range of industrial applications. The finest such deposits are used in the construction industry, particularly to make flooring and facing, and in the manufacture of ceramics and glass. The rock's low sensitivity to heat also makes it useful as a refractory material (*see* photo of quartzite refractory accessory, above), in the walls of kilns and ovens. Rough gray quartzite is widely used as railroad ballast (the coarse bed on which the tracks are laid).

Left: The component grains of quartzite are tightly compressed and the rock is therefore very tough and highly resistant to cutting.

QUARTZ PORPHYRY

This rock often contains valuable accessory minerals. It is sometimes used as an ornamental stone.

Quartz porphyry is a widely distributed intrusive igneous (derived from magma) rock. It is generally light colored—usually gray, pink, reddish, or violet. Formations of this type are further classified as acidic because they contain more than 65 percent total silica and more than 10 percent quartz. The essential mineralogical components of quartz porphyry are **feldspar**, **mica**, and **quartz**.

The most industrially important accessory mineral in quartz porphyry is **chalcopyrite**, which is mined as an important copper ore. The rock also commonly contains **apatite**, **calcite**, **hornblende**, **ilmenite**, **magnetite**, **molybdenite**, and **zircon**.

PORPHYRITIC ROCK

The essential physical characteristic of quartz porphyry is its phenocrysts (large crystals) of feldspar and quartz set in a finer-grained matrix (base). It is because of these large crystals that the rock is described as porphyritic. The rough surface of quartz porphyry may sometimes contain tiny but visible fragments of partially devitrified glass.

This rock solidifies in two distinct phases—the phenocrysts form during the first, hotter, phase, while the fine-grained groundmass coalesces later, at lower temperatures.

USED FOR BUILDING

In addition to being mined for its accessory minerals, the finest quartz porphyry may be cut and polished to make ornamental stones and building façades. Inferior deposits, on the other hand, may be used for gravel and ballast.

Above: Quartz porphyry is formed in two distinct temperature phases and has large, distinct crystals (phenocrysts) set in a base (matrix) of tiny grains.

Quartz porphyry is formed from magma in small intrusive structures, such as dikes and sills, which were usually formed at no great depth. (The use of the term "small" is relative—some quartz porphyry sills extend for over 2,000 sq.miles (5,180 sq.km).

Main Sources: *Found all over the world, some fine examples of quartz porphyry may be seen along the Pacific seaboard of the United States in California, Oregon, and Washington.*

REALGAR

An important source of arsenic, realgar is also valued for its physical properties and brilliant red coloration.

*Realgar occurs in hydrothermal veins with valuable metal sulfide ores. Its bright red color can be an aid to prospectors. It may also be found in hot spring deposits and as a volcanic sublimation product, meaning that it crystallizes from vapors. It is almost always formed with **orpiment**, but other associated minerals include **calcite** and **stibnite**.*

Main Sources: ◆ *China* ◆ *France* ◆ *Italy* ◆ *Japan* ◆ *Macedonia* ◆ *Peru* ◆ *Romania* ◆ *Switzerland* ◆ *California, Nevada, South Dakota, Utah, and Washington, United States*

Realgar is one of the three main industrial ores of arsenic—the others are **arsenopyrite** and orpiment. Its English name comes from the Arabic *rahj al ghar*, meaning "powder of the mine." This derivation is possibly because it was first found as an accessory in silver workings. Realgar has been known since ancient times and was described in detail by the Roman historian Pliny the Elder (A.D. 23–79) in his encyclopedia, *Naturalis historia*.

PROPERTIES AND CARE

Realgar is a sulfide of arsenic with the chemical formula AsS. Crystals of this mineral conform to the monoclinic system of symmetry. Externally, they are often prismatic and striated with diamondlike cross-sections and terminate in wedgelike domes. Realgar is also found as grains, crusts, and earthy masses. Massive aggregates are also common.

When it is exposed to light for long periods, realgar decomposes into a powder known as pararealgar. Hence, specimens of realgar should be stored in complete darkness and brought out only for short periods for inspection. Rarely, realgar may fluoresce under ultraviolet light, while some crystals are pleochroic between dark red and orange red.

HAZARDOUS FIREWORKS

Realgar was once used to color fireworks, but today minerals containing strontium are used for this purpose. This is because strontium minerals are less hazardous than minerals such as realgar that contain arsenic.

Left: This mass of granular realgar shows the mineral's striking red color.

RHODOCHROSITE

Related to calcite and siderite, rhodochrosite often occurs in distinctive pink-colored bands and has a number of ornamental uses.

*Rhodochrosite occurs in veins of **copper**, lead, and **silver** that have been altered by hydrothermals, and as a secondary deposit in sedimentary layers of manganese oxide. It is associated mainly with **calcite**, and may also occur with **quartz**.*

Main Sources: ◆ *Argentina* ◆ *Canada* ◆ *Germany* ◆ *Mexico* ◆ *Namibia* ◆ *Peru* ◆ *Romania* ◆ *Russia* ◆ *South Africa* ◆ *Arizona, Colorado, Montana, Utah, and Washington, United States*

This mineral derives its name from its dark red to brownish coloration. This color, in turn, is derived from the manganese it contains. Rhodochrosite—from the Greek, *rhodo-khros*, meaning "rose-colored"—is a minor ore of manganese and an ornamental and semiprecious stone. Although it has been known and used for thousands of years, it was not confirmed as a distinct mineral until 1813.

SERIES OF THREE

Chemically, rhodochrosite is a carbonate of manganese with the formula $MnCO_3$. However, in some deposits this metal may be replaced by calcium or iron to form two entirely separate minerals, calcite and **siderite** respectively. Where this process of gradual atomic substitution occurs, the three minerals form a solid solution series.

Crystals of rhodochrosite conform to the trigonal system of symmetry. They sometimes appear in rhombohedrons and scalenohedrons with rounded faces that can obscure the crystal shape. More commonly, however, the mineral appears in masses, which may be botryoidal (grapelike), globular, stalactitic, layered, or granular.

Massive rhodochrosite with pink and white bands is used as an ornamental stone, for example being

carved into figurines or sliced into circles with concentric bands. Slabs of the mineral are also used to make a wide range of ornaments, including trinket boxes, mosaics, and pots. Fine crystals of rhodochrosite are sometimes cut into cameo brooches, polished *en cabochon*, or tumbled into beads, but the mineral's softness (Mohs scale 3½ to 4) and brittleness limit its uses as a gemstone.

Above: Rhombohedral crystals of rodochrosite on a base (matrix) of ore-bearing rock.

INCA ROSE

The world's oldest surviving rhodochrosite mine is at San Luis, Argentina. Banded specimens from there are sold under the name "Inca rose."

RHODONITE

A brilliant pink or red colored mineral, rhodonite's bright colors may be obscured by black marks—a result of oxidation.

*Rhodonite is formed mainly in manganese-bearing metamorphic rocks, especially **marble** and **skarn**, which were previously **limestone**. It is also found in sediments that have been altered by metasomatism (chemical change). Among the minerals with which rhodonite is most commonly associated are **calcite**, **garnet**, and **pyrite**.*

Main Sources: ◆ *Australia* ◆ *Brazil* ◆ *Canada* ◆ *England* ◆ *Finland* ◆ *Hungary* ◆ *India* ◆ *Italy* ◆ *Japan* ◆ *Madagascar* ◆ *New Zealand* ◆ *Russia* ◆ *South Africa* ◆ *Sweden* ◆ *Tanzania* ◆ *California, Colorado, Maine, Massachusetts, Montana, and New Jersey, United States*

The English name of this mineral is derived from the Greek *rhodon*, meaning "rose," this being a reference to its bright pink to reddish coloration. Rhodonite was confirmed as a distinct species in 1819. A silicate of manganese with the chemical formula $Mn^{2+}SiO_3$, it is a minor ore of this metal. However, the main use of rhodonite is as an ornamental or semiprecious stone.

Crystals of rhodonite conform to the triclinic system of symmetry, and distinct individual specimens have a blocky, prismatic habit. Such formations are unusual, however, and those that do occur are rarely suitable for faceting because of their brittleness and sensitivity to heat. Indeed, one of the key tests for this mineral is that when it is held in an open flame, it fuses easily and turns into a reddish glass.

BEADS AND BROOCHES

Most rhodonite formations are massive, coarse, and fine granular aggregates, and it is these that are faceted for use as jewelry and ornaments. Such specimens are good for tumbling and polishing. The most popular use for low-grade rhodonite is beads, while the better-quality stones are usually fashioned into cabochons. The finest rhodonite samples may be cut into cameo brooches.

When freshly extracted from the Earth, the surface of rhodonite may sometimes be discolored by unsightly black marks and veins of manganese oxide. However, these impurities can be easily removed by carefully dabbing the surface of the stone with dilute hydrochloric acid. This removes the marks but does not damage the mineral, rhodonite itself being insoluble in acids.

Left: A massive aggregate of rhodonite showing its characteristic dark pink coloration.

RHYOLITE

Formed from particularly sticky, viscous molten lava, rhyolite's gray, brown, or reddish color often darkens with age.

Like all igneous rocks, rhyolite was originally created through the cooling and solidification of magma (molten volcanic lava).

Main Sources: *This rock is widely distributed across many parts of the Earth's surface, but it is most commonly visible in plugs at the throats of volcanoes. Such deposits do not normally extend over large areas because molten rhyolite is highly viscous so does not flow far before cooling down and solidifying.*

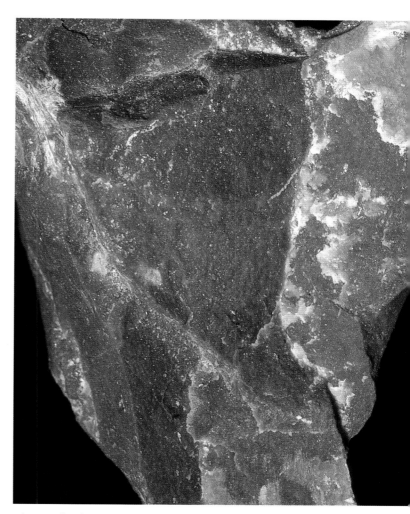

Above: Rhyolite is a hard, flinty rock that breaks to give sharp edges.

Rhyolite is an extrusive igneous rock formation that has many similarities to granite. Its English name comes from the Greek, *rhuax*, meaning "a torrent" or "a stream." This is a reference to the fluid lava from which it formed.

Many rhyolite deposits still bear visible signs of their liquefied origins—they have round, mineral-filled cavities (amygdales) and hollow sacs (vesicles), which are the solidified remains of what were once bubbles in a solution. The most vesicular forms of rhyolite may be classified as **pumice**.

VISCOUS LAVA

Rhyolite originates from highly viscous lava that is often so sticky it clogs up the vents through which it is trying to emerge onto the surface. These blockages can be eased only when the pressure of further lava builds up and causes an explosion. The viscosity also prevents rhyolite lava from flowing very far from its point of issue. As a result, volcanoes made of rhyolite lava are often very steep-sided.

The essential mineralogical components of rhyolite are **feldspar**, **mica**, and **quartz**. The numerous possible accessories include **hornblende**. Rhyolite may also contain glass, this being a common occurrence in rocks that have cooled too quickly for crystallization to take place.

Rhyolite often appears in prominent swirling layers of different colors and grain types—this phenomenon is known as flow banding. Although most formations consist of tightly packed micro crystals, some specimens may also feature large, single crystals of quartz and feldspar known as phenocrysts. This gives the rock a porphyritic texture.

RIEBECKITE

A member of the amphibole group, riebeckite is an accessory mineral in granite and syenite.

*Riebeckite is formed at low temperatures in a wide range of igneous rocks, especially **granite, pegmatite, rhyolite, syenite,** and **trachyte**. It is mainly associated with **hornblende, feldspar, augite,** and other pyroxenes and micas.*

Main Sources: ◆ *Australia* ◆ *Austria* ◆ *France* ◆ *Greenland* ◆ *Madagascar* ◆ *Nigeria* ◆ *Portugal* ◆ *Scotland* ◆ *South Korea* ◆ *Romania* ◆ *Russia* ◆ *South Africa* ◆ *South Yemen* ◆ *Spain* ◆ *Arizona, California, Colorado, Massachusetts, Rhode Island, and Washington, United States*

Above: When riebeckite forms in long strands or threads like these it is said to be asbestiform.

This mineral is named after Emil Riebeck (1853–85), the German explorer who first collected it on Socotra Island (South Yemen). Riebeckite is a hydrous silicate of sodium, ferrous iron, magnesium, and ferric iron. Its chemical formula is $Na_2(Fe^{2+},Mg)_3Fe^{3+}_2Si_8O_{22}(OH)_2$. It is further classified as an amphibole, one of a group of chain silicates that also includes **glaucophane**.

This mineral may be dark blue or black, the darkness of the color increasing with the amount of iron it contains. Pure riebeckite is iron-rich. Specimens where the iron has gradually been substituted by magnesium form a separate species known as magnesioriebeckite. The two minerals form a solid solution series.

FORM OF ASBESTOS

Crystals of riebeckite conform to the monoclinic system of symmetry. Externally, they may appear in prismatic shapes with parallel striations (grooves) along their surfaces. The finest may show a chatoyancy (cat's eye effect), and these are sometimes used in jewelry. Most deposits, however, form in fibrous strands. This variety of riebeckite, known as crocidolite, is one of the many forms of asbestos, a material that was used as an insulating and fireproofing material until it was found to cause lung cancer in humans. Although scientists are divided about whether **chrysotile**, the main mineral used in asbestos, is a carcinogen, there is general agreement that all amphiboles are extremely dangerous.

RUBY

One of the most precious gemstones on Earth, ruby is a very hard gemstone, with a fiery red brilliance like that of a glowing ember.

*Rubies are found in some forms of **marble** and in alluvial gravel along the banks of certain rivers.*

Main Sources: ◆ *Afghanistan* ◆ *Cambodia* ◆ *China* ◆ *India* ◆ *Kenya* ◆ *Madagascar* ◆ *Myanmar (Burma)* ◆ *Norway* ◆ *Pakistan* ◆ *Sri Lanka* ◆ *Tanzania* ◆ *Thailand* ◆ *North Carolina, United States* ◆ *Zimbabwe*

A form of **corundum**, ruby gets its red coloration from impurities of chromium and iron. In addition, the gemstone often contains traces of liquids and gases. Some rubies also contain **rutile**—when these inclusions form geometric shapes, they may reflect incident (incoming) light into shiny six-pointed stars, giving the gemstone a distinctive sparkle. This optical effect, known as asterism, adds greatly to the commercial value of the stone.

For more than 500 years the finest rubies have come from a small area near Mogok, Myanmar (Burma), where they are washed and sieved from limestone gravels.

Rubies are also used industrially. Since 1902, when Auguste Verneuil developed the flame-fusion process, artificial rubies have been produced from ammonia alum and chrome alum. In 1960 an artificial ruby was used in the first working laser.

SIMULATIONS

Some of the gemstones commonly known as ruby are, in fact, red varieties of **spinel**. One of the most famous examples is the Black Prince's Ruby in the British crown jewels.

Rubies are also sometimes imitated by garnet and glass, which are fused (melted) together in combinations known as doublets. In such a combination, the garnet—which provides the hardness and the

BIRTHSTONE

Ruby is the birthstone of people born under the sign of Leo (23 July to 22 August). It represents—and, according to some, inspires—passion.

sheen—is placed on the upper side of the gem. The glass beneath it is colored red to resemble ruby. Doublets are heated and cooled very quickly in order to create visible internal fractures similar to those that characterize the genuine stone.

Below: Small, non-precious rubies set in a mass of metamorphic rock.

RUTILE

Although it is sometimes used in jewelry, rutile is most often seen as a gemstone when it occurs as an inclusion within other stones.

Left: Slender, acicular rutile in transparent quartz crystal. Formations like this are highly valued by mineral collectors.

The English name of this mineral is derived from the Latin *rutilus*, meaning "red," this being a reference to its typical color. Rutile is the most abundant of the three naturally occurring forms of the chemical compound titanium oxide—the others are **anatase** and **brookite**.

USED AS A GEMSTONE

All three of these minerals are important as ores of titanium, but rutile is the only member of the trio that is used as a gemstone. The finest crystals, which conform to the tetragonal system, give off a greater fire (reflected light) than **diamond**, but this effect is often masked by the mineral's body color. Such crystals are generally faceted into rectangles or mixed cuts to bring out their sparkle to good effect.

Microscopic inclusions of rutile in quartz, tourmaline, **ruby**, **sapphire**, and other gemstones produce a range of optical effects such as chatoyancy (cat's eye) and asterisms (stars). A beautiful stone produced by large inclusions of rutile needles in clear quartz is known as rutilated quartz.

RUTILE STAR

Sometimes, rutile itself contains inclusions. When these are of trigonal hematite, the stone in question may display a six-rayed asterism making it highly valued as a jewel.

Crystals of rutile often appear in eight-sided prisms and blocky crystals with pyramidal terminations. Another very common habit is thin acicular needles (especially as inclusions in other minerals) or as blades. Twinning is common. Other habits include compact, granular, and massive.

*Rutile forms as an accessory mineral in igneous rocks and in metamorphic **gneiss** and **schist**. It may also form through the alteration of preexistent **mica** or **sphene**. It is often associated with **barite**, **hematite**, **quartz**, and **tourmaline**.*

Main Sources: ◆ *Austria* ◆ *Brazil* ◆ *Canada* ◆ *Czech Republic* ◆ *France* ◆ *Germany* ◆ *Italy* ◆ *Madagascar* ◆ *Norway* ◆ *Romania* ◆ *Russia* ◆ *Sweden* ◆ *Switzerland* ◆ *Arizona, Arkansas, California, Florida, Georgia, North Carolina, Pennsylvania, South Dakota, Utah, Virginia, and Washington, United States*

SANDSTONE

This common sedimentary rock, made up of tiny grains of quartz held together by a type of cement, is an important building material.

Sandstone is a product of sand, which is derived from the weathering of older rocks. Erosion by ice, water, or wind carries grains of varied sizes and shapes away from the parent rock. After these grains have been redeposited, groundwater percolating through the pores between the grains of sand will precipitate cement and convert it into sandstone. The most common cements are calcium carbonate, silica, and iron oxide. Coastal dunes, river and tidal sandbars, and shallow ocean bottoms all tend to be resting places for sands that will become sandstones.

Main Sources: *Sandstone is common and easy to find. There are many outstanding formations in the western United States, most notably in Zion Canyon, Utah.*

Sandstone is made of tiny grains of **quartz** held together by one of several types of cement or a fine, muddy matrix. If deposits of this broad type contain significant amounts of **feldspar**, they are known as **arkose**.

The grain size ranges between ¼₀₀ and ½ in. (0.06 and 2 mm) in diameter. Grains often appear with others of similar size because, as the sand is transported by air, water, or ice, the smallest grains are carried further than the heaviest, which are redeposited first.

The shape of the grains reflects the amount of abrasion that they have undergone during transport. Those carried by wind are the most evenly rounded; those carried by glaciers are the most uneven.

TYPES OF LAYERING

Sandstones are deposited on relatively flat surfaces and are stratified, or bedded. In most cases the stratification is parallel to the deposition surface, but subordinate layering may occur. Most common is fine-scale layering at angles of up to 30° above the dominant surface—this is known as cross bedding.

Another type of layering is graded bedding, in which the coarsest grains are at the bottom of a stratum and the finer grains at the top. This formation occurs when sand is transported in suspension within a churning mixture of water and sediment, known as a turbidity current—as the current's speed decreases, the grains settle in order of decreasing size.

BROWNSTONE

The brownstone houses seen in many U.S. cities of the northeast are really made of sandstone, a major construction material (*see* photo, above)

Left: Brown sandstone with numerous grains of quartz cemented together by silica and iron oxides.

SAPPHIRE

Sapphire is the blue variety of corundum, the second hardest natural mineral known. Red forms of corundum are known as ruby.

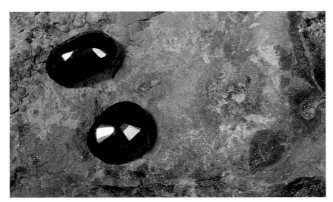

Above: Two small cut and polished sapphires resting on a massive slab of sapphire.

Sapphires are found in alluvial gravels in river beds. They settle in river beds after having been eroded by weather, dislodged from their original locations, and swept downstream.

Main Sources: ◆ *Australia* ◆ *Cambodia* ◆ *India* ◆ *Myanmar (Burma)* ◆ *Sri Lanka* ◆ *Thailand* ◆ *Montana, United States*

Sapphire is generally synonymous with blue, yet although some of the finest specimens are of this color, the gemstone may also be orange-pink, golden, white, or even black.

Classic blue sapphire is colored by impurities of iron and titanium that are lodged within the body of the corundum crystal. Oriented rutile inclusions cause a six-pointed effect known as asterism to form the popular "star sapphire" variety.

Sapphires are hard-wearing and highly resistant to electricity and heat. The finest specimens are cut in a variety of styles to make jewelry (*see* photo, above right) and other forms of ornamentation. Even

inferior stones are useful—sapphires have been mined extensively for the mechanisms of clocks, watches, and electrical measuring instruments, such as household meters. Elsewhere, they are used in the apertures and windows of very high-temperature furnaces, and in the rolling nibs of expensive ballpoint pens.

IMITATIONS

Synthetic sapphires are made by a flame-fusion technique in which powdered corundum is melted at high temperatures with iron and titanium.

Among the natural gemstones that resemble sapphire are blue spinel and blue tourmaline. Blue tanzanite also looks similar, but it is softer, scoring only 6½ to 7 on the Mohs Scale of Hardness (genuine sapphire has a Mohs rating of 9).

THE STAR OF INDIA

One of the largest sapphires ever discovered, the Star of India, was extracted from the Earth in Sri Lanka, the world's most productive source of this gemstone. This amazing specimen—which weighs 563 carats (4 oz.)—is now housed in the New York Museum of Natural History.

SCHEELITE

One of the most important ores of tungsten along with wolframite, scheelite is used for its high heat resistance to make television tubes.

*This mineral occurs in hydrothermal veins, in placer deposits, in contact metamorphic rocks, and in **pegmatite**. It is associated with **apatite, cassiterite, epidote, fluorite, garnet, gold, magnetite, molybdenite, quartz, silver, topaz, vesuvianite,** and **wolframite**.*

Main Sources: ◆ *Australia* ◆ *Austria* ◆ *Bolivia* ◆ *Brazil* ◆ *Canada* ◆ *Czech Republic* ◆ *England* ◆ *France* ◆ *Germany* ◆ *Japan* ◆ *Malaysia* ◆ *Mexico* ◆ *Myanmar (Burma)* ◆ *Peru* ◆ *Russia* ◆ *South Korea* ◆ *Switzerland* ◆ *Arizona, California, Colorado, Connecticut, Idaho, Montana, Nevada, New Mexico, South Dakota, Utah, Washington, and Wyoming, United States*

Confirmed as a distinct mineral in 1821, scheelite was named in honor of the great Swedish chemist Karl Wilhelm Scheele (1742–86). Its crystals often appear in pseudo-octahedrons and may weigh more than 1 lb. (40 g). Specimens measuring between six and 13 in. (15 and 33 cm) in length have been found in Japan and Korea. Most deposits, however, take the form of massive or granular aggregates. Some scheelite shows a bright blue to white or yellowish fluorescence under ultraviolet light.

Scheelite forms an isomorphous series with powellite. Both conform to the tetragonal system of symmetry and can appear externally identical. Yet scheelite is a tungstate of calcium, whereas powellite is a molybdate of calcium—the tungsten in the former is gradually replaced by molybdenum in a continuous atomic substitution process. The minerals thus form a solid solution series.

USES OF TUNGSTEN

Tungsten has the highest heat resistance of any metal—it melts only at temperatures above 6,170° F (3,410° C). It is therefore used to make the nose cones of rockets (*see* photo, above), which need to withstand the heat generated by re-entry into Earth's atmosphere from outer space. It is also used in electric lamp filaments, television tubes, and high-speed drill bits. Because heat causes it to expand at about the same rate as glass, tungsten is used in glass-to-metal seals.

CHEMICAL FORMULAE	
Powellite:	$CaMoO_4$
Scheelite:	$CaWO_4$

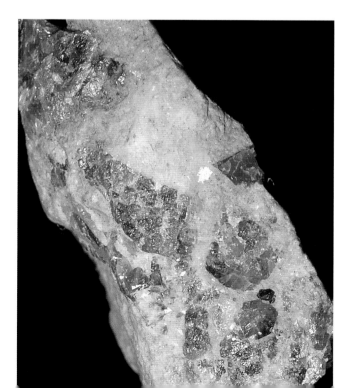

Left: Dark, brownish crystals of scheelite set in pale dolostone rock.

SCHIST

A number of different minerals can be found in this metamorphic rock, but schist usually contains mica, feldspar, and quartz.

Schist is a medium- to coarse-grained metamorphic rock. It is formed mainly from finely layered sheets of platy or elongated minerals such as **mica***. These sheets (or lamellae) are interleaved with* **feldspar** *and* **quartz***.*

Main Sources: *Schist is common where continental land masses have collided, as in the European Alps and the Himalayas of Asia.*

The essential visible characteristic of schist is that its crystals or microcrystals are aligned, meaning that they face in largely the same direction.

SCHIST TYPES

Although the minerals most commonly found in any schist are feldspar, mica, and quartz, the specific mineral composition of a schist may be indicated by placing the name or names of significant accessory minerals in front of the word "schist." Common types include biotite schist, garnet-mica schist, hornblende schist, muscovite-chlorite schist, and staurolite-kyanite schist.

The general composition or texture of the schist can also be indicated by the use of prefixes. Thus, for example, we may encounter folded schist—a variety that has been bent and twisted deep beneath the surface of the Earth in mountain-forming belts—and spotted schist, which has large, dark individual crystals (porphyroblasts) in a finer-grained and lighter-colored matrix.

DEGREES OF METAMORPHISM

Schists are generally the products of moderate pressure and heat during regional metamorphism. Porphyroblasts are most commonly found in schists that have undergone the highest degrees of

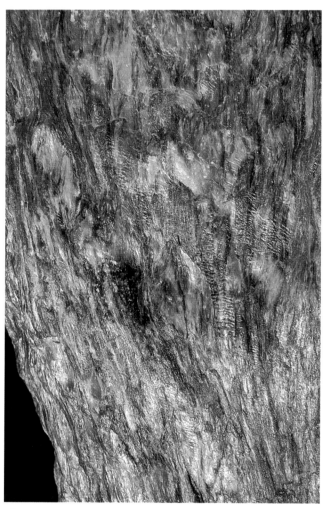

Above: During metamorphism, the component crystals of schist become aligned in parallel.

metamorphism. Among the minerals that may appear as porphyroblasts in schist are **andalusite**, **cordierite**, **garnet**, **kyanite**, and **staurolite**. Some porphryoblasts are very large, but garnets are typically about 1/16 in. (1 mm) in diameter, while crystals of mica in muscovite schist may be twice that size.

SCOLECITE

Scolecite gets its name from the Greek for "worm," a reference to the physical change it undergoes when heated.

*Scolecite occurs mainly in crystal-lined cavities in **basalt**. It is sometimes also found in areas of contact metamorphism—small segments of rock whose composition has been changed from that of its immediate surroundings by locally applied heat and pressure. It is often associated with **apophyllite**, **heulandite**, **quartz**, and **stilbite**.*

Main Sources: ◆ *Antarctica* ◆ *Austria* ◆ *Brazil* ◆ *Canada* ◆ *Faroe Islands* ◆ *Germany* ◆ *Greenland* ◆ *Hungary* ◆ *Iceland* ◆ *India* ◆ *Italy* ◆ *Scotland* ◆ *Switzerland* ◆ *Thailand* ◆ *Arizona, California, Colorado, New Jersey, and Washington, United States*

Scolecite was first identified as a distinct mineral in 1813 by the German scientists A.F. Gehlen and J.N. von Fuchs. Its name comes from the Greek *scolex*, meaning "a worm"—a reference to the fact that, when heated, it tends to curl up and form worm-like shapes.

A hydrated silicate of calcium and aluminum, scolecite's chemical formula is $CaAl_2Si_3O_{10}.3H_2O$. It is a member of the zeolite group (*see* **analcime**) and a tektosilicate—that is, a silicate in which each atom of oxygen is shared with adjacent molecules of the same mineral. Minerals of this type often form in long lines, and are therefore commonly referred to as chain silicates.

LACKING SODIUM

Externally, scolecite may appear almost indistinguishable from **mesolite** and **natrolite**, but it is the only one of the three that contains no sodium. Crystals conform to the monoclinic system—the finest specimens have long, thin, prismatic shapes, often with striations along their surfaces. Fibrous clusters—in which acicular crystals radiate outwards from a central hub—are particularly popular with collectors.

Below: Thin, prismatic crystals of scolecite. The rock on which it has formed is basalt.

SCORODITE

Scorodite is one of three closely related minerals that make up the variscite group.

Scorodite is a secondary deposit formed mainly through the alteration of preexisting arsenic-bearing minerals—particularly arsenopyrite—in the oxidation zones of copper and zinc belts. Small amounts of the mineral may also be found as crusts precipitated on the outer rims of hot springs. Scorodite is commonly associated with adamite, limonite, olivenite, pharmacosiderite, and quartz.

Main Sources: ◆ *Algeria* ◆ *Australia* ◆ *Brazil* ◆ *Canada* ◆ *England* ◆ *Greece* ◆ *Mexico* ◆ *Namibia* ◆ *Arizona, California, Georgia, Nevada, New Jersey, New York, South Dakota, Utah, Washington, and Wyoming, United States*

Confirmed as a distinct species in 1818, the English name of this mineral is derived from the Greek *scorodion*, meaning "garlic"—this is a reference to the smell it gives off when heated in an open flame. (The garliclike odor emitted when the mineral is heated is in fact arsenic.)

THE VARISCITE GROUP

In its pure form, scorodite is a hydrated arsenate of ferric iron. In nature, however, it almost always contains at least some aluminum, which replaces some of the iron. When this substitution is complete, the result is a new mineral, mansfieldite—a hydrated arsenate of aluminum. The two minerals therefore form a solid solution series; they are also dimorphous

Above: Small, dark, pyramidal crystals of scorodite on a groundmass of arsenic-rich rock.

(have the same chemistry but different forms) and are very difficult to tell apart without detailed analysis. Both minerals are closely related to **variscite**, a hydrated phosphate of aluminum, and are categorized as members of the variscite group.

CRYSTAL SHAPES AND SIZES

Scorodite crystals conform to the orthorhombic system of symmetry. Externally, they may appear in pseudo–octahedral prismatic or pyramidal shapes; the largest, from Tsumeb, Namibia, are about 2 in. (6 cm) in diameter. Massive aggregates are also common.

VARISCITE GROUP	
Mansfieldite:	$Fe^{3+}AsO_4.2H_2O$
Scorodite:	$AlAsO_4.2H_2O$
Variscite:	$AlPO_4.2H_2O$

SERPENTINITE

Deriving its name from its surface texture's resemblance to snakeskin, serpentinite is sometimes carved into jewelry and figurines.

*Serpentinite was originally formed as **peridotite** in the lower part of the Earth's oceanic crust and its upper mantle. Subsequently, it was altered by heat and pressure to form a range of low-temperature serpentine minerals. It often occurs in dikes, lenses, and stocks of folded metamorphic rock.*

Main Sources: *Serpentinite may be seen in many parts of the world—some of the most spectacular formations are found around the Lizard in Cornwall, England, and in the European Alps in Austria, France, Italy, and Switzerland.*

Serpentinite is a dark, intrusive altered igneous rock that contains less than 45 percent total silica and is therefore described as ultrabasic. It is composed almost entirely of serpentine minerals, such as **antigorite** and **chrysotile**.

SERPENTINIZATION

The igneous process by which peridotite is converted into serpentinite is known as serpentinization. The name itself is derived from the surface patterns of the rock, which often resemble snakeskin. The alteration from peridotite into serpentinite is not always complete, however, and this accounts for the frequent presence in serpentinite of relics of **olivine**, the main mineralogical component of peridotite.

Serpentinite may contain other ferro–magnesian (mafic) minerals such as **garnet**, **hornblende**, and **mica**; **chromite** may also be found in large enough quantities to be mined industrially for its chromium.

Serpentinite deposits are medium- to coarse-grained and sometimes form in banded or veined layers. The shape of the component crystals is widely variable—they may be well formed (euhedral) or have no discernible shape at all (anhedral).

The finest serpentinite slabs may be cut and polished into ornamental stones. Some of the antigorite in the rock may be the semiprecious form bowenite—a green or bluish green stone that is carved into jewelry, figurines, and statuettes, and may be used to imitate the even more valuable **jade**.

Below: The surface of this serpentinite from Cornwall, England, is mottled red and green.

SHALE

Shale is rich in fossils and dinosaur tracks have been found imprinted in this sedimentary rock.

Shale is formed in quiet water environments, such as lake bottoms, river floodplains, tidal flats, marshes, and the floors of deep oceans, where the finest particles carried by the water have settled at the bottom.

Main Sources: *Shale may be seen in almost every country on Earth. It is commonly associated with other argillaceous rocks, especially more loosely consolidated clays and more tightly compacted mudstones. In North America, the largest formations are the Burgess Shale in the Rocky Mountains of British Columbia, Canada, and the Nonesuch Shale in Michigan.*

Below: Shale forms in well-marked bedding planes and may be rich in fossils.

Shale is a sedimentary rock formed by the gradual lithification (petrification) of successive layers of **clay**. It is finely bedded and fissile (splits readily into layers). Formations of this type may also contain the minerals **feldspar**, **mica**, and **quartz**. The color of red shale is caused by the presence of oxides of iron, including **goethite** and **hematite**.

DINOSAUR TRACKS

Many shale deposits are rich in fossils, which are clearly visible because they contrast so clearly with the fine-grained texture of the rock in which they are preserved. Some shales have revealed dinosaur tracks. The name shale is derived from the Old English *scealu*, meaning "shell."

Shale is closely related to mudstone, but the key difference between them is the extent to which they have been compacted together—mudstones are fairly well consolidated and massive, while shales form in much thinner laminations or layers.

ARGILLACEOUS FORMATIONS

Argillaceous rocks are clayey sedimentary rocks of fine-grained sediments composed of particles that are less than $1/500$ in. (0.05 mm) in size. In addition to shale, other examples include mudstones, clays, marls, and silts. Most argillaceous rocks contain material of two types: clay minerals and rock flour, the latter consisting of very fine particles of quartz, feldspar, and other rock-forming minerals. Most argillaceous rocks have been deposited in water, whether in the sea, in estuaries, or in lakes. There are also terrestrial deposits such as loess and clays, which are products of glacial deposition.

SIDERITE

Siderite is an ore of iron, but it is rarely mined for this metal unless it is found along with more valuable iron-bearing minerals.

*Most siderite is formed in sedimentary rocks such as **clay** and **shale**, where it often appears in bog iron ore. It may also be a minor component of ore veins that have been formed by hydrothermals, and is sometimes found in igneous rocks such as **basalt** and **pegmatite**. It is often associated with **pyrite**, **quartz**, and **sphalerite**.*

Main Sources: ◆ *Australia* ◆ *Austria* ◆ *Bolivia* ◆ *Brazil* ◆ *Canada* ◆ *Czech Republic* ◆ *England* ◆ *France* ◆ *Germany* ◆ *Greenland* ◆ *Italy* ◆ *Portugal* ◆ *Switzerland* ◆ *Colorado, Connecticut, South Dakota, and Washington, United States*

Above: A magnificent cluster of rhombohedral siderite crystals in which twinning can be seen.

Confirmed as a distinct species in 1845, the English name of this mineral is derived from the Greek *sideros*, meaning "iron." Siderite is a carbonate of iron. It is sometimes mined as an ore of this metal, but only when it occurs in association with other, more valuable, iron-bearing minerals.

A MEMBER OF TWO SERIES

Siderite forms two solid solution series—one with **magnesite** and the other with **rhodochrosite**. All three minerals are carbonates of the **calcite** group, but while pure siderite contains up to 48 percent iron, magnesite is a carbonate of magnesium and rhodochrosite is a carbonate of manganese. The metals replace each other in a process of continuous atomic substitution.

CURVED CRYSTALS

Crystals of siderite conform to the trigonal system of symmetry. They commonly appear in curved rhombohedrons that are sometimes flattened to

appear bladed; many are twinned. Botryoidal and earthy habits are also found. Some of the most attractive aggregates have a lens-shaped (lenticular) habit. Specimens may be magnetic when heated.

NAME CALLING

Iron meteorites are also known as siderites, but this name is misleading because the mineral siderite is formed only on the Earth and, as far as is known, has no extraterrestrial sources.

CHEMICAL FORMULAE

Calcite:	$CaCO_3$
Magnesite:	$MgCO_3$
Rhodochrosite:	$MnCO_3$
Siderite:	$FeCO_3$

SILLIMANITE

Sillimanite is noted for its ability to change color from green to blue depending on the light and the angle from which it is viewed.

Left: A fibrous mass of sillimanite composed of tiny crystals that are all prismatic and almost square in cross-section.

Sillimanite is formed in metamorphic rocks such as **gneiss** and **schist**. In addition to **andalusite** and **kyanite**, it is often found in association with **feldspar, garnet, mica,** and **quartz**.

Main Sources: ◆ *Austria* ◆ *Brazil* ◆ *Canada* ◆ *Czech Republic* ◆ *France* ◆ *Germany* ◆ *India* ◆ *Ireland* ◆ *Italy* ◆ *Kenya* ◆ *Madagascar* ◆ *Myanmar (Burma)* ◆ *North Korea* ◆ *Scotland* ◆ *South Africa* ◆ *South Korea* ◆ *Sri Lanka* ◆ *Switzerland* ◆ *Tanzania* ◆ *Arizona, Connecticut, Delaware, Idaho, New York, North Carolina, Oklahoma, Pennsylvania, South Carolina, South Dakota, and Washington, United States*

First identified as a distinct species in 1824, this mineral was named in honor of Benjamin Silliman (1779–1864), a professor of chemistry at Yale University. Sillimanite is sometimes mined for use in the manufacture of automobile sparking plugs.

With the chemical formula Al_2SiO_5, sillimanite is a silicate of aluminum. It is a nesosilicate—in other words, a silicate whose molecules are free standing rather than formed in chains or rings.

Sillimanite is trimorphous with andalusite and kyanite. Indeed the three were often confused as late as 1852. A polymorph is a mineral that has the same chemistry as at least two other minerals but has a different specific gravity and/or crystal structure.

With a specific gravity (SG) of 3.2 to 3.3, sillimanite is denser than andalusite (SG 3.16 to 3.20), but less dense than kyanite (SG 3.5 to 3.7). Both sillimanite and andalusite conform to the orthorhombic system of crystal symmetry. However, crystals of kyanite are triclinic.

Crystals of sillimanite often appear in elongated prisms, but may also take the form of tiny, matted fibers. (Fibrous, massive varieties of sillimanite are sometimes known as fibrolite.) The finest crystals display a strong pleochroism—in other words, their color varies depending on the direction of the light source and the angle from which they are viewed. Sillimanite may appear to change from yellowish green to dark green or blue and pleochroic specimens may be faceted in cushion cuts or cut *en cabochon* to enhance their natural lights. The crystals are quite easy to work on because they are hard—6½ to 7½ on the Mohs scale. Massive aggregates of this mineral are also common.

SILVER

Historically used in jewelry and coinage, today silver is more often used in photography and other industrial applications.

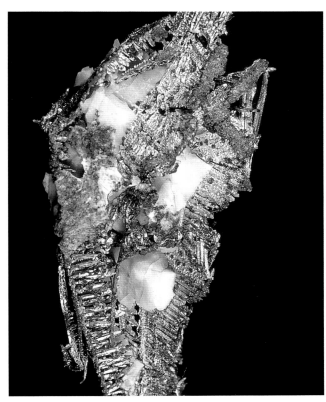

Above: Some of this recently extracted silver retains its original color, while other parts have begun to tarnish in air.

*Elemental silver occurs with **acanthite** in hydrothermal veins and in the oxidized regions of ore deposits, where it is formed through through the action of hot waters on silver sulfides or of arsenides on silver chloride. Among the other minerals with which it may be associated are **cobaltite, copper, galena, gold**, and **quartz**.*

Main Sources: ◆ *Australia* ◆ *Bolivia* ◆ *Canada* ◆ *Chile* ◆ *Czech Republic* ◆ *England* ◆ *France* ◆ *Germany* ◆ *Italy* ◆ *Mexico* ◆ *Norway* ◆ *Peru* ◆ *Arizona, Colorado, Idaho, Michigan, Montana, and Nevada, United States*

Silver has been mined for thousands of years for use in jewelry (*see* photo of bracelet, below) and coinage. Today, however, only about six percent of world production of silver goes to coinage, and only about 10 percent to jewelry, silver plate, and sterling ware. More than 40 percent of all the silver produced is used in photography because of silver's sensitivity to light. Although the main industrial ore of silver is acanthite, this valuable metal does sometimes occur in its native state.

Crystals of silver conform to the cubic system. Individual crystal specimens are extremely rare, but those that do occur tend to appear in cubes, octahedrons, or dodecahedrons. The metal more commonly appears in massive and disseminated grains, plates, or wires. These can form coiled clusters that resemble ram's horns. Other characteristic habits include arborescent sheets and scales.

THE BEST CONDUCTOR

Silver is a better conductor of heat and electricity than any other metal and is second only to diamond in the mineral world. Next to gold, it is also the most malleable and ductile metal known. It is harder than gold but softer than copper. This softness (Mohs scale 2½ to 3) limits its use, even for coinage, unless it is alloyed with about 10 percent copper. When alloyed with 7.5 percent copper, it is known as sterling silver.

The largest active silver mine in the United States is near Virginia City, Nevada. Canada has productive mines in British Columbia, near Sudbury, and Cobalt, Ontario, and in the Yukon.

SKARN

Formed from preexistent limestone and dolostone, skarns are mineral-rich rocks often mined for the valuable ores they contain.

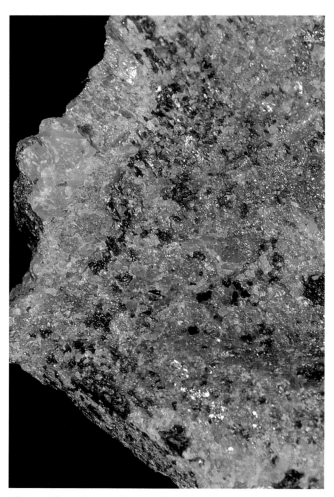

Above: Skarn has well-shaped (euhedral) crystals of numerous mineral types.

*Skarn is formed when molten magma at about 1,292 to 2,192° F (700 to 1,200° C) escapes from the Earth's mantle or lower crust and becomes injected into the upper crust, where it forms igneous intrusions. When this magma heats surrounding nonigneous rocks, it alters their chemical and physical composition. Skarn is formed from preexistent impure **limestone** or **dolostone** that has been altered, not only by heat, but also by the addition or replacement of various chemicals—the scientific term for this process is metasomatism.*

Main Sources: *Skarn occurs on all continents. One of the most productive deposits in the United States occurs at Carr Fork in Bingham Canyon copper pit, Utah.*

A contact metamorphic rock in which metasomatism has occurred, skarn also forms around igneous intrusions and along the joints between limestone and **syenite**. Its essential mineralogical component is **calcite**.

Rocks of this type have a banded, veined, or zoned appearance. Their grain size is medium to coarse, and their component crystals are euhedral (well formed). The numerous minerals associated with skarn are often concentrated into dark patches and nodules scattered across and within a lighter-colored calcite groundmass.

RICH IN ORES

Limestone and dolostone, the rocks from which skarn is formed, are sedimentary rocks that are rich in carbonate compounds, especially calcium carbonate. When they are invaded by magma (which typically contains aluminum, iron, magnesium, and silica) a whole range of new minerals may be formed. A few of these are oxides of iron, but most are calcareous (calcium–bearing) minerals such as **axinite**, calcite, **diopside**, **epidote**, **garnet**, and **wollastonite**. As a result, many skarns are rich in mineral ores, especially **chalcopyrite**, **galena**, **magnetite**, **pyrite**, and **sphalerite**. These are often mined industrially. Some skarns are rich in minerals containing manganese and molybdenum. One of the world's finest skarns may be seen at Crestmore, California.

SKUTTERUDITE

Named for its type locality, skutterudite usually forms in hydrothermal veins with other nickel- and cobalt-bearing ores.

*Skutterudite forms in veins that have been altered by the action of hot water (hydrothermals). It is commonly associated with **cobaltite** and may also form weathering crusts with **annabergite, arsenopyrite, bismuth, erythrite,** and **silver**.*

Main Sources: ◆ *Canada* ◆ *Germany* ◆ *Iran* ◆ *Italy* ◆ *Morocco* ◆ *Norway* ◆ *Arizona, Colorado, and New Jersey, United States*

Skutterudite is a minor ore of both cobalt and nickel. The principal industrial sources of cobalt are cobaltite and erythrite, while nickel comes mainly from **garnierite** and **pentlandite**. Confirmed as a distinct species in 1845, skutterudite is named after its type locality, Skutterud in Norway.

Chemically, skutterudite is an arsenide of cobalt, iron, and nickel. Iron–rich specimens are rare, however, and this mineral is almost always the cobalt-rich end member of the solid solution series it forms with nickel-skutterudite (also known as cloanthite). Both minerals conform to the same cubic crystal system, but nickel-skutterudite is an arsenide of, as its name suggests, nickel alone.

RAINBOWLIKE COLORS

Skutterudite crystals are mainly cubic in appearance but may also be octahedral or dodecahedral. However, even these shapes are often modified with cubic faces. Most deposits take the form of massive aggregates. The mineral is usually white or gray, but some specimens have a rainbowlike play of colors about their surface. The scientific term for this optical effect is iridescence.

The mineral is moderately hard, Mohs scale 5½ to 6, and weighs between 6.5 and 6.9 times more than

Above: Although skutterudite conforms to the cubic system of symmetry, its finest crystals appear in eight-sided shapes.

the equivalent volume of water at room temperature. Skutterudite has a distinct cleavage. When it breaks up, it leaves behind surface markings that resemble the surface patterns on a seashell—the mineral is thus said to display conchoidal fracture.

CHEMICAL FORMULAE	
Nickel-skutterudite:	$NiAs_{2-3}$
Skutterudite:	$(Co,Fe,Ni)As_{2-3}$

SLATE

A fine-grained metamorphic rock with a distinctive cleavage, slate is used to provide roofing tiles and a wide range of domestic surfaces.

Slate is commonly found in areas where shale has been subjected to low-grade regional metamorphism (low pressure and very little heat) during episodes of mountain building.

Main Sources: *Slate is common in folded mountain chains, such as the Appalachians.*

One of the world's most widely used roofing materials (*see* photo, right), slate is a dense, fine-grained, metamorphic rock. Its English name comes from the French *esclate*, meaning "fragment"—this is a reference to the distinctive way it breaks under pressure into thin, roughly parallel sheets. Scientifically, slate is said to split into microscopically

divided planes. This phenomenon, described as slaty cleavage, results from recrystallization under pressure.

Slates are formed through the metamorphism of preexistent sedimentary material, especially **clay** and **shale**, as well as from volcanic ash and dust. The metamorphism is low grade, meaning that it takes place at relatively low temperatures and pressures. One consequence of this is that not all slate has been fully converted from its parent rock and may contain some of the original minerals and sedimentary bedding planes more or less intact.

In some slates, fossils may even be visible, although they are almost always distorted by heat and pressure. By contrast, any fossils that were once present in high-grade metamorphic rocks have always been obliterated by heat and pressure.

Quartz is abundant in slate and may form as much as 70 percent by weight of the rock. Other essential components are **andalusite**, **cordierite**, and **mica**. The main accessory mineral is **graphite**. Although slate grains are generally too small to be seen without a microscope, large porphyroblasts of **magnetite** and **pyrite** may sometimes be visible.

Because of its physical characteristics and its cleavage, slate has been used for a great variety of surfaces in different forms of construction. Roofing tiles and pool-table tops are commonly made of sheets of slate about 3 in. (7.6 cm) thick.

Left: Slate may contain distinct crystals of minerals—such features are known as porphyroblasts.

SMITHSONITE

A bright green, transluscent variety of smithsonite is sometimes used as an ornamental stone.

Smithsonite is a secondary mineral formed in parts of **copper** *and zinc deposits that have been oxidized by the action of air and water. It is particularly likely to occur in dry climates as a weathering product of primary sulfides such as* **sphalerite**.

Main Sources: ◆ *Algeria* ◆ *Australia* ◆ *Austria* ◆ *Belgium* ◆ *England* ◆ *France* ◆ *Germany* ◆ *Greece* ◆ *Italy* ◆ *Mexico* ◆ *Namibia* ◆ *Poland* ◆ *Spain* ◆ *Tunisia* ◆ *Arizona, Arkansas, Colorado, Idaho, Montana, New Mexico, South Dakota, and Utah, United States* ◆ *Wales* ◆ *Zambia*

This carbonate of zinc is named after James Smithson (1765–1829), the British chemist and mineralogist who founded the Smithsonian Institution in Washington, D.C. It was confirmed as a distinct mineral in 1832.

After sphalerite, smithsonite is the world's second most important industrial ore of the metal zinc. In its pure form, the mineral (chemical formula $ZnCO_3$) is made up of 65 percent zinc oxide and 35 percent carbon dioxide. However, smithsonite is seldom pure, and its metal is almost always substituted to some extent by iron, cobalt, or manganese.

ASSOCIATED MINERALS

Among the many minerals with which smithsonite is commonly associated are **aurichalcite**, **azurite**, **calcite**, **cerussite**, **dolomite**, **galena**, **hemimorphite**, **limonite**, **malachite**, **mimetite**, **pyromorphite**, sphalerite, and **wulfenite**. It may also sometimes appear as a replacement of **limestone**. In addition, many other zinc ore minerals may originally have

Above: The yellow color of these curved faces of smithsonite crystals indicate the presence of cadmium impurities.

been smithsonite before they were altered by metamorphism or metasomatism.

Crystals of smithsonite conform to the trigonal system of symmetry. Distinct specimens are rare, but those that do form resemble rhombohedrons (six-sided prisms) with rough, curved faces. The mineral usually forms in botryoidal (grapelike) or reniform (kidney-shaped) masses and may also appear as stalactites or encrustations around a rock or another mineral. One of the world's leading smithsonite sources is at Leadville, Colorado.

SODALITE

Sometimes mistaken for lapis lazuli, dark blue sodalite may be used as an ornamental stone and in jewelry.

Most sodalite is formed in igneous rocks, especially **syenite**, *but it may occur in metasomatised calcareous rocks and sometimes in* **meteorites**. *It may also be found in silica-poor dikes and lavas. The mineral is commonly associated with* **calcite**, **cancrinite**, *and* **nepheline**.

Main Sources: ◆ *Angola* ◆ *Bolivia* ◆ *Brazil* ◆ *Canada* ◆ *Ecuador* ◆ *Germany* ◆ *Greenland* ◆ *Italy* ◆ *Myanmar (Burma)* ◆ *Norway* ◆ *Romania* ◆ *Russia* ◆ *Scotland* ◆ *South Africa* ◆ *South Korea* ◆ *Arkansas, Maine, Massachusetts, Montana, New Hampshire, New Jersey, and South Dakota, United States* ◆ *Zambia*

PRINCESS BLUE

Gem-quality sodalite from Bancroft, Ontario, Canada, is known as Princess Blue, after Princess Margaret of England.

Confirmed as a mineral in 1811, sodalite's name is taken from that of its chief metal—it is a chlorosilicate of sodium and aluminum with the chemical formula $Na_4Al_3Si_3O_{12}Cl$.

Sodalite is closely related to **haüyne**. Both minerals are among the principal constituents of lapis lazuli, a rock that is also a gemstone. Indeed, sodalite is sometimes confused with lapis lazuli, but the mineral has a lower specific gravity (2.27 to 2.33) and does not contain the brass-colored specks of **pyrite** that give lapis lazuli its distinctive sparkle.

VALUABLE CRYSTALS

Crystals of sodalite conform to the cubic system of symmetry. Distinct specimens are rare, but those that do occur are dodecahedral and often twinned. These are cut in a wide variety of ornamental styles for use in jewelry. One of the leading sources of sodalite crystals is the lava on the slopes of the volcanic Mount Vesuvius in Italy. Massive formations, which are much more common, are sometimes polished into ornamental stones.

There are two variant forms of sodalite. One, known as hackmanite, contains more sodium than the basic version—up to 6.25 percent by weight. The other is molybdosodalite, which has less chlorine and up to 2.87 percent by weight of molybdenum oxide.

Left: Sodalite, such as this massive aggregate, is characterized by its dark blue coloration.

SPHALERITE

This mineral is the world's most important source of zinc, an element used to coat metals in order to prevent corrosion.

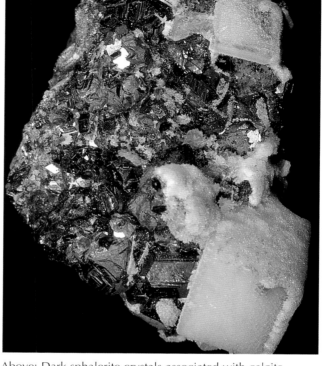

*Sphalerite is formed mainly in hydrothermal veins and as a replacement for **limestone**. It may also occur in metamorphic rocks, **meteorites**, and **pegmatite**. The mineral is commonly found in association with **calcite**, **chalcopyrite**, **fluorite**, **galena**, **magnetite**, **pyrite**, **pyrrhotite**, and **quartz**.*

Main Sources: ◆ *Australia* ◆ *Belgium* ◆ *Brazil* ◆ *Canada* ◆ *Czech Republic* ◆ *England* ◆ *France* ◆ *Germany* ◆ *Italy* ◆ *Japan* ◆ *Mexico* ◆ *Morocco* ◆ *Myanmar (Burma)* ◆ *Namibia* ◆ *Peru* ◆ *Poland* ◆ *Romania* ◆ *Scotland* ◆ *Serbia* ◆ *Spain* ◆ *Sweden* ◆ *Arizona, Colorado, Idaho, Illinois, Kansas, Missouri, New York, Oklahoma, Tennessee, Utah, Washington, and Wisconsin, United States*

Above: Dark sphalerite crystals associated with calcite and quartz.

Also known as blende, sphalerite is the chief industrial ore of zinc and has been known since ancient times. When it was first used, sphalerite was heated to excessively high temperatures, making the zinc it contained evaporate unnoticed. This led early scientists to the mistaken conclusion that it contained no metal at all. Later, it was discovered that the mineral is a sulfide of zinc. It is named from the Greek, *sphaleros*, meaning "slippery."

Although, in its pure form, sphalerite may contain up to 67 percent zinc, it also contains iron. Its chemical formula—$(Zn,Fe)S$—is the same as that of **wurtzite**, so the two minerals are dimorphous. The difference between them lies in their internal symmetry: wurtzite is either hexagonal or trigonal, while sphalerite is cubic.

Sphalerite may contain a wide range of impurities that do not appear in the chemical formula. These include the metals cadmium, gallium, **gold**, indium, iron, manganese, and mercury.

ZINC AND ITS ALLOYS

Zinc, the 25th most abundant element on Earth, is a strong reducing agent, meaning that it will save iron from corrosion when the two metals are alloyed. Metals that have been coated with a protective layer of zinc are said to have been galvanized. The best-known zinc alloy is brass, which is made of copper with between three and 45 percent zinc. A quarter of all the zinc produced in the world each year is used in die-casting alloys. This useful metal is also an important component of dry-cell batteries (*see* photo, left).

SPHENE

Found in a wide range of colors, sphene is distinctive for its brilliant sparkle and unusual optical properties.

Above: Many of these prismatic and wedge-shaped crystals of sphene are twinned.

*Sphene is a minor component of the igneous rocks **granite** and **syenite**. It is found in association with **anatase**, **calcite**, **feldspar**, **ilmenite**, **quartz**, **rutile**, and **zircon**.*

Main Sources: ◆ *Austria* ◆ *Brazil* ◆ *Canada* ◆ *Czech Republic* ◆ *England* ◆ *Finland* ◆ *France* ◆ *Greenland* ◆ *India* ◆ *Italy* ◆ *Madagascar* ◆ *Mexico* ◆ *New Zealand* ◆ *Norway* ◆ *Pakistan* ◆ *Russia* ◆ *Switzerland* ◆ *Arizona, Arkansas, California, Connecticut, New Jersey, New York, Pennsylvania, South Dakota, Utah, and Washington, United States*

Unusually, sphene, the common old name for this mineral is still used more widely than its new scientific name, titanite. The English word comes from the Greek, *sphen*, meaning "wedge"—this is a reference to the typical external shape of its crystals, which conform internally to the monoclinic system of symmetry. Twinning is common.

In its pure form, sphene is a silicate of calcium and titanium with the chemical formula $CaTiSiO_5$. However, it often contains appreciable amounts of fluorine and sometimes niobium, sodium, and various rare earth metals such as cerium and lanthanum. A few specimens have also been found with more than 6.5 percent aluminum oxide.

Other metal impurities sometimes affect the color of particular sphene specimens. Browns and yellows, for example, are caused by traces of iron, while pink sphene is colored by manganese. The rare and valuable green form of this mineral owes its appearance to traces of chromium.

BRIGHT SPARKLE

Sphene is sometimes a source of titanium oxide, used as a yellow pigment by artists. However, its main use is as a gemstone. Despite only moderate hardness—Mohs scale 5 to 5½—the mineral is valued for its fire (sparkle), which is even stronger than that of **diamond**. Sphene is also pleochroic. This means that it shows different colors, depending on the relative position of the light source and the angle from which it is viewed.

However, sphene's most spectacular property is probably its birefringence—the mineral's capacity to split each ray of incident light into two. Because of this optical effect, which is also known as double refraction, faceted sphene may show a different shade on every face.

SPINEL

An oxide of magnesium and aluminum, spinel is often dark red in color and may be confused with ruby.

*Formed in metamorphic rocks, spinel is commonly associated with **calcite**, **corundum**, **dolomite**, and **garnet**.*

Main Sources: ◆ *Afghanistan* ◆ *Australia* ◆ *Brazil* ◆ *Cambodia* ◆ *Canada* ◆ *Finland* ◆ *France* ◆ *Germany* ◆ *India* ◆ *Italy* ◆ *Madagascar* ◆ *Myanmar (Burma)* ◆ *Pakistan* ◆ *Russia* ◆ *Sri Lanka* ◆ *Sweden* ◆ *Thailand* ◆ *Turkey* ◆ *Alabama, Arizona, California, Colorado, Massachusetts, Montana, New Jersey, New York, North Carolina, and Washington, United States*

First positively identified in 1779, this mineral takes its English name from the Latin *spina* ("thorn")—an allusion to its typical crystal shapes. The finest specimens are semiprecious gemstones.

Usually red, green, black, blue, or brown in color, spinel conforms to the cubic system of symmetry. Crystals may appear in octahedrons, dodecahedrons, and combinations of other isometric forms. Inclusions of **rutile** may create four- or six-rayed stars in an effect known as asterism. Specimens with this optical quality are often polished *en cabochon* to heighten the effect. Other habits include rounded grains in alluvial placer deposits.

THE BRITISH CON JEWEL?

The gemstone known as the Black Prince's Ruby, which is set in the British Imperial State Crown, is actually spinel. It is not known whether this was a genuine mistake or an attempt to dupe the King of England, but today that hardly matters because any stone in the Crown Jewels is priceless. Besides, although spinel is less valuable than **ruby**, both are highly precious gemstones.

SPINEL GROUP

Spinel minerals are oxides with the general formula AB_2O_4 in which *A* may be cobalt, copper, germanium, iron, magnesium, manganese, titanium, or zinc, and *B* may be aluminum, chromium, iron, magnesium, manganese, titanium, or vanadium. There are more than 20 of them altogether.

Chromite: $Fe^{2+}Cr_2O_4$
Franklinite: $(Zn,Mn^{2+},Fe^{2+})(Fe^{3+},Mn^{3+})_2O_4$
Gahnite: $ZnAl_2O_4$
Hercynite: $Fe^{2+}Al_2O_4$
Magnesiochromite:
$(Mg,Fe^{2+})(Al,Cr)_2O_4$
Magnetite: $Fe^{2+}Fe^{3+}_2O_4$
Spinel: $MgAl_2O_4$

Below: Fine red crystals of spinel bear more than a passing resemblance to rubies.

SPODUMENE

The chief source of an industrially important metal, lithium, transparent, colored varieties of spodumene are also used for gemstones.

*Spodumene forms in igneous rocks such as lithium-bearing **granite** and **pegmatite**. It is commonly found in association with **beryl**, **feldspar**, **quartz**, **topaz**, and **tourmaline**.*

Main Sources: ◆ *Afghanistan* ◆ *Brazil* ◆ *Canada* ◆ *Italy* ◆ *Madagascar* ◆ *Mexico* ◆ *Myanmar (Burma)* ◆ *Pakistan* ◆ *Russia* ◆ *Scotland* ◆ *Sweden* ◆ *California, Connecticut, Maine, Massachusetts, North Carolina, and South Dakota, United States*

Spodumene is the most important ore of the metal lithium. Confirmed as a distinct species in 1800, the English name is derived from the Greek *spodumenos*, meaning "reduced to ashes." This is what happens to spodumene that is heated in a blowpipe flame.

Spodumene is a silicate of lithium and aluminum with the chemical formula $LiAlSi_2O_6$. Crystals conform to the monoclinic system. Externally, they often appear in prisms with deep striations and domed terminations. Twinning is common. Some of the largest crystals ever found are over 40 ft. (12.2 m) long and weigh nearly 88 tons (90 tonnes).

The finest spodumene crystals display pleochroism and may be cut as gemstones known as hiddenite or kunzite. Hiddenite is colored a bright emerald green by impurities of chromium, while the pink tones of kunzite are caused by the presence of manganese. When these varieties are faceted, the gemcutters take special care to orient the stone in the best position to obtain the deepest and most variable plays of color.

USES OF LITHIUM

The lithium obtained from spodumene is used in wide range of useful compounds. Lithium reacts with water to form lithium hydroxide, used as a carbon dioxide bonding agent in the ventilating systems of submarines and spaceships. Lithium hydride is used to inflate lifeboats and balloons, while other compounds are used in glazes in ceramics. Lithium salts are used as antidepressant drugs. Lithium deuteride is the explosive material in hydrogen bombs.

Below: Crystals of spodumene are prismatic, flattened, and often vertically striated.

STAUROLITE

This mineral is distinctive for its dark color, hardness, and for the unusual cross-shaped form of some of its crystals.

Above: These crystals of staurolite are twinned in a cross-like (cruciform) shape.

Staurolite forms in metamorphic rocks, particularly **gneiss** *and* **schist**.

Main Sources: ◆ *Brazil* ◆ *Canada* ◆ *Czech Republic* ◆ *Finland* ◆ *France* ◆ *Germany* ◆ *Greenland* ◆ *Ireland* ◆ *Italy* ◆ *Ivory Coast* ◆ *Russia* ◆ *Scotland* ◆ *Switzerland* ◆ *Uganda* ◆ *Arizona, Connecticut, Georgia, Maine, Massachusetts, Montana, New Hampshire, New Mexico, North Carolina, South Dakota, Tennessee, Virginia, and Washington, United States* ◆ *Zambia*

Confirmed as a distinct mineral in 1792, staurolite often forms in distinctive cruciform shapes that are highly sought after by collectors. Its English name is taken from the Greek *stauros* ("the Cross").

Staurolite, also known as cross stone, is a complex hydrous silicate of iron, magnesium, zinc, and aluminum. Some specimens also contain sodium, while in others traces of manganese have been detected.

FAIRY CROSSES

Staurolite crosses are strongly associated with Christianity and the finest specimens are worn as as amulets (good luck charms). They are sometimes known as fairy stones or fairy crosses.

Manganese-bearing staurolite fuses (melts) more easily than pure forms of the mineral. There are three varieties of staurolite: lusakite, which may contain up to eight percent by weight of cobalt oxide; nordmarkite, which includes up to 2.5 percent manganese oxide; and zinkstaurolith, the zinc-rich form.

Crystals of staurolite conform to the monclinic system of symmetry and are typically prismatic or tabular. Some have a pseudo-orthorhombic cross-section but most are flattened into diamond shapes with two of their four points truncated. Twinning is seen in about one in three cases. There are two types of twin—one an X-shape intersecting at about 60°, the other a 90° cross. This rarer cruciform variety is highly valued by collectors (*see* box, above).

Staurolite crystals sometimes grow onto crystals of **kyanite**. Among the other minerals with which it may be associated are **garnet**, **mica**, and **quartz**.

CHEMICAL FORMULAE

Lusakite: $(Fe,Mg,Co)_2Al_9Si_4O_{23}OH$
Nordmarkite:
$Fe^{2+}_2(Al,Mn,Fe^{3+})_9Si_4O_{23}(OH)$
Staurolite:
$(Fe^{2+},Mg,Zn)_2Al_9(Si,Al)_4O_{22}(OH)_2$
Zinkstaurolith:
$(Fe,Mg,Zn)_4Al_{18}Si_8O_{46}(OH)_2$

STELLERITE

Named after a German explorer, stellerite was mistaken for another mineral for centuries until geologists recognized some differences.

Stellerite is frequently formed in mineral-filled cavities in **basalt**. *These cavities are known as vesicles, while the minerals they contain are called amygdales. Although the mineral may be associated with* **apophyllite, calcite, heulandite, natrolite,** *and* **quartz,** *it is most likely to be found with* **stilbite.**

Main Sources: ◆ *Canada* ◆ *India* ◆ *Italy* ◆ *Russia* ◆ *New Jersey and Oregon, United States*

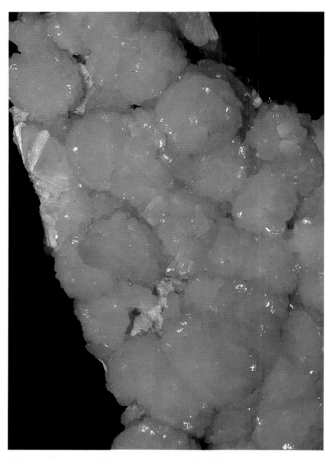

Above: These globular aggregates of stellerite may be described as mammillated (with small protruberances).

Stellerite is of particular interest to mineralogists because of its similarities to and differences from the closely related stilbite. Both minerals are members of the zeolite group (*see* **analcime**).

Confirmed as a distinct mineral in 1909, stellerite is named after Georg Wilhelm Steller (1709–46), the German explorer and naturalist who, along with the Danish navigator Vitus Bering (1681–1741), discovered the Komandorskiye Islands in the Bering Sea between Russia and Alaska, where the mineral was originally located.

Chemically, stellerite is a hydrated silicate of calcium and aluminum. Crystals often appear in globular aggregates or in radiating, acicular masses.

Stilbite and stellerite are so similar that it took geologists over a hundred years to recognize the presence of another mineral in deposits that they had previously considered to be of stilbite alone. The key differences between the two minerals are their chem-ical composition and their internal shapes—stellerite is the sodium-free end member of a solid solution series that has stilbite as its other extreme. Stilbite conforms to the monoclinic system of symmetry, while crystals of stellerite are orthorhombic.

Another closely related mineral is barrerite, a hydrated silicate of sodium, potassium, calcium, and aluminum. It was formerly known as sodium stellerite but confirmed as a distinct mineral in 1975.

CHEMICAL FORMULAE	
Barrerite:	$(Na,K,Ca)_2Al_2Si_7O_{18}.7H_2O$
Stellerite:	$CaAl_2Si_7O_{18}.7H_2O$
Stilbite:	$NaCa_2Al_5Si_{13}O_{36}.14H_2O$

STIBICONITE

Stibiconite has some unusual properties—it can split light passing through it into two rays and its crystals look the same from any angle.

*Stibiconite is a secondary mineral formed through the oxidation of **stibnite**. It commonly occurs with this mineral and is sometimes pseudomorphous with it—in other words, it may replace the primary mineral but retain the old orthorhombic shape.*

Main Sources: ◆ *Algeria* ◆ *Australia* ◆ *Bolivia* ◆ *Borneo* ◆ *Canada* ◆ *England* ◆ *Germany* ◆ *Italy* ◆ *Mexico* ◆ *Namibia* ◆ *Peru* ◆ *Romania* ◆ *Russia* ◆ *Spain* ◆ *Turkey* ◆ *Arizona, Arkansas, California, Idaho, Nevada, South Dakota, Utah, and Washington, United States*

Confirmed as a distinct species in 1832, the English name stibiconite is derived from *stibium*, the Latin for "antimony," and the Greek *konis*, meaning "powder." Stibiconite is sometimes mined as an ore of antimony, but the main industrial source of this metal is stibnite.

Chemically, stibiconite is a hydrous oxide of antimony with the formula $Sb^{3+}Sb^{5+}_2O_6(OH)$. Crystals of this mineral conform to the cubic system of symmetry. Some have swordlike, bladed habits or appear in radiating clusters. Most deposits, however, take the form of earthy crusts and botryoidal (grapelike) or powdery masses.

ISOTROPY

One of stibiconite's strangest and most interesting physical properties is that it may appear the same from all angles, rather like a cube. This phenomenon is known as isotropy. Another well-known isotropic mineral is **halite**.

Stibiconite is able to split light that passes through it into two rays, which then reemerge at divergent angles. This phenomenon is known as double refraction or birefringence.

The mineral scores between 3 and 7 on the Mohs Scale of Hardness, depending on whether it is scraped along the grain or against it. Its specific gravity is widely variable, and ranges between 3.3 and 5.5 times more than the equivalent volume of water at room temperature.

WHITE WHEN PURE

Although stibiconite is often yellow or orange, and may also appear black, brown, or gray, these colors are caused by various impurities. It can appear transparent or translucent and its luster varies from pearly to earthy. The irreducible color of its powder is white—this can be confirmed by the streak test, which involves scraping a rough specimen of the mineral along a piece of unglazed porcelain.

Below: This stibiconite is a pseudomorph of stilbite, having replaced the latter and taken on its external shape.

STIBNITE

Stibnite is used in the manufacture of alloys, matches, fireworks, and percussion caps.

*Stibnite is found in hydrothermal veins and hot spring deposits, where it is a replacement mineral in **limestone**. It is commonly associated with **cinnabar, galena, orpiment, pyrite, quartz,** and **realgar**.*

Main Sources: ◆ *Algeria* ◆ *Bolivia* ◆ *Borneo* ◆ *Brazil* ◆ *Canada* ◆ *China* ◆ *Czech Republic* ◆ *France* ◆ *Germany* ◆ *Italy* ◆ *Japan* ◆ *Mexico* ◆ *New Zealand* ◆ *Peru* ◆ *Romania* ◆ *South Africa* ◆ *Thailand* ◆ *Alaska, Arkansas, California, Colorado, Idaho, Montana, Nevada, Oregon, and Washington, United States*

S tibnite is the main industrial source of antimony, and the mineral's English name is derived from *stibium*, the Latin for this metal.

Stibnite is a sulfide of antimony with the chemical formula Sb_2S_3. It is dimorphous with metastibnite, a mineral with the same chemical composition but a different structure. (The exact internal symmetry of metastibnite remains undetermined and, until it is, for want of a precise term, it is described as amorphous.)

Crystals of stibnite conform to the orthorhombic system of symmetry. Externally, they are prismatic with surface grooves (striations) that may be vertical or lateral. One of the largest ever found—over 2 ft. (60 cm) long and weighing 15 lbs. (7 kg)—now forms part of the Wada Collection of the Mitsubishi Mining Company in Japan. Other habits include acicular, columnar, or radiating aggregates.

USES OF ANTIMONY

Antimony occupies about one part per 10,000 of the Earth's crust. It is extracted from stibnite by roasting the ore in air to form senarmontite (Sb_2O_3) and then reducing this antimony oxide with carbon to obtain the pure metal.

The addition of antimony to a soft metal such as lead produces an alloy of increased hardness and stiffness that is mostly used in the manufacture of grids for lead storage batteries. Another important alloy is type metal, which comprises variable amounts of antimony, tin, and lead, often with a trace of copper. Molten type metal expands slightly on solidifying to give sharp reproduction in molds or castings. High-purity antimony is used in semiconducting materials.

Left: A group of radiating, prismatic stibnite crystals. This mineral is always lead-gray and has a metallic luster.

STILBITE

This widely distributed zeolite mineral is notable for its glassy to diamondlike luster (sheen).

Stilbite is a secondary mineral formed by the action of hydrothermals on preexistent minerals. It occurs in both extrusive and intrusive igneous rocks, where some of the finest crystals form inside petrified bubbles (vesicles), and is particularly common in metamorphic **gneiss** *and* **schist**. *It is also found in hot spring deposits. Among the many minerals with which stilbite is commonly associated are* **apophyllite, calcite, heulandite, natrolite,** *and* **quartz**.

Main Sources: ◆ *Australia* ◆ *Austria* ◆ *Canada* ◆ *Czech Republic* ◆ *Faroe Islands (Denmark)* ◆ *Germany* ◆ *Iceland* ◆ *Ireland* ◆ *India* ◆ *Italy* ◆ *Mexico* ◆ *New Zealand* ◆ *Norway* ◆ *Poland* ◆ *Scotland* ◆ *Switzerland* ◆ *California, Connecticut, New Jersey, Oregon, Pennsylvania, and Washington, United States*

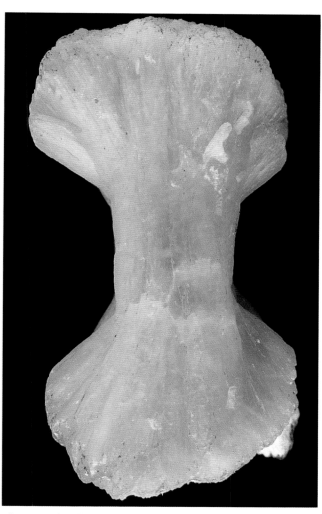

Above: A sheaflike aggregate of stilbite. Many of the component crystals are twinned.

Like the mineral **analcime**, stilbite is a member of the zeolite group. Stilbite was confirmed as a distinct mineral in 1797. Its English name comes from the Greek *stilbein*, meaning "to shine." This is a reference to its striking vitreous (glassy) and adamantine (diamondlike) luster.

PERFECT CLEAVAGE

Stilbite is a hydrated silicate of sodium, calcium, and aluminum and has the chemical formula $NaCa_2Al_5Si_{13}O_{36}.14H_2O$. It scores $3\frac{1}{2}$ to 4 on the Mohs scale and has a specific gravity of 2.2. When pressure is applied to its crystals, they break up cleanly along their weakest structural lines—in scientific terms they are said to display perfect cleavage. Most stilbite is white, but some specimens are colored by impurities and surrounding minerals to appear pink, red, or yellow.

Crystals of stilbite conform to the monoclinic system of symmetry. Externally, they may often appear in sheaflike aggregates. Many specimens share a face or faces to make cruciform (crosslike) penetration twins. Such habits bear a close resemblance to **stellerite**, and the two minerals are often difficult to tell apart without detailed analysis. Stilbite may also form in radiating nodules.

STILPNOMELANE

Scientists are divided over whether stilpnomelane is a simple mineral or a mixture of closely related species.

*Stilpnomelane forms dark coatings in **schist** and may also be found in **iron** ore deposits. It is commonly associated with **epidote** and **mica**.*

Main Sources: ◆ *Australia* ◆ *Canada* ◆ *Czech Republic* ◆ *Finland* ◆ *Germany* ◆ *Greenland* ◆ *Italy* ◆ *Japan* ◆ *New Zealand* ◆ *Poland* ◆ *Russia* ◆ *Scotland* ◆ *Sweden* ◆ *Switzerland* ◆ *California, Colorado, Michigan, Minnesota, New Jersey, New York, North Carolina, and Washington, United States*

Above: A thin deposit of dark stilpnomelane on the surface of an iron-rich schist.

Confirmed as a distinct species in 1827, the English name of this mineral comes from the Greek *stilpnos* ("shining") and *melanos* ("black").

Stipnomelane is a hydrous silicate of potassium, ferrous and ferric iron, magnesium, and aluminum. Its chemical formula is generally written as $K(Fe^{2+},Mg,Fe^{3+})_8(Si,Al)_{12}(O,OH)_{27}$.

However, not all scientists agree about this. Some believe that stilpnomelane is not a single mineral, but rather two end members of a solid solution series in which one form of iron is gradually substituted by the other. Others take the view that the two forms of iron coexist in varying amounts without atomic substitution. A few analysts have stated that the mineral's hydrogen and oxygen do not appear in the form of hydroxyl radicals (chemical formula OH) but are an indefinite number of attached molecules of water of crystallization (nH_2O). But none of these theories has been proved and there are clearly still large gaps in our knowledge of this mineral.

Crystals of stilpnomelane may conform to either the triclinic or the monoclinic system of symmetry, depending on the conditions in which they were formed. Externally, they often appear in thin, foliated plates or coatings on the surface of other minerals or rocks. The mineral scores 3 to 4 on the Mohs Scale of Hardness and weighs 2.5 to 2.9 times more than the equivalent volume of water at room temperature.

FRAGILE

The mineral is easily damaged and specimens should therefore be cleaned with distilled water only—ordinary tap water contains impurities that may damage the delicate surface of the crystals.

Pure stilpnomelane contains more ferric iron than ferrous iron. Specimens containing more ferrous iron than ferric iron are sometimes known as chalcodite or ferrostilnomelane.

STRONTIANITE

The mineral strontianite is the principal ore of the metal strontium, which is extracted to make tracer bullets and treat bone cancer.

The mineral forms principally in hydrothermal veins but may also occur in hollows in **limestone** *and marl. It is commonly associated with* **aragonite, barite, calcite, celestine, dolomite, fluorite, galena,** *and* **quartz.**

Main Sources: ◆ *Australia* ◆ *Austria* ◆ *Canada* ◆ *Germany* ◆ *India* ◆ *Italy* ◆ *Mexico* ◆ *Scotland* ◆ *Switzerland* ◆ *California, Colorado, Illinois, Louisiana, New Mexico, New York, Ohio, Pennsylvania, South Dakota, Texas, and Washington, United States*

Strontianite is the principal ore of strontium. Both the mineral and the metal are named after Strontian—the region of Argyll, Scotland, in which they were originally found.

Chemically, strontianite is a carbonate of strontium with the formula $SrCO_3$. The crystals of strontianite conform to the orthorhombic system of symmetry and generally appear in acicular (needle-like), prismatic, or tabular habits, although twinned pseudohexagons are sometimes found. The mineral may also take the form of fibrous, granular, concretionary, and massive aggregates.

EXTRACTING STRONTIUM

Strontium is extracted from strontianite first by roasting, a process that reduces the carbonate to an oxide. A further chemical reaction with aluminum then removes the remaining atoms of oxygen to leave the pure metal. Strontium was first isolated from strontianite in 1808 by Sir Humphry Davy.

USES OF STRONTIUM

As a soft metal that is a good conductor of electricity, strontium gives off a bright red light when it is burned. For more than 100 years, the latter property made strontium an important ingredient of pyrotechnics, especially fireworks and distress flares. However, strontium contains radio-active isotopes that make it potentially hazardous to humans—it is widely regarded as the most dangerous of all atomic fallout products. As a result, it has now largely been replaced in fireworks by less toxic materials, although it is still used in tracer bullets.

Strontium is an important aid in the treatment of bone cancer. The heat generated by its radioactive decay is sometimes converted into electricity that is used to light navigation buoys, and to power remote weather stations, and space vehicles.

Below: These twinned crystals of strontianite show its distinctive glassy sheen (vitreous luster).

STRUNZITE

A relative newcomer to the list of minerals, strunzite was classified as laueite until the discovery of certain anomalies in its make up.

Crystals of strunzite appear as coatings and tufts on the surface of granite pegmatite, where they formed through the alteration of primary triphylite (a phosphate of lithium and iron). Strunzite is commonly associated with limonite and quartz.

Main Sources: ◆ *Brazil* ◆ *England* ◆ *Germany* ◆ *Alabama, Connecticut, Idaho, Maine, New Hampshire, New Jersey, North Carolina, and South Dakota, United States*

Above: Tufty crystals of strunzite on the surface of a granite pegmatite rock formation.

Confirmed as a distinct species in 1957, this mineral was named after Hugo Strunz, who was professor of mineralogy at Berlin Technical University in Germany around this time.

During the 1950s, geologists discovered an unidentified mineral in Bavaria, Germany. After extensive tests, it was confirmed as a hydrous hydrated phosphate of manganese and iron with triclinic crystals. In 1954, it was named laueite, after German Professor Max von Laue (1879–1960), a pioneer of the use of X-rays in crystallography and winner of the 1914 Nobel Prize for Physics.

SEPARATE SPECIES

Afterwards, scientists found that some of the crystals they had previously thought to be laueite in fact conformed to the monoclinic system of symmetry. On closer examination, the electrical charge (valency) of the manganese turned out to be different, too. In 1956, crystals of this type were confirmed as a separate mineral and given the name pseudolaueite.

All the manganese in pseudolaueite was at first thought to be monovalent (chemical symbol Mn). Within a year, however, it was shown that some crystals contained divalent atoms of the same metal (Mn^{2+}). Specimens with this composition were then reclassified as strunzite, a hydrated phosphate of manganese and ferric iron with the chemical formula $Mn^{2+}Fe^{3+}_2(PO_4)_2(OH)_2.8H_2O$.

CHEMICAL FORMULAE

Name	Chemical Formula	Crystal System
Laueite:	$Mn^{2+}Fe^{3+}_2(PO_4)_2(OH)_2.8H_2O$	Triclinic
Pseudolaueite:	$Mn^{2+}Fe^{3+}_2(PO_4)_2(OH)_2.8H_2O$	Monoclinic
Strunzite:	$Mn^{2+}Fe^{3+}_2(PO_4)_2(OH)_2.8H_2O$	Monoclinic

SULFUR

People have used sulfur since ancient times for its ability to ignite easily, but today its uses range from insecticides to skin treatments.

Sulfur originates from volatile gases given off by volcanoes and hot springs. It may also occur as a secondary deposit in many ore deposits. When it cools, it goes straight from gas to solid without passing through the normal intermediate liquid stage—a process known as sublimation.

Main Sources: ◆ *Argentina* ◆ *Chile* ◆ *Iceland* ◆ *Italy* ◆ *Japan* ◆ *Mexico* ◆ *Poland* ◆ *Arizona, California, Colorado, Hawaii, Louisiana, Michigan, Nevada, Ohio, Texas, Utah, and Wyoming, United States*

A nonmetallic element with the chemical symbol S, sulfur has been used since prehistoric times in a wide range of applications, such as religious ceremonies and for fumigation. It was first classified as an element in 1777 by Antoine Lavoisier (1743–94).

MINING FOR SULFUR

Before the development of modern mining methods, sulfur was collected by men lowered in baskets into dormant volcanoes, where the element would be scraped from the vent walls. Today sulfur is obtained from underground sedimentary deposits by the Frasch process, in which a system of concentric pipes is sunk into the earth. One pipe carries superheated water into the deposit in order to melt the sulfur, which is then forced up another pipe to the surface, where it is recovered in nearly pure form.

Pure sulfur crystals conform to the orthorhombic system of symmetry. Externally, they often appear in tabular or bipyramidal shapes but may also take the form of powdery encrusting masses. However, sulfur is a polymorphous mineral—the same element may sometimes appear in monoclinic forms, and these are classified as rosickyite. Orthorhombic sulfur is otherwise known as α-sulfur; rosickyite is β-sulfur.

Sulfur is used in the commercial production of sulfur dioxide, sulfuric acid, and hydrogen sulfide. It is essential in the vulcanization of rubber and in the production of chemicals used in detergents. It is also used in insecticides, fungicides, and plant fertilizers. Elemental sulfur is non-toxic and is used in a finely divided form to treat some skin diseases.

Below: This encrusting mass of sulfur shows its characteristic yellow color and resinous luster.

SYENITE

Sometimes mistaken for granite because of its color, syenite is easily differentiated by its lower silica content.

*Syenite usually forms in major intrusions, and in dikes and sills. It is often associated with **granite**.*

Main Sources: *Found worldwide, there are large syenites in St. Francois County, near Farmington, Missouri.*

A coarse-grained, intrusive igneous rock that originated deep in the Earth, syenite is therefore said to be plutonic. Its English name is derived from the Latin *lapis syenites*, which means "stone from Syene (Egypt)."

Syenite is an intermediate rock, containing 55 to 65 percent total silica, which takes the form of sodium- or potassium-rich **feldspar**, ferro-magnesian minerals, and **quartz**. The feldspar is commonly of the orthoclase, albite, perthite, or, more rarely, microcline type. The dark-colored ferro-magnesian mineral is usually **biotite mica**, **hornblende**, or a pyroxene such as **augite**.

Some syenites also contain feldspathoid minerals such as **nepheline**. Nepheline syenite is formed in rocks that are particularly rich in feldspar.

A TELLTALE AMOUNT OF QUARTZ

Syenite is light colored, and is thus often confused with granite. The two rocks sometimes grade into one another. The major difference between them is the amount of silica they contain—granite has more than 65 percent silica while syenite has 55 to 65 percent total silica.

Syenite is so coarse-grained that all its component minerals can usually be seen with the naked eye. It is also largely equigranular. Some deposits contain large crystals set in a finer-grained matrix; textures of this type are described as porphyritic.

COLOR INDEX

The color index is used to differentiate the proportions of dark ferro-magnesian minerals in igneous rocks. It ranges between 0 and 100. Syenite is at the lower end of the scale, with a rating of 0 to 40. Nepheline syenite is usually even lower (0 to 30). (Granite also has a color index rating of 0 to 30). The darkest igneous rocks are **pyroxenite** and **serpentinite**, which are both over 90.

Left: Syenite is a light-colored igneous rock with a coarse-grained texture.

SYLVINE

Sylvine, the main mineral ore of potassium, is found mostly in dried-up salt lakes in deserts and around the vents of volcanoes.

*Sylvine is an evaporite mineral formed mainly from dried-out salt lakes and seas in deserts and other arid areas. It is commonly associated with minerals of the same type, especially **halite**. Smaller deposits may be formed around the fumaroles of volcanoes—two of the richest sources of this type are Mount Etna and Mount Vesuvius in Italy.*

Main Sources: ◆ *Canada* ◆ *Chile* ◆ *China* ◆ *England* ◆ *Germany* ◆ *Iran* ◆ *Israel* ◆ *Italy* ◆ *Peru* ◆ *Poland* ◆ *New Mexico, Texas, and Utah, United States*

Above: This sylvite specimen is composed of tiny, interlocking cubic crystals.

Although it was confirmed as a distinct mineral as recently as 1832, sylvine—also known as sylvite—was known at least 200 years previously. Its English name comes from the Latin *sal digestivus Sylvii* ("digestive salt of Sylvius"). This refers to François Sylvius de la Boe (1614–72), a chemist and physician of Leiden, Netherlands, who used it as a potion to cure excess stomach acid in humans.

Sylvine is a chloride of potassium with the chemical formula KCl. Although more than 70 percent of the world's supplies of this metal are obtained from seawater, sylvine is its principal mineral ore. It is extracted by electrolytic reduction.

Crystals of sylvine conform to the cubic system of symmetry. They often take the external shape of cubes, too, although some specimens are octahedral. Massive aggregates are even more common.

This mineral is usually white or colorless, but some specimens may have a red coloration caused by the presence of minute inclusions of **hematite**. Purple sylvine derives its color from the natural radioactivity in the Earth's atmosphere.

MIXED WITH POTASSIUM

Potassium makes up about 2.6 percent of the Earth's crust and it is the world's seventh most abundant element. It has a wide range of industrial uses, especially in its salt form. Historically, one of the most important of these has been potassium nitrate, which, when combined with 15 percent charcoal and 10 percent sulfur, makes gunpowder.

TALC

Closely related to minnesotaite and willemseite, talc is an extremely soft mineral with a wide range of industrial applications.

*A secondary mineral, talc is found mainly in igneous rocks, but may also form through the metamorphic alteration of dolomitic sediments. It is commonly associated with **dolomite, magnesite, mica, olivine,** and **quartz**. Talc may be pseudomorphous with these minerals, taking on their shape while retaining its own chemistry.*

Main Sources: ◆ *Australia* ◆ *Austria* ◆ *Brazil* ◆ *Canada* ◆ *China* ◆ *England* ◆ *France* ◆ *Germany* ◆ *India* ◆ *Italy* ◆ *Norway* ◆ *Russia* ◆ *Scotland* ◆ *South Africa* ◆ *Sweden* ◆ *Switzerland* ◆ *Arizona, California, Colorado, Georgia, Massachusetts, New Hampshire, New York, North Carolina, Pennsylvania, South Dakota, Texas, Utah, Vermont, Virginia, and Washington, United States*

Above: Talc occurs typically in massive habits with a distinctively greasy luster.

The softest mineral on the Mohs Scale of Hardness, the English name for talc derived from the Arabic, *talq,* meaning "mica." The mineral has a greasy look and feel, which is why it is sometimes known alternatively as soapstone or steatite (from the Greek, *stear,* meaning "fat").

Talc is a hydrous silicate of magnesium. Crystals may conform to either the monoclinic or the triclinic system, depending on the conditions in which they formed. Externally, they may appear in tabular shapes with hexagonal cross-sections. However, clearly defined, individual crystals are rare and most deposits take the form of thin lamellar (sheetlike) masses or leaflike (foliated) agglomerations.

CARVINGS AND ORNAMENTS

Talc has been used for thousands of years to make carvings, ornaments, and utensils. Notable examples include ancient Egyptian scarabs and Chinese statues.

Talc is fairly resistant to electricity and heat and has many practical applications, notably in the manufacture of lubricants. It is also used as a surface for laboratory counter tops and electrical switchboards. The smallest talc particles may be purified, scented, and sold as talcum powder for perfuming the skin.

Closely related are minnesotaite, in which some of talc's magnesium has been replaced by ferrous iron (Fe^{2+}), and willemseite, which contains nickel.

CHEMICAL FORMULAE

Minnesotaite:	$(Fe^{2+},Mg)_3Si_4O_{10}(OH)_2$
Talc:	$Mg_3Si_4O_{10}(OH)_2$
Willemseite:	$(Ni,Mg)_3Si_4O_{10}(OH)_2$

TANTALITE

This mineral is the chief source of tantalum, a metallic element used in industry and medicine.

*This mineral is formed in igneous rocks, especially granite **pegmatite**, and in placer deposits. It is associated with **amblygonite, apatite, beryl, cassiterite, feldspar, quartz, spodumene,** and **tourmaline**.*

Main Sources: ◆ *Afghanistan* ◆ *Australia* ◆ *Brazil* ◆ *Canada* ◆ *Finland* ◆ *France* ◆ *Japan* ◆ *Madagascar* ◆ *Mozambique* ◆ *Norway* ◆ *Russia* ◆ *Sweden* ◆ *California, Colorado, Connecticut, Maine, New Mexico, South Dakota, Virginia, and Wyoming, United States* ◆ *Zimbabwe*

Tantalite is the main ore of tantalum. Both the mineral and the metal are named for Tantalus, the mythological Greek king who wanted to drink but was unable to, because water kept moving away from him whenever he tried to grasp it. This is a reference to the fact that neither tantalite nor tantalum will absorb ("drink") acid.

Tantalite forms a solid solution series with **columbite** in which tantalum is gradually substituted by niobium. In addition, tantalite is closely related to two other minerals: ferrotantalite, in which manganese has been replaced by iron and there is no niobium, and manganotantalite, a tantalate of manganese alone, with no iron or niobium.

Crystals of tantalite conform to the orthorhombic system. Externally, they appear in tabular shapes and many share a face or faces with one or more of their neighbors—a phenomenon known as twinning.

TANTALUM AND ITS USES

Tantalum is extracted from tantalite by dissolving the mineral ore in hydrofluoric acid and separating the resulting niobium fluoride. The residual tantalum fluoride is then reduced with the aid of sodium.

Tantalum is highly resistant to chemical attack. In addition, its high melting point, 5,425° F (2,996° C), is exceeded only by that of tungsten and rhenium. As a result, the metal has a number of applications—most tantalum is used to make electrolytic capacitors and vacuum furnace parts. Because of its low reactivity, it is not irritating to body tissue so is also safe to use as surgical pins to join badly broken bones.

CHEMICAL FORMULAE	
Ferrotantalite:	$Fe^{2+}Ta_2O_6$
Manganotantalite:	$MnTa_2O_6$
Tantalite:	$(Fe,Mn)(Ta,Nb)_2O_6$

Left: A common occurrence of tantalite is in sand deposits in river bed sediment.

TEKTITE

Named for the regions in which they occur, it is not known whether tektites are terrestrial or extraterrestrial in origin.

Tektites occur in broad bands in specific localities in different parts of the world. These bands produce characteristically similar tektites and are sometimes loosely associated with meteorite craters or suspected craters.

Main Sources: *Some scientists believe that the tektite fields in Texas are fallout from the impact of a meteorite that landed on Chesapeake Bay.*

Above: This tektite specimen is from Thailand and shows a typical dark color and shiny surface.

Mysterious and unexplained, tektites are small, irregularly shaped glassy nodules that have no crystal structure and are therefore similar to **obsidian**. Individual tektites measure between ¼ in. (6 mm) and 1¼ in. (3 cm) in diameter. Most weigh 7 to 10 oz. (198 to 283 g), although some have tipped the scales at over 26 lbs. (11.8 kg). The shape of these objects is enormously variable, but they commonly appear in discoids, lensoids, tear shapes, or spheres. Some are smooth and shiny, but others have rough, strongly etched, and abraded surfaces. Most tektites have grooves that reflect flow patterns inside the glass. They are mainly jet black, but some are brown and moldavites (*see* box, right) are green. Chemically, tektites are composed of a silica–rich glass that also contains alumina, lime, and potash.

No one knows where tektites come from, and the main debate is about whether they are extraterrestrial or terrestrial in origin. Some scientists believe that they are produced by meteorite impacts, the glass being formed by the enormous heat and pressure generated by entry into the Earth's atmosphere and impact with its surface.

This theory is now losing ground to another that postulates a volcanic origin. However, the great unanswered question is why they often form in areas in which there is no other evidence of vulcanism.

MANY VARIETIES

Of the 750,000 tektites that have been gathered, two-thirds have been philippinites.

Tektite	Provenance
Australites:	southern Australia and Tasmania
Bediasites:	Texas, United States
Georgia tektites:	Georgia, United States
Indochinites:	Cambodia, Laos, Thailand, and Vietnam
Ivory Coast tektites:	Ivory Coast
Javaites:	Java
Malaysianites:	Malaysia
Moldavites:	Czech Republic
Philippinites:	Philippines and southern China

TELLURITE

A soft mineral, tellurite is composed mainly of tellurium, a nonmetal used in semiconductors and as a strengthener added to steel.

*Tellurite is a secondary mineral formed through the oxidation of preexistent tellurium compounds or of the element itself, which sometimes occurs in the native state. Tellurite is most commonly associated with paratellurite, a mineral with a similar appearance and chemical formula but which crystallizes in the tetragonal crystal system—the two are said to be dimorphous. Among other associated minerals are **galena**, **gold**, **quartz**, and **silver**. In addition, it may be associated with native tellurium.*

Main Sources: ◆ *Australia* ◆ *Japan* ◆ *Mexico* ◆ *Romania* ◆ *Russia* ◆ *California, Colorado, and Nevada, United States*

Confirmed as a distinct mineral species in 1845, tellurite is named after its main elemental component, tellurium. This mineral is an oxide of tellurium with the chemical formula TeO_2. It conforms to the orthorhombic system of symmetry and crystals sometimes appear in small prisms. However, tellurite occurs mainly as powdered sprinklings on the surface of rocks. Both tellurite and tellurium have the same type locality—Sibenburgen in Transylvania, Romania.

A very soft mineral, tellurite scores only 2 on the Mohs Scale of Hardness. It is fairly heavy, weighing 5.9 times more than the equivalent volume of water at room temperature.

USES OF TELLURIUM

Tellurium is a nonmetal named after *tellus*, a Latin word for "Earth." It melts and boils at fairly low temperatures—844° F (451° C) and 1,814° F (990° C) respectively—and has a wide range of industrial applications. Tellurium is an important component in semiconductors, in which it is combined with bismuth. In addition, small amounts may be added to steel as a strengthener and to increase its ductility (the ease with which the alloy may be drawn out into strands). Tellurium is also used in petrol refining and in the purification of zinc. It is mixed with 0.1 percent of lead to make cable sheaths and pipe casings. It is also one of the chemicals used to color glass blue or brown.

Below: Tellurite is a subtranslucent to opaque mineral that may be orange, yellow, or white in color.

TETRAHEDRITE

Often containing economically valuable impurities such as silver and zinc, this mineral is named for its distinctive, tetrahedral crystals.

Above: Twinned, gray crystals of tetrahedrite, many of which have characteristically triangular faces. The associated white mineral is quartz.

*Tetrahedrite is a product of low- to medium-temperature hydrothermals. It is formed mainly in lead-silver ore veins with a wide range of other minerals, including **barite**, **bornite**, **calcite**, **chalcopyrite**, **fluorite**, **galena**, **pyrite**, **quartz**, and **sphalerite**. Elsewhere, some specimens occur in igneous contact metamorphic rocks.*

Main Sources: ◆ *Algeria* ◆ *Australia* ◆ *Bolivia* ◆ *Canada* ◆ *Chile* ◆ *England* ◆ *France* ◆ *Germany* ◆ *Mexico* ◆ *Peru* ◆ *Romania* ◆ *Sweden* ◆ *Switzerland* ◆ *Arizona, California, Colorado, Idaho, Montana, Nevada, New Mexico, and Utah, United States*

A minor ore of copper, tetrahedrite was confirmed as a distinct mineral species in 1845. It was named after its typical crystals, which have four faces of equal size (tetrahedrons). Crystals of tetrahedrite conform to the cubic system of symmetry. Externally, they often have triangular faces and many are penetration twins. Other habits (external shapes) are compact, granular, and massive.

TWO DIFFERENT SERIES

In its pure form, tetrahedrite is a sulfide of copper, iron, and antimony. However, some deposits contain varying quantities of arsenic, and by degrees this element may replace antimony. When the atomic substitution is complete, a new mineral, tennantite, is formed. Another mineral that is closely related to tetrahedrite is freibergite, which is a sulfide of silver, copper, iron, antimony, and arsenic. Tetrahedrite forms two different solid solution series with each of these minerals. The three minerals often occur together and some deposits of this type are valuable ores of **silver**.

Tetrahedrite and tennantite are so closely related that it is often difficult to tell them apart without testing for antimony or arsenic. Often the only other way to distinguish the two is by weighing them: tennantite has a specific gravity (SG) of 4.60 to 4.75, while tetrahedrite is heavier, with an SG of 4.60 to 5.10. In certain conditions, tetrahedrite may be altered into **azurite** or **malachite**.

CHEMICAL FORMULAE	
Freibergite:	$(Ag,Cu,Fe)_{12}(Sb,As)_4S_{13}$
Tennantite:	$(Cu,Fe)_{12}As_4S_{13}$
Tetrahedrite:	$(Cu,Fe)_{12}Sb_4S_{13}$

THENARDITE

This mineral may form as dipyramidal, prismatic, or tabular-shaped crystals, or as crusts on the surface of other minerals or rocks.

*A sulfate of sodium with the chemical formula Na_2SO_4, thenardite is an evaporite mineral that is precipitated as an efflorescence in playas, dried-out salt water in caves and mines, and as a crusty deposit around fumaroles. It is commonly associated with **borax**, **glauberite**, **gypsum**, **halite**, **sylvine**, and **trona**.*

Main Sources: ◆ *Canada* ◆ *Chile* ◆ *Egypt* ◆ *Italy* ◆ *Kazakhstan* ◆ *Libya* ◆ *Russia* ◆ *Spain* ◆ *Arizona, California, and Nevada, United States*

Confirmed as a distinct mineral in 1826, thenardite is named after Baron Louis-Jacques Thénard (1777–1857), professor of chemistry at the University of Paris, France. It is an important source of sodium, used to produce soda, and has various other applications in the glass and paper industries.

Crystals of thenardite conform to the orthorhombic system of symmetry. Externally, they may appear in dipyramidal, prismatic, or tabular shapes. Many are twinned. The mineral is soft, scoring only 2½ to 3 on the Mohs Scale of Hardness, and weighs approximately 2.7 times more than the equivalent volume of water at room temperature.

PROPERTIES

Thenardite is easily soluble in water, decomposing into mirabilite, a hydrated sodium sulfate with the formula $Na_2SO_4.10H_2O$. To prevent this reaction, specimens should be stored with desiccant. Another property of thenardite is that it is sometimes fluorescent, showing a white color under shortwave ultraviolet light and a yellow-green color under longwave.

Popular with collectors, many of the finest thenardite specimens originated at Searles Lake in San Bernardino County, California. Its type locality is the Espartinas salt lake, Aranjuez, near Madrid, Spain.

PLAYAS

Some of the finest thenardite deposits are found in playas. A playa is a dry lake bed in a desert region—the word is Spanish, meaning "beach" or "shore." Playa basins are sometimes hundreds of miles across.

Although normally completely dry, exceptionally severe rain storms may cause a playa to be inundated by a thin sheet of water that rarely remains for more than a few weeks. True playas do not have any outlets and lose this water entirely by evaporation into the atmosphere.

Below: Pyramidal crystals of thenardite. This mineral is transparent to translucent and has a resinous (greasy) luster.

THOMSONITE

A member of the zeolite group of minerals, thomsonite often forms in mineral-rich cavities in lava flows.

*Thomsonite forms in vesicles (mineral-filled cavities) in lava (especially basaltic lava), and as a decomposition product of **nepheline** in **schist**. The mineral is commonly associated with **analcime, calcite, chabazite, heulandite, natrolite, quartz,** and **stilbite.***

Main Sources: ◆ *Canada* ◆ *Czech Republic* ◆ *Faroe Islands (Denmark)* ◆ *Germany* ◆ *Greenland* ◆ *India* ◆ *Ireland* ◆ *Italy* ◆ *Scotland* ◆ *Arkansas, California, Colorado, Minnesota, New Jersey, and Oregon, United States*

Confirmed as distinct in 1820, this mineral was named after Thomas Thomson (1773–1852), a Scottish chemist and geologist. A hydrated silicate of sodium, calcium, and aluminum with the chemical formula $NaCa_2Al_5Si_5O_{20}.6H_2O$, thomsonite is one of the less common members of the zeolite group.

In many specimens, calcium and aluminum may be partially replaced by further sodium and silicon. Elsewhere, sodium alone may replace some of the basic calcium, while another variant form of thomsonite may contain no sodium at all. Yet another type has also been reported to contain nearly 10 percent by weight of strontium oxide—this variety is known as strontian thomsonite.

Crystals of thomsonite conform to the orthorhombic system of symmetry. Externally, they often appear in radiating, pseudotetragonal, acicular (needlelike) clusters or in sphericules. Many of these crystals have deep, vertical striations. Fibrous, lamellar, prismatic, and tabular crystals also occur.

UNEVEN FRACTURE

Thomsonite is moderately hard, Mohs scale 5 to 5½, and has a specific gravity of only 2.25 to 2.40. The mineral has a distinct cleavage and fractures unevenly. Its basic color and streak are white, and the luster is vitreous (glassy) to mother-of-pearl.

When a specimen is immersed in hydrochloric acid, it dissolves with gelatinization. This is a method of distinguishing thomsonite from some other zeolites, although the test does not help with natrolite, which has the same reaction to acids. The type locality of thomsonite is Old Kilpatrick in Scotland.

Left: Small, white crystals of thomsonite on a groundmass of basalt rock.

TOPAZ

Rare pink or blue varieties of this hard mineral make valuable gemstones. Colorless topaz may be mistaken for diamond.

*Topaz forms in igneous rocks such as **granite** and **pegmatite** and may also be found as waterworn pebbles in alluvial sands. It is often associated with **apatite, beryl, cassiterite, feldspar, fluorite, quartz,** and **tourmaline.***

Main Sources: ◆ *Australia* ◆ *Brazil* ◆ *Germany* ◆ *Ireland* ◆ *Italy* ◆ *Japan* ◆ *Madagascar* ◆ *Mexico* ◆ *Mozambique* ◆ *Myanmar (Burma)* ◆ *Namibia* ◆ *Nigeria* ◆ *Norway* ◆ *Pakistan* ◆ *Russia* ◆ *Sri Lanka* ◆ *Sweden* ◆ *Arizona, California, Colorado, Connecticut, Maine, New Hampshire, Texas, Utah, and Virginia, United States*

Above: Topaz often occurs in large crystals, which may weigh over 220 lbs. (100 kg).

The English name of this precious gemstone is derived from the Greek, *topazios*, which may come from either *tapas*, the Sanskrit for "fire," or from the ancient Greek name for an island in the Red Sea. Topaz occurs in many colors. Pink stones are the most valuable, not only because of their great beauty but also because they are extremely rare. However, most pink topaz is actually a yellow form of the material that has been artificially irradiated.

Topaz is a hydrous fluorosilicate of aluminum with the chemical formula $Al_2SiO_4(F,OH)_2$. Its crystals conform to the orthorhombic system and often appear in lozenge shapes. Topaz can also form in granular or massive habits.

TEAR-SHAPED CAVITIES

Although topaz is hard enough (Mohs scale 8) to be used as an abrasive, it almost never is because it is too valuable as jewelry. Some of the finest specimens have tear-shaped internal cavities that contain immiscible gas bubbles or liquids.

Colorless topaz bears a strong resemblance to **diamond** and is sometimes used to simulate it: the 1,600-carat (11-oz.) Braganza Topaz in the old Portuguese royal crown was originally thought to have been the more precious gemstone. Some topaz crystals are up to 3 ft. (92 cm) in length. The Smithsonian Institution in Washington, D.C., has a topaz weighing 3,270 carats (23 oz.).

LUCKY STONE

Topaz is the lucky stone for natives of Sagittarius, people born between the dates of 22 November and 21 December.

TORBERNITE

Chemically unstable and radioactive, this green colored mineral is a minor ore of uranium.

*Torbernite is a secondary mineral formed when **uraninite** in uranium and **copper** veins is altered by contact with oxygen in air and water.*

Main Sources: ◆ *Australia* ◆ *Czech Republic* ◆ *Democratic Republic of the Congo (formerly Zaire)* ◆ *England* ◆ *France* ◆ *Gabon* ◆ *Germany* ◆ *Italy* ◆ *Mexico* ◆ *Portugal* ◆ *North Carolina and Utah, United States*

Confirmed as a distinct species in 1793, this mineral is named for Swedish professor, Torbern Olof Bergman (1735–84), who was the first person to obtain nickel in the pure state.

Torbernite is a hydrated copper uranyl phosphate with the formula $Cu(UO_2)_2(PO_4)_2.8\text{-}12H_2O$. Its attached water of crystallization behaves like that of a zeolite, although torbernite is not a member of this group. In some specimens, the phosphorus may be partly substituted by arsenic, and the copper may be replaced by lead.

When torbernite is exposed to the atmosphere for long periods, it will partially dehydrate to form metatorbernite, a closely related mineral with almost the same formula but only eight attached molecules of water of crystallization. This alteration increases the specific gravity of affected crystals from 3.2 (pure torbernite) to 3.7 (metatorbernite).

Crystals of torbernite conform to the tetragonal system of symmetry. Externally, they usually appear in rectangular, octagonal, or tabular shapes. The mineral also forms as crusts, and in micaceous, foliated, or scaly aggregates.

In addition to metatorbernite and uraninite, torbernite is also commonly associated with **autunite** and is a member of the autunite group.

The presence of torbernite crystals has been used by prospectors as an indicator of profitable uranium ores in the area. The mineral itself is also sometimes used as a source of this radioactive metal.

Above: Green crystals of torbernite on a groundmass of iron-rich rock.

TOURMALINE

With its variable chemical composition, the gemstone tourmaline occurs in a wide range of different varieties and colors.

*Tourmalines form in **granite** and **pegmatite**, as well as in some metamorphic rocks and alluvial deposits. They are commonly found in association with **beryl**, **feldspar**, **quartz**, and **zircon**.*

Main Sources: ◆ *Afghanistan* ◆ *Australia* ◆ *Austria* ◆ *Brazil* ◆ *Canada* ◆ *Czech Republic* ◆ *England* ◆ *Germany* ◆ *Greenland* ◆ *Italy* ◆ *Japan* ◆ *Madagascar* ◆ *Mexico* ◆ *Mozambique* ◆ *Myanmar (Burma)* ◆ *Namibia* ◆ *Nepal* ◆ *Norway* ◆ *Pakistan* ◆ *Russia* ◆ *Sri Lanka* ◆ *Switzerland* ◆ *California, Colorado, Connecticut, Maine, Massachusetts, Montana, New Hampshire, New Jersey, New York, North Carolina, Pennsylvania, South Dakota, and Washington, United States*

Top-quality tourmalines are among the world's most precious gemstones (*see* photo, right). They may be carved into figurines, cut *en cabochon*, faceted, or sliced into cross-sections. Some specimens are so beautiful that they need no improvement and are displayed in their natural, uncut state.

CHEMICAL FORMULA

$(Na,Ca)(Li,Mg,Fe^{2+},Al)_3(Al,Fe^{3+})_6B_3Si_6O_{27}(O,OH,F)_4$

Although generally categorized as a distinct mineral, the exact composition of tourmaline is so variable that it is more accurately described as a group. Tourmaline is a hydrous fluoroborosilicate of sodium, calcium, lithium, magnesium, aluminum, and ferrous and ferric iron. Within this broad definition there are many different types. This is because several of these chemical elements are interchangeable within the structure of the mineral.

VALUABLE ELBAITE

The most valuable tourmaline is elbaite, a lithium-rich form that may appear in a variety of colors. These include achroite (a colorless stone), dravite (colored brown by magnesium), indicolite (dark blue), and rubellite (red). The black, iron-rich variety of tourmaline is known as schorl. Some forms, known as watermelon tourmaline, are particolored, with clearly delineated zones of green and pink.

Crystals of tourmaline conform to the trigonal system of symmetry. Externally, they appear in prisms, often with striations. Tourmaline crystals are pleochroic, so they may appear darker in color when viewed down their long axis than when looked at from the side. This property may be enhanced by judicious cutting.

Left: A prismatic crystal of watermelon tourmaline, the green and pink variety, showing vertical surface striations.

TRACHYTE

Deriving its name from the Greek word for "rough," this craggy and hard-wearing rock is sometimes used as paving material.

Trachyte is formed from lava flows and pyroclastics (explosive volcanic activity), often in association with **basalt**. *It is the extrusive equivalent of* **syenite**.

Main Sources: *Trachytes occur mainly in small lava flows—they do not extend far because of their viscosity.*

The English name of this extrusive igneous rock is derived from the Greek word *trakhus*, meaning "rough." This is a reference to its pitted, craggy surface.

The total silica content of trachytes is between 55 and 60 percent. Trachytes are therefore classified as intermediate igneous rocks. They are rich in alkali **feldspar** and also contain either **nepheline** or up to 10 percent **quartz**. Darker mafic minerals, such as **aegirine**, **augite**, **hornblende**, and **mica**, are also present in small amounts. The rock is usually gray but may be brownish, pinkish, reddish, or whitish. Whatever its color, it is always light in overall tone, scoring no more than 40 on the color index.

Trachytes are basically fine grained, but some have larger interspersed crystals (phenocrysts)—such deposits are said to be porphyritic. The feldspar crystals are often lath shaped and aligned with the flow direction of the lava, giving rise to the typical trachytic texture.

As the amount of alkali feldspar in trachyte diminishes, there is a corresponding increase in the amount of plagioclase; when this replacement is complete, or nearly so, the rock becomes classified as the closely related extrusive igneous rock latite.

Where it occurs in large and accessible quantities, trachyte is sometimes used as a paving material because it is hard-wearing and does not become shiny when rubbed.

Trachytes are widespread in many parts of the world. Some of the most striking deposits occur along the Rift Valley of central Africa.

PHENOCRYSTS

The rectangular phenocrysts that may sometimes be seen in trachytes are sanidine, a potassium feldspar, which is a glassy high-temperature form of orthoclase.

Left: This trachyte is made up of a multitude of tiny crystals with small phenocrysts (larger, distinct crystals) of feldspar.

TREMOLITE

Named after its discovery site in Val Tremola, Switzerland, this mineral converts to diopside under very high temperatures.

*Tremolite is a fairly common mineral in some metamorphic rocks and is also found in **serpentinite**, an igneous formation. It is formed with **calcite** and carbon dioxide during the conversion of **dolomite**, silica, and water. It is commonly associated with the minerals **garnet** and **talc**.*

Main Sources: ◆ *Austria* ◆ *Brazil* ◆ *Canada* ◆ *England* ◆ *Finland* ◆ *Italy* ◆ *Myanmar (Burma)* ◆ *Russia* ◆ *Scotland* ◆ *Sierra Leone* ◆ *Switzerland* ◆ *Tanzania* ◆ *Arizona, California, Connecticut, Massachusetts, New York, South Dakota, Utah, and Washington, United States*

Above: Often colorless, white, or gray in color, tremolite has a vitreous (glassy) to silky luster.

Confirmed as a distinct species in 1796, this mineral is named after its discovery locality in Val Tremola, near St. Gotthard, Switzerland. Like **chrysotile**, it is a form of asbestos.

THE INFLUENCE OF IRON

Tremolite is a hydrous silicate of calcium, magnesium, and iron. The chemical formula—$Ca_2(Mg,Fe^{2+})_5Si_8O_{22}(OH)_2$—shows that it may contain varying quantities of magnesium and iron. Magnesium-rich specimens are creamy white, but with increased amounts of iron the color darkens to brown or green and the specific gravity rises from 2.9 to 3.2 times more than the equivalent volume of water at room temperature. Minerals with the same chemical formula but a specific gravity of 3.2 to 3.4 are classified as **actinolite**. Tremolite and actinolite therefore form a solid solution series.

Crystals of tremolite conform to the monoclinic system of symmetry and twinning is very common.

Externally, the crystals often appear in long, bladelike shapes but they may also appear in columnar, granular, plumelike, or radiating forms, as well as in massive aggregates.

One variety of tremolite, sometimes known as mountain leather or mountain cork, is a fibrous, felted mass that looks and feels like cloth and often has attached crystals of calcite.

Tremolite is sensitive to heat and converts at high temperatures to **diopside**, a silicate of magnesium and calcium. Therefore the presence of tremolite and the absence of diopside in a given rock indicates that it is a low–temperature deposit.

TRONA

This mineral is commonly found in the world's deserts, where it may occur in dried-up salt beds or caves.

*Trona is formed in arid regions, where it is associated with other similar products such as **borax, dolomite, glauberite, gypsum, halite,** and **sylvine**. It also occurs in salt flats formed from evaporated lakes.*

Main Sources: ◆ *Armenia* ◆ *Canada* ◆ *Chad* ◆ *China* ◆ *Egypt* ◆ *Greenland* ◆ *Iran* ◆ *Kenya* ◆ *Libya* ◆ *Mongolia* ◆ *Tanzania* ◆ *Tibet* ◆ *Uganda* ◆ *California, Nevada, and Wyoming, United States* ◆ *Venezuela*

Above: Trona may be grayish white, pale yellow, or pale brown and forms typically in massive, layered habits.

Confirmed as a distinct mineral in 1773, trona's English name comes from *tron*, a shortened form of *natrun*, the Arabic for "salt." Chemically, trona is a hydrated bicarbonate of sodium with the formula $Na_3H(CO_3)_2.2H_2O$.

The richest deposits of this evaporite product are sometimes used as a commercial source of sodium. They are fairly easy to gather because they form mainly on the Earth's surface. The type locality of trona is in Sweetwater County, Wyoming—the site of the world's largest known deposit of this mineral.

Trona is quite soft—2½ to 3 on the Mohs Scale of Hardness—and has a low specific gravity of 2.1. It has perfect cleavage. In other words, when struck with a hammer or pressurized, it will break off cleanly along its weakest lines of structure.

Crystals of trona are monoclinic and may appear in prismatic or tabular shapes. More commonly, however, the mineral takes the form of powdery surface layers (efflorescence) on the walls of caves and mines or in soils in desert regions.

CARBONATE MINERALS

Carbonate minerals—those containing the ion CO_3—react readily with acids to produce carbon dioxide and water, often with effervescence. There are four main types.

Type	Examples
Anhydrous normal carbonates	Calcite, dolomite magnesite, siderite, smithsonite
Hydrated normal carbonates	Natron (also known as washing soda)
Bicarbonates	Trona
Carbonates with a hydroxyl (OH) or a halogen	Azurite, malachite

TUFF

A rock that forms around active volcanoes, tuff is made up of ash and materials that have been thrown out of the Earth during an eruption.

The exact form and compositon of tuff depend on the nature of the material from which it originates. Thus we see crystal tuffs, lithic tuffs (composed of rock particles), and vitric tuffs (fragments of a glassy nature).

Main Sources: *Tuff may be seen around nearly all of the Earth's active volcanoes. Extensive deposits may be seen on the slopes of Mount Shasta—a 14,162-ft.- (4,317-m-) high dormant volcano in the Cascade Range of California.*

A loosely consolidated igneous rock, tuff is composed of ash and larger fragments that have been thrown out of the Earth during volcanic eruptions. It is therefore classified as a pyroclastic formation. Its name is derived from the Latin *tofus*, meaning "soft stone."

Tuff is a fine-grained rock—most of its component particles are less than ⅒ in. (2 mm) in diameter. However, this groundmass may be interspersed with much larger fragments. Some tuffs contain lumps of **pumice** and other rocks measuring more than 2 in. (5 cm) in diameter. Such formations are known as lithic tuffs. Individual rock fragments within a body of tuff are known as lapilli, from the Latin *lapillus*, meaning "little stone."

The surface of some tuff shines with sparkling minerals—such formations are known as crystal tuffs. Rocks that contain many shards of glass are vitric tuffs, whereas tuffs formed from rivers of ash that have flowed downhill before solidifying are known as ash-flow tuffs.

During an eruption, the largest fragments of ash tend to fall closest to the volcano since they are less easily carried on the wind. Smaller particles of tuff may be deposited many miles from the source of the lava. Tuff that has been erupted in a hot gas cloud may be hot enough upon deposition to form a hard, massive rock known as a welded tuff, or ignimbrite.

The essential mineralogical components of tuff are **feldspar**, **mica**, and **quartz**. The most important accessory mineral in tuff is **hornblende**.

WELDED TUFF

Welded tuff, also known as ignimbrite, is an unsorted rock deposited from a *nuée ardente*—a hot glowing ash flow that moves rapidly down volcanoes—while the particles are still in a plastic condition. When the ash flow cools, the plastic material welds these particles together. Ignimbrites may be very thick and cover large areas.

Below: Lithic tuff is made up of rock particles that have been ejected from a volcano and fused (melted) together.

TURQUOISE

Treasured since ancient times for its striking blue to green color, the
the most precious turquoise gemstones now come from Iran.

*Turquoise is a secondary product of the action of water
on phosphate rocks containing **copper** and aluminum.
It is commonly associated with clay minerals such as
kaolinite, together with **limonite**, **pyrite**, and **quartz**.*

Main Sources: ◆ *Afghanistan* ◆ *Argentina* ◆ *Australia*
◆ *Belgium* ◆ *Chile* ◆ *Egypt* ◆ *England* ◆ *France*
◆ *Germany* ◆ *Guatemala* ◆ *Iran* ◆ *Russia* ◆ *Tanzania*
◆ *Tibet* ◆ *Alabama, Arizona, California, Colorado,
Nevada, New Mexico, Pennsylvania, Utah, and Virginia,
United States*

Above: Turquoise rarely forms in distinct crystals—most
deposits are crusts on the surface of rocks.

Turquoise has been mined and used
as jewelry (*see* photo, left) for at least
8,000 years. The earliest recorded deposits
were found in the Sinai Peninsula (part of
modern Israel) and transported to Western
Europe through Turkey. Its English name
comes from *turqueise*, which is the medieval
French word for "Turkish."

Chemically, turquoise is a hydrous
hydrated phosphate of copper and
aluminum. It forms a solid solution series
with chalcosiderite, a mineral that is
almost identical apart from the fact
that it contains ferric iron instead of
aluminum. During this process of atomic
substitution, the distinctive blue of the
finest turquoise—which is caused by
copper—shades into green due to the increasing presence of iron.

BIRTHSTONE

Turquoise is the lucky stone for natives of the
astrology sign Sagittarius—those people who are
born between 22 November and 21 December.

Turquoise crystals conform to the triclinic system
of symmetry, but individual specimens are very
rare—most deposits are in fact granular or massive in
habit. Despite its great value as a gemstone, turquoise
is not without its limitations in this regard—it is brittle and very porous, which may lead it to fade and
crack. To prevent this, stones are often impregnated
with wax or resin.

Today, the most precious turquoise comes from
Neyshabur in the deserts of northeast Iran. One of
the oldest and most magnificent turquoise artefacts
is a breastplate from the reign of Sesostris II (king of
Egypt 1844–1837 B.C.), which is now stored in the
Metropolitan Museum of Art in New York.

CHEMICAL FORMULAE

Chalcosiderite: $CuFe^{3+}_6(PO_4)_4(OH)_8.4H_2O$
Turquoise: $CuAl_6(PO_4)_4(OH)_8.5H_2O$

ULEXITE

This mineral has one distinctive variety in which light is able to be transmitted from one end of a crystal to the other without bending.

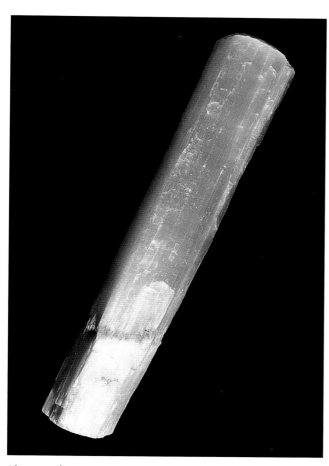

Above: A fine prismatic crystal of ulexite clearly showing the fibrous structure of this mineral.

*An evaporite product, ulexite forms in geodes (mineral-filled cavities) with **borax** in sedimentary rocks. When the two occur in large and accessible quantities they are mined for their boron content. The other main associated minerals are **anhydrite, colemanite,** and **glauberite.***

Main Sources: ◆ *Argentina* ◆ *Azerbaijan* ◆ *Canada* ◆ *Chile* ◆ *Italy* ◆ *Kazakhstan* ◆ *Peru* ◆ *Russia* ◆ *Turkey* ◆ *California and Nevada, United States*

Ulexite is named in honor of George Ludwig Ulex (1811–83), the German chemist who in 1850 first correctly analysed this mineral, which had previously been known as hydroborocalcite.

COTTON BALLS

This mineral is a hydrous hydrated borate of sodium and calcium with the chemical formula $NaCaB_5O_6(OH)_6.5H_2O$. Its crystals conform to the triclinic system of symmetry. Externally, they are often acicular (needle-shaped) and form in rounded aggregates that are sometimes likened to and known as cotton balls. Fibrous, tufted, or veinlike masses may also occur. Ulexite is generally either white or colorless and has a vitreous or silky luster.

UNALTERED LIGHT

TV stone is a transparent variety of ulexite that is remarkable for its capacity to transmit light unaltered from one end of its crystals to the other. (Light is usually bent when it passes from air into and out of any solid, a process known as diffraction.)

Ulexite is a very soft mineral—the hardest crystals have a Mohs scale rating of only 2½, while aggregates may score only 1, the same as **talc**. Ulexite also has a low specific gravity, weighing only 1.9 times more than the equivalent volume of water at room temperature. The mineral displays perfect cleavage, meaning that when it is struck by a hammer or subjected to pressure, it will break up cleanly along its weakest structural lines. Ulexite melts very easily and will also swell and turn a yellow color when it is heated. It does not dissolve in cold water but will dissolve slightly in hot water.

The type locality of ulexite is at Iquique, Tarapaca, which was formerly in Peru but is now part of Chile.

URANINITE

As the main source of the metal uranium, uraninite is mined for use in nuclear reactors and in weaponry.

Uraninite forms in granite **pegmatite,** *in hydrothermals, in bedded sedimentary rocks, and in coal seams. It is commonly associated with* **autunite, monazite, silver, torbernite, tourmaline,** *and* **zircon.**

Main Sources: ◆ *Australia* ◆ *Canada* ◆ *Czech Republic* ◆ *Democratic Republic of the Congo (formerly Zaire)* ◆ *England* ◆ *France* ◆ *Germany* ◆ *Italy* ◆ *Portugal* ◆ *South Africa* ◆ *Arizona, Colorado, Connecticut, New Hampshire, New Mexico, New York, North Carolina, South Dakota, Texas, Utah, and Washington, United States*

Above: A typical dark colored specimen of uraninite with a "pitchy" luster.

Uraninite (uranium oxide, chemical formula UO_2) is the chief ore of uranium. It is also an important source of radium and helium, which are produced during the course of uranium's natural radioactive decomposition into lead.

Early 18th-century Germans knew uraninite as *Pechblende* (English: pitchblende), meaning "false pitch," because, although it resembled coal tar, they could not extract anything useful from it. In 1789, however, German chemist Martin Heinrich Klaproth (1743–1817) found within it a new metal that he named uranium, and, from 1845, the source of this metal became known by its present name.

In 1898, the husband and wife chemist team Pierre and Marie Curie identified another new metal in uraninite—radium. Marie later successfully isolated this metal, for which she was awarded the 1911 Nobel Prize for Chemistry.

Radium is a highly radioactive element that is used in luminous paints and in radiotherapy—a form of medical treatment in which cancerous cells are bombarded with alpha and beta particles.

Uranium is widely distributed and occupies about one in every 2,500 parts of the Earth's crust—it is thus more abundant than **antimony**, mercury, or silver. Apart from traces of neptunium and plutonium, uranium is the heaviest atom found in nature.

The metal is a source of nuclear energy in reactors and weaponry. Because it decomposes over a known, finite period, geologists used to calculate the age of rocks in which it was formed by measuring the relative quantities of uranium and lead in a given deposit. However, this method has now been superseded because it is less accurate than measuring the rate at which potassium decomposes into argon.

Crystals conform to the cubic system. Although four-, eight-, and 12-sided individuals sometimes occur, most deposits take the form of botryoidal clusters or tightly packed granular aggregates.

The largest quantities of uranium ore are mined from the Blind River area of Canada.

VANADINITE

Vanadinite is the main ore of vanadium, a very strong metal that is used to make industrial steel alloys.

Above: A mass of stubby prismatic vanadinite crystals with hexagonal outlines.

*Vanadinite is a secondary mineral that forms in the oxidation zones of sulfide ore deposits. It is usually found in association with **barite**, **galena**, **limonite**, and **wulfenite**.*

Main Sources: ◆ *Algeria* ◆ *Argentina* ◆ *Australia* ◆ *Austria* ◆ *Italy* ◆ *Mexico* ◆ *Morocco* ◆ *Namibia* ◆ *Russia* ◆ *Scotland* ◆ *South Africa* ◆ *Tunisia* ◆ *Arizona, California, Colorado, Nevada, New Mexico, South Dakota, and Utah, United States*

With **carnotite**, vanadinite is one of the main industrial ores of vanadium. The mineral is named after the metal, which is itself named after Vanadis—better known as Freya—the Scandinavian goddess of beauty and youth.

Confirmed as a distinct mineral in 1838, vanadinite is a chlorovanadate of lead, with the chemical formula $Pb_5(VO_4)_3Cl$. Its lead content accounts for its high specific gravity of 6.88. Vanadinite is a member of the **apatite** group and forms a series with **pyromorphite**.

Vanadinite conforms to the hexagonal system of symmetry, and this internal structure may be reflected in six-sided crystal shapes. Prismatic shapes may also occur. Other habits include crusts or rounded masses that resemble pyromorphite. Some specimens are prized for their vivid red color, although it can also appear brownish red, orange-red, yellow, or brown.

VANADIUM

Vanadium was discovered in 1801 by Spanish mineralogist Andrés Manuel del Río (1764–1849), who named it erythronium. He later rejected his own findings, however, after he became convinced that what he had found was not a new element after all, but merely an impure form of chromium.

Del Río should have stuck to his guns. In 1830, the metal was analyzed afresh by Swedish chemist Nils Gabriel Selfström, who gave it its present name and now usually takes the credit for its discovery. Vanadium was first isolated in 1867 by English chemist Sir Henry Enfield Roscoe (1833–1915).

Vanadium is the 22nd most abundant element in the Earth's crust. It has great structural strength and is therefore used in a large number of alloys—about 80 percent of the amount produced annually is used to make ferrovanadium or as a steel additive.

VARISCITE

It is variscite's impurities of iron and chromium that give it its unusual color and make it an attractive stone for use in jewelry.

*Variscite is a secondary mineral that forms when aluminum-bearing rocks are altered by water containing phosphate materials. Many deposits are found as encrustations on rock surfaces and in gaps between fractures. Among the minerals with which it is commonly associated are **apatite**, **chalcedony**, and **limonite**.*

Main Sources: ◆ *Australia* ◆ *Austria* ◆ *Bolivia* ◆ *Brazil* ◆ *Czech Republic* ◆ *England* ◆ *France* ◆ *Germany* ◆ *Italy* ◆ *Poland* ◆ *Spain* ◆ *Arizona, Arkansas, California, Nevada, North Carolina, Pennsylvania, South Dakota, and Utah, United States*

Confirmed as a distinct species in 1837, this mineral is named after Variscia, the ancient name for Voigtland in Saxony, Germany, the locality in which it was first discovered.

In its pure form, variscite is hydrated phosphate of aluminum with the chemical formula $AlPO_4.2H_2O$. In nature, however, it nearly always contains impurities of iron and sometimes of chromium—it is these metals that give some variscite specimens their distinctive green color though some specimens are a delicate pink.

If this mineral is left exposed to sunlight, its water of crystallization will evaporate and the dehydrated material that is left behind is known as metavariscite. In some deposits, the aluminum in variscite is replaced by ferric iron (Fe^{3+}) to form strengite. The two minerals therefore form a solid solution series.

Crystals of variscite conform to the orthorhombic system of symmetry. Some may take the form of pseudo-octahedrons, but these are rare—most deposits are massive aggregates, although nodules, fine-grained masses, crusts, or veins may also occur.

RESEMBLANCE TO TURQUOISE

The mineral sometimes resembles, and may be mistaken for, the gemstone **turquoise**. Variscite crystals found in Queensland, Australia, are misleadingly called "Australian turquoise." Specimens may sometimes be tumbled to make beads that are cheap imitations of precious turquoise, but variscite does not lend itself well to this form of treatment—it is quite soft (3½ to 4½ on the Mohs Scale of Hardness), brittle, porous, and so sensitive to heat that it may lose its green color when it is polished.

Left: This variety of variscite from Ghana shows pinkish botryoidal (grapelike) masses.

VESUVIANITE

Named after its type locality (Mount Vesuvius, Italy) vesuvianite may be cut as a gemstone but is usually only displayed in collections.

Above: Small, brown and yellow prisms of vesuvianite set in volcanic rock.

*Vesuvianite forms mainly in areas of contact metamorphism, especially in calcareous (calcium-rich) rocks. It may also occur in veins in ultrabasic igneous rocks, and in **nepheline syenite**. It is associated with many other minerals, including **calcite**, **diopside**, **epidote**, **garnet**, **mica**, and **wollastonite**.*

Main Sources: ◆ *Australia* ◆ *Canada* ◆ *Czech Republic* ◆ *Finland* ◆ *France* ◆ *Italy* ◆ *Japan* ◆ *Kenya* ◆ *Mexico* ◆ *Norway* ◆ *Pakistan* ◆ *Romania* ◆ *Russia* ◆ *South Korea* ◆ *Switzerland* ◆ *Taiwan* ◆ *Arizona, Arkansas, California, Maine, Montana, Nevada, New Jersey, New York, Utah, Vermont, and Washington, United States*

Confirmed as a distinct mineral in 1795 after analysis of a specimen found in Asbestos, Quebec, Canada, vesuvianite was named after its type locality—Mount Vesuvius in Italy. It is alternatively known as idocrase.

Vesuvianite is a hydrous silicate of calcium, magnesium, iron, and aluminum with the chemical formula $Ca_{10}(Mg,Fe)_2Al_4Si_9O_{34}(OH)_4$. Within this broad definition, several variations are possible— some of the silicon or calcium may be replaced by further atoms of aluminum, and some specimens contain only minuscule amounts of iron or magnesium. Some deposits have been found to contain appreciable amounts of fluorine, while in others traces of antimony oxide and beryllium oxide have also been reported.

Crystals of vesuvianite conform to the tetragonal system of symmetry. Externally, most specimens are thick prisms with square cross-sections and their surfaces are often marked with parallel grooves (striations). Some crystals may display a slight pleochroism. In other words, they appear to change color, depending on the direction of the light source and the angle from which they are viewed. Vesuvianite also often occurs in columns and in granular or massive aggregates.

SEMIPRECIOUS VARIETIES

There are several semiprecious gem varieties of vesuvianite: green californite from California, blue cyprine from Norway, green wiluite from Russia, and yellowish green xanthite from New York. These stones are sometimes faceted, but only for display in collections—they are too brittle to withstand frequent use as jewelry. They resemble, and may be used to imitate, other more precious stones, including **tourmaline** and **zircon**.

VIVIANITE

Although known for its blue color, which was once used as an artist's pigment, vivianite is colorless in the ground, until it hits the air.

*Vivianite forms in manganese ore veins and in **pegmatite** through the alteration of preexistent phosphate materials. It may also occur in **limestone**, where it sometimes replaces the fossilized bones of animals. It is often associated with **quartz, siderite**, and **sphalerite**.*

Main Sources: ◆ *Australia* ◆ *Bolivia* ◆ *Brazil* ◆ *Cameroon* ◆ *Canada* ◆ *Czech Republic* ◆ *England* ◆ *France* ◆ *Germany* ◆ *Italy* ◆ *Japan* ◆ *Mexico* ◆ *Romania* ◆ *Russia* ◆ *Scotland* ◆ *Serbia* ◆ *Ukraine* ◆ *California, Colorado, Delaware, Florida, Georgia, Idaho, Maine, Maryland, New Hampshire, New Jersey, North Carolina, South Dakota, Utah, Virginia, and Washington D.C., United States*

Confirmed as a distinct mineral in 1817, vivianite is named in honor of J.G. Vivian, the English mineralogist who discovered it in Cornwall, England. It was formerly known as "blue iron earth" and was used to make an artists' pigment that resembled Prussian blue.

Vivianite is a hydrated phosphate of iron with the chemical formula $Fe_3^{2+}(PO_4)_2.8H_2O$. Its crystals conform to the monoclinic system and may form in sheets that are very easy to cut. Specimens 4 ft. (1.2 m) long have been found in Cameroon. Other habits include radiating clusters of prismatic, acicular or fibrous crystals, or earthy and encrusting masses.

TURNING BLUE

Vivianite is usually colorless when first removed from the Earth but turns blue on contact with oxygen in the atmosphere. Up to 28 percent of its mass is made of water of crystallization, and this may evaporate in dry air. Therefore collectors should keep specimens away from direct light in airtight compartments with small bowls of water.

Vivianite is very soft—it scores only 1½ to 2 on the Mohs Scale of Hardness—and weighs 2.6 to 2.7 times more than the equivalent volume of water at room temperature. When hit with a hammer or subjected to pressure, it will break up cleanly along its weakest structural lines. In scientific terms, it is said to display perfect cleavage.

Above: Striking prismatic crystals of vivianite from South America.

WAVELLITE

Named after the doctor who found it in southern England, wavellite stands out because of its unusual crystal shapes.

Above: Wavellite often occurs in rounded spherical masses that have internal radiating structures.

*Wavellite is a secondary mineral formed mainly through the alteration of **apatite** and found in the joints and cavities of metamorphic rocks, most notably **slate**. It may also occur on ore bodies containing **limonite** and in hydrothermal veins. Among the other minerals with which it is associated are **mica**, **quartz**, and **turquoise**.*

Main Sources: ◆ *Australia* ◆ *Bolivia* ◆ *Bulgaria* ◆ *Czech Republic* ◆ *England* ◆ *France* ◆ *Germany* ◆ *Ireland* ◆ *Italy* ◆ *Portugal* ◆ *Romania* ◆ *Alabama, Arkansas, California, Colorado, Florida, Pennsylvania, and Wisconsin, United States*

Confirmed as a distinct species in 1805, wavellite is named after William Wavell (1756–1829), a physician who discovered it in clay near Barnstaple in Devon, England.

This mineral is a hydrous hydrated fluorophosphate of aluminum with the chemical formula $Al_3(PO_4)_2(OH,F)_3.5H_2O$. Wavellite may be used to make phosphated manure, but this is by no means common because it rarely appears in economically worthwhile deposits.

HEMISPHERES AND GLOBES

Crystals of wavellite conform to the orthorhombic system. Acicular (needle-shaped) habits may occur, but these are rare and, externally, the mineral nearly always appears in unusual hemispherical or globular aggregates, which tend to be fibrous and radiate outwards from a central hub. It may also sometimes occur in tiny, prismatic crystals or encrustations.

NO COLOR OF ITS OWN

Wavellite has a specific gravity of 2.3 to 2.4 and a hardness of 3½ to 4 on the Mohs scale. Although the mineral may appear in a wide range of colors— green is classic, but it may also be blue, brown, gray, white, or yellow—it has a white streak and is basically an allochromatic mineral. In other words, it has no color of its own and is easily colored by the elements in surrounding minerals.

The mineral's luster can range from vitreous to resinous or pearly. The mineral also has a perfect cleavage, meaning that if it is hit with a hammer or subjected to pressure it will split cleanly along its weakest structural lines.

Wavellite does not melt, even under high temperatures, but does give off water when it is heated in a sealed test tube.

WILLEMITE

Willemite has some unusual properties—it has trigonal crystals, which is rare for a silicate mineral, and can be fluorescent.

*Willemite is found mainly in crystalline **limestone** and **marble**. It is a secondary mineral formed through the metamorphism of preexistent zinc minerals such as **hemimorphite** and **smithsonite**. It may also occur in the oxidized zones of zinc deposits with the closely related zinc oxides **franklinite** and **zincite**. Willemite may also be associated with **calcite**, **greenockite**, and **rhodonite**.*

Main Sources: ◆ *Algeria* ◆ *Belgium* ◆ *Canada* ◆ *Democratic Republic of the Congo (formerly Zaire)* ◆ *Greece* ◆ *Greenland* ◆ *Iran* ◆ *Mexico* ◆ *Namibia* ◆ *Russia* ◆ *South Africa* ◆ *Sweden* ◆ *Arizona, California, Colorado, New Jersey, New Mexico, and Utah, United States* ◆ *Zambia*

This mineral is named after Willem I, King of the Netherlands (1772–1843), and was confirmed as a distinct species in 1830.

Willemite is a silicate of zinc with the chemical formula Zn_2SiO_4. When the mineral occurs in large enough quantities, it is sometimes mined as a minor ore of this metal, the main industrial source of which is **sphalerite**.

Crystals of willemite are trigonal—very few silicate minerals conform to this system of symmetry. Externally, they may appear in long prisms with steep rhombohedral terminations, but the mineral more commonly appears in granular, lamellar, and fibrous masses. Its color is usually a greenish yellow, but can also range from white to brown.

FLUORESCENT

Some specimens of willemite are both fluorescent and phosphorescent. When placed under an ultraviolet lamp, they may give off a bright green light of their own, which continues to shine even after the UV has been switched off.

Willemite reacts unusually when placed in hydrochloric acid—it decomposes into a powder, leaving behind a residue of silica. This is one of the key identification tests.

There are variant forms of willemite that may contain up to 12 percent by volume of manganese in the form of manganese oxide. Such deposits have the chemical formula $(Zn,Mn)_2SiO_4$ and are sometimes known as troostite.

The world's leading sources of willemite were in the amazingly rich but now defunct mines at Franklin and Sterling Hill, New Jersey.

Left: Green massive willemite showing a typically resinous (waxy) luster.

WITHERITE

As an important ore of barium, witherite has many industrial roles and is used to make optical glass, barium salts, and in sugar refining.

*Witherite forms at low temperatures in hydrothermal veins. It is most commonly associated with **aragonite** and **barite**, and may also occur with **anglesite**, **calcite**, **celestite**, **fluorite**, **galena**, and **quartz**.*

Main Sources: ◆ *Australia* ◆ *Canada* ◆ *Czech Republic* ◆ *England* ◆ *France* ◆ *Germany* ◆ *Japan* ◆ *Russia* ◆ *Arizona, California, Illinois, Kentucky, and Montana, United States*

Above: A mass of small, prismatic witherite crystals from a cavity in a hydrothermal vein.

Confirmed as a distinct species in 1789, this mineral is named after William Withering (1741–99), the English physician and naturalist who first described it.

USES OF WITHERITE

Although witherite is not common, it is still important in industry because it is the second most abundant barium ore after barite. It is preferred to barite in the preparation of barium salts, because witherite is soluble in acids, whereas barite is not. Witherite is also used to make flux for ceramics and in the manufacture of some forms of optical glass. It is an important component of various types of steel and is used in sugar-refining.

RELATED TO ARAGONITE

Witherite is a carbonate of barium with the chemical formula $BaCO_3$. It is closely related to aragonite, and a member of the aragonite group.

One of the tests for this mineral is that it effervesces when placed in dilute solutions of hydrochloric acid. It may also fluoresce light blue under both long- and short-wave ultraviolet light. Some specimens are also phosphorescent under short-wave UV. Because of its barium content, witherite is fairly heavy for a carbonate mineral, with a specific gravity of 4.3. Crystals of witherite conform to the orthorhombic system of symmetry. Externally, they appear in dipyramidal or pseudo-hexagonal shapes with vertical grooves (striations) and are almost invariably twinned. Other habits include columnar, botryoidal (grapelike), fibrous, granular, or massive.

WOLFRAMITE

This mineral is one of the two main ores of tungsten, a metallic element used industrially to harden alloys.

*Wolframite occurs in igneous rocks, especially **pegmatite**, and in high-temperature hydrothermal veins. It is commonly associated with **scheelite**, as well as with **cassiterite, galena, hematite, mica, pyrite, quartz, rhodochrosite, sphalerite,** and **tourmaline.***

Main Sources: *◆ Australia ◆ Bolivia ◆ Canada ◆ China ◆ Czech Republic ◆ England ◆ France ◆ Germany ◆ Greenland ◆ Malaysia ◆ Myanmar (Burma) ◆ Peru ◆ Portugal ◆ Russia ◆ Spain ◆ South Korea ◆ Arizona, California, Colorado, Idaho, Nevada, New Mexico, South Dakota, and Washington, United States*

Above: A cleaned specimen of wolframite showing the mineral's characteristic metallic luster.

Wolframite is one of the world's two main ores of tungsten; the other is scheelite.

In 1783, Spanish chemists José and Fausto d'Elhuyar isolated from this mineral a new metal, which they named wolfram. This element is now known as tungsten, but its chemical symbol (W) still recalls the original name. The word "wolfram" is thought to be derived from the German words *Wolf* ("wolf") and *Rahm* ("froth"). This is taken to be a reference to the scum that forms during the smelting of tin ores that contain impurities of tungsten.

A tungstate of iron and manganese with the formula $(Fe,Mn)WO_4$, wolframite's chemical composition is intermediate between **hübnerite** and ferberite, forming the middle section of a solid solution series, with the other two minerals as end members.

Wolframite is a heavy mineral, weighing between 7.0 and 7.5 times more than the equivalent volume of water at room temperature. It is moderately hard, scoring 5 to 5½ on the Mohs scale.

Wolframite may contain as much as 60 percent of tungsten by weight. The metal is extracted by heating the ore with concentrated caustic soda—more

scientifically known as sodium hydroxide, with the chemical formula NaOH. The resulting compound, which is soluble, is reduced to pure tungsten by reacting it with hydrogen gas. Tungsten has a range of electrical uses and is also used to harden alloys.

Wolframite crystals conform to the monoclinic system of symmetry. Externally, they often appear in prismatic or flat, heavily modified tabular shapes, and are often twinned. Other habits include columnar aggregates and lamellar masses.

WOLLASTONITE

Wollastonite is an interesting and useful mineral—it can glow with a pink fluorescence and is used in paint fillers and ceramic tiles.

Although wollastonite sometimes occurs in alkaline igneous rocks, most deposits are formed when impure **limestone** *is metamorphosed by hot magma containing silica. It is particularly likely to be found in* **skarn**, *where it is often associated with* **calcite, diopside, epidote, feldspar, garnet,** *and* **vesuvianite.**

Main Sources: ◆ *Canada* ◆ *China* ◆ *Finland* ◆ *France* ◆ *Germany* ◆ *Greece* ◆ *Italy* ◆ *Mexico* ◆ *Norway* ◆ *Romania* ◆ *Switzerland* ◆ *California, Colorado, New Jersey, New York, and Texas, United States*

Confirmed as a distinct species in 1818, this mineral is named in honor of William Hyde Wollaston (1766–1828), a versatile English scientist who was a physician, chemist, physicist, mineralogist, and inventor—his main claim to fame is as the discoverer of the elements palladium and rhodium.

Chemically, wollastonite is a silicate of calcium, with the formula $CaSiO_3$. Crystals conform to the triclinic system of symmetry. Externally, they appear in prismatic or tabular shapes and many are twinned. Other habits include compact, fibrous, or massive.

THREE-WAY CLEAVAGE

The mineral displays cleavage in three directions—perfect in one and good in the other two. The perfect cleavage breaks off at nearly 90°, forming prisms with rectangular cross-sections. Cleavage fragments generally appear as elongated splinters. Some wollastonite specimens—notably those from the mines at Franklin, New Jersey—may display an orange or pink fluorescence when put under ultraviolet light.

Closely related to wollastonite is parawollastonite, which has exactly the same chemical formula but conforms to the monoclinic system of symmetry.

In 1978, a third polymorph was identified. It has crystals that conform to the triclinic system and it is known as wollastonite-7T.

Wollastonite is widely used in the manufacture of ceramic tiles, as a filler in paints, and in a wide variety of electricity- and heat-resistant products, such as porcelain insulating plugs.

Below: A mass of radiating woollastonite crystals with a silky luster.

WULFENITE

The lead that this mineral contains is often partly replaced by another metal, calcium.

*Wulfenite is a secondary mineral derived from **molybdenite** and forms in ore veins that have been altered by circulating water. It is often found in association with **calcite, cerussite, galena, limonite, malachite, mimetite, pyromorphite, smithsonite,** and **vanadinite**.*

Main Sources: ◆ *Algeria* ◆ *Australia* ◆ *Austria* ◆ *Czech Republic* ◆ *Germany* ◆ *Italy* ◆ *Mexico* ◆ *Morocco* ◆ *Namibia* ◆ *Arizona, Massachusetts, Nevada, New Mexico, Pennsylvania, South Dakota, and Utah, United States*

With molybdenite, wulfenite is one of the main ores of molybdenum. It is a member of the scheelite group.

Confirmed as a distinct species in 1845, this mineral is named after Franz Xavier Wülfen (1728–1805), an amateur geologist who made a lifelong study of the mineralogy of Carinthia in his native Austria.

Chemically, wulfenite is a molybdate of lead with the formula $PbMoO_4$. Although lead may comprise up to about 56 percent of the weight of each molecule, the mineral is never mined for this metal because it is often partly replaced by calcium.

SHARING FACES

Crystals of wulfenite conform to the tetragonal system of symmetry. Externally, they resemble slightly elongated cubes or octahedral pyramids. Some share a face or faces with one or more of their neighbors—a phenomenon known as twinning. The mineral may also form in encrustations.

As with all lead-bearing minerals, wulfenite has a high specific gravity—it weighs between 6.5 and 7 times more than the equivalent volume of water at room temperature.

LEAD MOUNTAIN

The Austrian province of Carinthia, in which the mineral wulfenite was first discovered, is particularly rich in lead minerals—one of the towns here is called Bleiburg, which means "lead mountain" in German.

Left: A mass of tabular wulfenite crystals showing the mineral's typical yellowish-brown coloring.

WURTZITE

This rare mineral has an unusual crystal symmetry, which can be either hexagonal or trigonal, depending on how it formed.

*In nature, wurtzite is formed mainly with other sulfide ores in hydrothermal veins. It is sometimes also found in concretions in sedimentary rocks such as **clay** and **ironstone** and in contact metamorphosed **limestone**. In addition to **galena** and **sphalerite**, wurtzite may also be found in association with **pyrite**.*

Main Sources: ◆ *Bolivia* ◆ *Czech Republic* ◆ *England* ◆ *Germany* ◆ *Italy* ◆ *Namibia* ◆ *Peru* ◆ *Portugal* ◆ *Romania* ◆ *Arizona, California, Connecticut, Idaho, Missouri, Montana, Nevada, Ohio, Pennsylvania, and Utah, United States*

Above: An aggregate mass of dark wurtzite crystals, some of which show a metallic luster.

This minor ore of zinc was confirmed as a distinct mineral in 1861 and named after Karl Adolph Wurtz (1817–84), French chemist and dean of the medical faculty at the University of Paris, France.

HEMIMORPHISM

Chemically, wurtzite is a sulfide of zinc and iron. It is trimorphous with matraite and sphalerite. All three minerals have the same chemical formula, $(Zn,Fe)S$, but conform to different systems of symmetry. Crystals of sphalerite are cubic, but wurtzite, most unusually, may be either hexagonal or trigonal, depending on the heat and pressure under which it formed. Externally, wurtzite crystals often appear in six-sided shapes or as pyramids. Many have a differently shaped termination at either end. The scientific term for this phenomenon is hemimorphism (*see* **hemimorphite**).

In laboratory conditions, wurtzite has been made to form a complete isomorphous series with **greenockite**, a sulfide of cadmium, and cadmoselite,

cadmium selenite. In other words, the three minerals can be made to appear externally identical.

ORNAMENTAL STONES

The external forms, or habits, of wurtzite include groups of radiating acicular (needlelike) crystal groups and layered, botryoidal (grapelike) crusts. Aggregates of botryoidal wurtzite crusts that form with layers of galena and sphalerite are known as *Schalenblende*. Such aggregates are sometimes cut and polished into ornamental stones.

When placed under an ultraviolet lamp, some specimens of wurtzite may display fluorescence, giving off an orange light of their own.

ZIRCON

The finest specimens of zircon resemble diamonds and are used in jewelry and ornamentation.

*Zircon is found as an accessory mineral in igneous rocks, especially **syenite**, in metamorphic rocks such as **gneiss** and **schist**, and as a detrital mineral in some sedimentary formations. It has also been found in **meteorites** and on the Moon. It is commonly associated with **feldspar, garnet**, and **monazite**.*

Main Sources: ◆ *Australia* ◆ *Brazil* ◆ *Cambodia* ◆ *Canada* ◆ *France* ◆ *Germany* ◆ *Italy* ◆ *North Korea* ◆ *Madagascar* ◆ *Myanmar (Burma)* ◆ *Nigeria* ◆ *Norway* ◆ *Pakistan* ◆ *Russia* ◆ *South Korea* ◆ *Sri Lanka* ◆ *Tanzania* ◆ *Thailand* ◆ *Arizona, Colorado, Maine, Massachusetts, New Jersey, New York, North Carolina, Oklahoma, South Dakota, Texas, and Washington, United States* ◆ *Vietnam* ◆ *Zimbabwe*

Used since antiquity to make a wide range of jewelry and other forms of ornamentation, zircon derives its English name from the Arabic *zargun*, meaning "golden colored."

Despite this etymology, the finest and most valuable zircons are colorless. Such specimens are cut into gemstones in a wide range of styles and are sometimes used to imitate the even more precious **diamond**, which they resemble.

MANY COLORED VARIETIES

Clear, transparent zircon is pure zirconium silicate ($ZrSiO_4$). The many colored forms—there are blue, brown, green, orange, red, and yellow varieties—have the same chemical formula but contain various impurities. Some zircon contains traces of thorium and uranium, two radioactive elements that will eventually cause a breakdown in the crystal structure of the gem. Undecayed stones are known as high zircon, whereas decayed stones are known as low zircon and their structure is said to be a metamict.

Crystals of zircon conform to the tetragonal system of symmetry. They may appear in various shapes, either in prismatic crystals with bipyramidal terminations or as fibrous aggregates that radiate out from a central focus. Twinning may occur.

High zircon has sharp corners and a glassy or diamondlike sheen (vitreous to adamantine luster), but metamicts have curved faces and edges and a generally duller appearance. Some of the largest crystals have been found in Canada—they measure 12 in. (30 cm) by 4 in. (10 cm).

INDUSTRIAL USE

Zircon is highly resistant to heat, and specimens that are not good-looking enough to be used in jewelry are used as refractory (heat resistant) materials for lining furnaces and kilns.

Below: Small, brownish zircon crystals set in an igneous rock matrix (base).

ZOISITE

Named after its discoverer, the finest specimens of zoisite may be cut and polished as gemstones or beads.

*The mineral zoisite can be found in a wide range of rocks, especially in metamorphic **limestone**. It may be associated with **calcite, corundum, garnet, hornblende, mica**, and **quartz**.*

Main Sources: ◆ *Australia* ◆ *Austria* ◆ *Canada* ◆ *Finland* ◆ *Germany* ◆ *Greenland* ◆ *India* ◆ *Italy* ◆ *Japan* ◆ *Kenya* ◆ *Mexico* ◆ *Namibia* ◆ *Norway* ◆ *Russia* ◆ *Scotland* ◆ *Switzerland* ◆ *Tanzania* ◆ *Arizona, California, Massachusetts, Nevada, North Carolina, Pennsylvania, South Dakota, Tennessee, and Washington, United States.*

A member of the **epidote** group, zoisite is a hydrous silicate of calcium and aluminum with the chemical formula $Ca_2Al_3(SiO_4)_3OH$. The precious gemstone variety is tanzanite.

Zoisite was first discovered by Baron Sigismund Zois von Edelstein (1747–1819), a Slovenian nobleman and mineralogist. He named it saualpite, after the Sau-Alp Mountains in which he found it, but when it was confirmed as a distinct mineral in 1805, it was renamed after him. Tanzanite was not discovered until 1967.

Crystals of zoisite conform to the orthorhombic system of symmetry. Many specimens are prismatic or tabular in appearance, usually with poorly developed terminations and deep surface striations. Massive and granular habits are also common.

Pure zoisite is colorless, but some varieties are colored by impurities: thulite, for example, is pink or reddish because of the presence of manganese while the sapphire-blue of tanzanite is due to vanadium. Many specimens display a strong pleochroism, appearing blue, gray, or purple depending on the direction of the light source and the angle from which they are viewed.

Above: This delicate pink variety of zoisite is known as thulite.

One of the most valuable forms of zoisite is a green massive aggregate that also contains **ruby** (red corundum) and hornblende. This variety may be carved, polished, or tumbled into cabochons, ornamental stones, or beads.

Zoisite may change color momentarily when it is placed under a normal electric light and more lastingly when it is heated. In fact, it is not uncommon to find stones that have been artificially enhanced by this method.

Zoisite is dimorphous with clinozoisite, a separate mineral species that conforms to the monoclinic system of symmetry but is otherwise identical. Although the chemical formula of clinozoisite is written slightly differently from that of zoisite—$Ca_2Al_3Si_3O_{12}(OH)$—this is merely to reflect the difference in crystal structure. All the component elements and their proportions are exactly the same in both minerals.

GLOSSARY

Accessory minerals
Any constituents of a rock that occur in such small quantities as to be insignificant, both in the chemistry and the definition of the rock.

Acicular
With an external shape (habit) that resembles a needle.

Adamantine
A sparkly luster, like that of a diamond.

Amorphous
Without obvious internal or external crystalline structure or shape (*see* amber).

Amphibole group
A group of rock-forming minerals, often rich in magnesium and iron.

Argillaceous rock
Clayey, sedimentary rock of fine-grained sediment composed of particles that are less than 0.002 in. across (*see* shale).

Arsenate
A mineral compound of arsenic and oxygen that often occurs as an oxidation product of arsenide ore minerals (*see* carminite).

Associated minerals
Minerals found near or mixed up with another mineral or rock.

Asterism
An optical effect in which a four- or six-rayed star can be seen in a mineral.

Basal cleavage
Cleavage parallel to the base crystal plane of a mineral.

Basic igneous rock
Igneous rocks are classified according to the silica they contain. A basic igneous rock contains between 45 and 55 percent total silica (*see* augite).

Birefringence
Where a mineral splits light passing through it into two rays that then reemerge at divergent angles. Also known as double refraction (*see* stibiconite).

Bladed
A habit resembling the blade of a knife.

Botryoidal
Habit resembling bunches of grapes.

Cabochon
A gemstone cut so as to have a domed upper surface. In such cases the gem is said to have been cut *en cabochon*.

Carbonates
Carbonate minerals are those that contain the ion CO_3 (*see* trona).

Chatoyancy
The cat's eye effect in which a single ray of light crosses the stone. This optical effect is shown by some gemstones when they are cut *en cabochon* (*see* apatite).

Cleavage
The structural lines along which a mineral will break up when it is hit with a hammer or subjected to pressure.

Colloid
Any substance that appears to be dissolved but nevertheless cannot pass through a membrane (*see* chert, limonite).

Color index
Igneous rocks are categorized according to the concentration of dark-colored minerals they contain. The color index gives each rock a score of between 0 and 100; the higher the number, the darker the rock (*see* granodiorite).

Compounds
Compounds are held together by a chemical force; their components are fixed and difficult to separate (*see* allophane).

Contact twinning
An intergrowth of two or more crystals of the same mineral through contact.

Crystal
A solid that has a definite internal structure producing a characteristic external shape.

Crystal structure
A crystal's internal atomic structure. There are seven different crystal structures.

Dendritic
A mineral habit with a plantlike or tree-like shape.

Dichroic
A gem that appears in two different colors, depending on the light and the angle from which it is viewed.

Double refraction
See birefringence (*see* calcite).

Dike
Sheet-shaped igneous intrusion, which cuts across preexisting rock structures.

Earthy
A dull, non-reflective sheen.

Essential mineral
The constituents of a rock that form an essential part of its makeup.

Evaporite deposit
A mineral or rock formed through the evaporation of salt water.

Faceting
Cutting the surfaces of a gemstone.

Ferric and ferrous iron
Iron can form two different bonds with other chemical elements. Ferrous iron (Fe^{2+}) has two links, while ferric iron (Fe^{3+}) has three (*see* arfvedsonite).

Foliated
A habit where the crystals form in thin, flat sheets, rather like the pages of a book.

Fracture
The way a mineral breaks up when hit or subjected to some form of pressure. It is usually used to describe breaks that are not along distinct lines of cleavage.

Gelatinization
The product of a reaction between a mineral and other chemicals that leaves a semi-solid, gelatin-like residue.

Gemstone
A mineral (usually) prized for its beauty, rarity, and/or durability.

Globular aggregate
A rounded mineral deposit made up of tiny individual crystals.

Groundmass
(*See* matrix.)

Habit
A mineral's characteristic shape or appearance (*see* boulangerite).

Halides
Minerals that contain one of the halogen elements: astatine, bromine, chlorine, fluorine, or iodine.

Hardness
A mineral's resistance to being scratched.

Hemimorphism
Where the crystals of a mineral lack a center of symmetry so that one end of each prism has a different shape from the other (*see* hemimorphite).

Hydrated minerals
Minerals with molecules of water of crystallization attached (*see* actinolite).

Hydrothermals
Fluids that carry elements from which vein minerals are crystallized and which alter preexistent minerals to form new species (*see* bornite).

Hydrothermal vein
A fracture in a rock where minerals have been deposited from hot flows of magma that were rich in water.

Hydrous minerals
Those that contain the elements of water (hydrogen and oxygen) even though they do not carry water itself (*see* actinolite).

Hydroxide
A compound in which a metallic element combines with water and hydroxl.

Hydroxyl
An ion that combines one atom of oxygen and one of hydrogen (formula OH).

Igneous rock
A rock formed from molten material. There are two main types: extrusive and intrusive. Extrusive igneous rocks are formed from volcanic material that has flowed onto the Earth's surface and resolidified, often as vast sheets. Intrusive varieties are formations that have forced themselves into preexistent strata, along a clearly defined structural feature such as a bedding plane, or in large, irregular masses cutting across preformed structures.

Inclusion
A fragment of another material enclosed in a crystal or rock.

Intergrown
When two minerals grow together.

Intermediate rock
An igneous rock with 55 to 65 percent total silica.

Intrusion
A mass of igneous rock that invades an older rock.

Isomorphous
Minerals with the same crystal structure but different chemical compositions.

Isotropic mineral
A mineral that appears the same from all angles, rather like a cube (*see* stibiconite).

Lamellar
Where a mineral forms in thin layers.

Lava
Molten volcanic rock.

Luster
The way light is reflected off the surface of a mineral.

Magma
Molten rock below the Earth's surface.

Mammillated
Smooth and rounded in shape.

Massive
A mineral habit with no definite shape.

Matrix
The rock base in which a crystal or gemstone is set. Also known as the groundmass, host, or parent rock.

Metamorphic rock
Rocks that have been altered by heat and/or pressure.

Metamorphism
Changes as a result of heat or pressure.

Metasomatism
Changes as a result of the addition or replacement of chemicals.

Mineral
An inorganic, naturally occurring material with both a constant chemical formula and a regular crystal symmetry (internal atomic structure).

Mixture
Any combination of substances that are not held together by a chemical force. A mixture's components can be of any proportions and may be separated by physical means (*see* allophane).

Mohs Scale of Hardness
A means of measuring a mineral's hardness in relation to other minerals.

Native elements
The smallest units of matter that may exist on their own in nature, uncombined with other elements to form compounds.

Oolites
Limestones composed of very small particles with concentric layers of spheroidal or ellipsoidal structures (*see* limestone).

Ore
A rock or mineral that contains a commercially valuable metal or other material.

Oxides
Compounds in which one or two metallic elements combine with oxygen.

Pegmatite
An igneous rock formed as magma solidifies, containing very large crystals.

Penetration twinning
An intergrowth of two or more crystals of the same mineral species through interpenetration.

Phenocrysts
Large crystals set in the matrix of an igneous rock.

Platy
A mineral habit with flat, thin crystals.

Playa
A dried-out lake bed in a desert region (*see* thenardite).

Pleochroism
A gemstone's capacity to appear in different colors when viewed from different directions (*see* andalusite).

Phosphates
Compounds in which the phosphate radical (PO_4) combines with one or more metallic elements.

Polymorphs
Substances with the same chemical composition that exist in two or more distinct forms (*see* anatase).

Porphyritic
The texture of an igneous rock whereby large crystals are set in a matrix of rock.

Primary mineral
A mineral that crystallizes straight from molten material or fluids in or on the Earth (*see* adamite).

Prismatic
A habit with a uniform cross-section.

Pseudocubes
Formations that have a cubic shape but do not actually conform to the cubic system of symmetry (*see* jarosite).

Pseudomorphism
Where one mineral replaces another species atom by atom but leaves the original crystal shape intact (*see* chalcosite).

Pyroxenes
Minerals that are chain silicates with the general formula $X_2Si_2O_6$ where X may be aluminum, calcium, iron, lithium, magnesium, manganese, sodium, or titanium (*see* pyroxenite).

Reniform
Kidney-shaped habit.

Resinous
A waxy luster (sheen).

Rock
An aggregate of mineral particles.

Rock-forming minerals
Minerals that typically comprise certain types of rock. Pyroxenes, for example, are known as rock-forming minerals because they occur as both major and minor components of a wide variety of igneous and metamorphic formations.

Scree
A mass of rock waste found below a cliff or on a mountain slope that has resulted from weathering.

Secondary mineral
A mineral that is formed from a primary mineral, or minerals (*see* adamite).

Sedimentary rock
A rock formed by the accumulation of layers of loose sediment or by the accumulation of chemicals that precipitate out of water.

Silicates
Minerals containing silicon and oxygen, with or without other chemical elements.

Sill
A sheet-shaped igneous intrusion, which follows the structures of preformed rocks (*see* dike).

Solid solution series
Where the atoms of one component of a mineral are gradually replaced by another component. When this atomic substitution is complete, a new mineral is formed (*see* ankerite).

Specific gravity
A comparison of the weight of a mineral with the weight of an equal volume of water at room temperature.

Spherulites
Minerals or rock formations with a roughly globe-shaped habit.

Stalactitic
Minerals with a habit that resembles the tapering growths of calcium carbonate that form upward from the ground.

Streak
The irreducible color of a particular mineral—all specimens of the mineral would be this color if they were reduced to powder (*see* bayldonite).

Striations
Parallel grooves or lines along the surface of a mineral.

Stromatolites
Laminated mounds of limestone formed by blue-green algae (*see* limestone).

Sulfates
Compounds in which one or more metallic elements combine with the sulfate (SO_4) ion.

Sulfides
A group of minerals in which sulfur has combined with metallic and/or semi-metallic elements.

Sulfosalts
Sulfides (chemical compounds of sulfur) that contain two or more metals (*see* bournonite).

Transparency
The way light passes through a mineral.

Twinning
When crystals share one or more faces with one or more of their neighbors.

Type locality
A particular place in the world that has provided geologists with a classic mineral specimen against which subsequent possible finds may be tested for authenticity (*see* actinolite).

Ultrabasic rocks
Igneous rocks that contain less than 45 percent silica and virtually no quartz (*see* augite).

Vanadates
Naturally occurring compounds containing vanadium and oxygen in the form of vanadate ions (*see* mottramite).

Vein
A sheetlike area of mineral material that often cuts through rock formations.

Vesicle
A hole in lava created by gas and left after the lava has solidified.

Vitreous
Glassy luster.

Water of crystallization
The elements of water (H_2O) attached to a mineral in solid form. It may be driven off by heating.

Weathering
The breakdown and decomposition of materials on or near the surface of the Earth (*see* anglesite).

Xenolith
Fragments of unrelated metamorphic or sedimentary rocks typically found in certain igneous rocks (*see* granite).

Zeolites
Minerals that, when heated, give off their attached water of crystallization in a single, continuous action (*see* analcime).

CHEMICAL SYMBOLS

Ag	silver
Al	aluminum
As	arsenic
Au	gold
B	boron
Ba	barium
Be	beryllium
Bi	bismuth
C	carbon
Ca	calcium
Cd	cadmium
Ce	cerium
Cl	chlorine
Co	cobalt
Cr	chromium
Cs	cesium
Cu	copper
F	fluorine
Fe	iron
H	hydrogen
Hg	mercury
K	potassium
La	lanthanum
Li	lithium
Mg	magnesium
Mn	manganese
Mo	molybdenum
N	nitrogen
Na	sodium
Nb	niobium
Nd	neodymium
Ni	nickel
O	oxygen
P	phosphorus
Pb	lead
Pd	palladium
Pt	platinum
Re	rhenium
S	sulfur
Sb	antimony
Se	selenium
Si	silicon
Sn	tin
Sr	strontium
Ta	tantalum
Te	tellurium
Th	thorium
Ti	titanium
U	uranium
V	vanadium
W	tungsten
Y	yttrium
Zn	zinc
Zr	zirconium

INDEX

Words shown in a bold typeface indicate a main rock, mineral, or gemstone entry.

abrasives 97, 206, 222
acanthite 6
achondrites 189
actinolite 7, 159, 281
adamite 8, 172, 205
adelite group 91
aegirine 9, 227
aerolites 189
agate 71, 76, 229
aggregates 33, 127, 133, 155
alabaster 142
albite 123
alchemists 208
alexandrite 79
allochromatic minerals 291
allophane 10
alloys 24, 65, 72, 78, 87, 112, 141, 149, 194, 213, 224, 255, 287
almandine 129
alum 12
aluminite 11
aluminum, 12, 42, 108
alunite 12, 161
amalgams 82
amazonite 123
amber 13
amblygonite 14
amethyst 229
amphiboles 28, 133, 152, 236
amphoteric minerals 177
analcime 15
anatase 16, 57
andalusite 17, 167, 248
andesite 18, 41
andradite 129
anglesite 19
anhydrite 20
ankerite 21, 112, 166
annabergite 22, 120, 165
anthracite 86
antigorite 23, 75
antimony 24, 54, 262
Apache tears 204
apatite 25
apophyllite 26
aquamarine 45
aragonite 27, 60, 293
arfvedsonite 28
argentite 6
argillaceous rocks 246
arkose 29, 239
arsenates 8, 62, 67
arsenic 30, 31, 87, 178, 208, 232
arsenopyrite 31
artinite 32
asbestos 81, 236
asphalt 48
asterism 237, 238, 240, 257
astrophyllite 33

atacamite 34
augite 35, 143, 148
aurichalcite 36
autunite 37, 278
axinite 38
azurite 39

barite 40, 66
barium 40, 293
basalt 18, **41**, 106
bauxite 42, 101, 108, 131
bayldonite 43, 91
benitoite 44
berthierine 75
beryl 45, 115, 143
beryllium 45
beudantite 161
birefringence 60, 256, 261
birthstones 45, 97, 107, 115, 207, 209, 229, 237, 240, 277, 284
bismuth 46, 47
bismuthinite 47
bitumen 48
Black Prince's Ruby 237, 257
blende 255
bloodstone 71
Blue John 124
boehmite 108
boleite 49
boracite 50
borax 50, **51**, 88
boric acid 51
bornite 52, 98
boron 50, 51, 88
boulangerite 53, 54, 160
bournonite 54
bowenite 23, 245
breccia 55, 90, 174
brochanitite 56
brookite 57
brownstone 239
brucite 58
bustamite 59

cadmium 141
calcite 27, **60**, 233, 247
californite 289
campylite 225
cancrinite 61
Cape emerald 220
carbon 107, 140
carbonate minerals 282
carminite 62
carnallite 63
carnelian 71, 229
carnotite 37, **64**
cassiterite 65
cat's eye see chatoyancy
celestine 66
ceruleite 67
cerussite 19, **68**, 170
chabazite 69

chalcanthite 56, **70**
chalcedony 71, 76, 229
chalcopyrite 72, 98, 231
chalcosiderite 96, 284
chalcosine 98
chalcosite 73
chalk 74
chamosite 75, 84
chatoyancy (cat's eye) 25, 68, 79, 187, 220
chert 76
chessylite 39
chiastolite 17, 153
childrenite 77
China clay 164
chlorite group 84
chondrites 189
chrome-enstatite 117
chromite 78, 257
chromium 78, 100
chrysoberyl 79
chrysocolla 80
chrysoprase 71, 229
chrysotile 23, **81**, 236
cinnabar 82
cinnamon 49
clay 83
clinochlore 75, **84**
clinopyroxenes 35
clinozoisite 85, 299
coal 86
cobalt 87, 120, 251
cobalt bloom 120
cobalt glance 87
cobaltite 87, 120
cockscombs 185
cogwheel ore 54
colemanite 88
colloids 175
Color index 138, 268
columbite 89, 271
conglomerate 55, **90**
conichalcite 91
connellite 92
copiapite 93
copper 34, 52, 54, 56, 70, 72, 73, 91, 92, **94**, 98, 102, 116, 182, 197, 205, 274
copper hydrous phosphates 96
copper sulfate minerals 56
cordierite 95, 153
cornelian see carnelian
cornetite 96
corundum 97, 237, 240
covellite 98
cristobalite 99, 204
crocidolite 236
crocoite 100
cryolite 101
cuprite 102
cumengéite 49
cymophane 79
cyprine 289

danaite 31
danalite 103
danburite 104
deliquescence 63
descloizite 105
desert rose 142
diabase 106
diamagnetism 46
diamond 107, 140
diaspore 108
dichroism 44, 110, 195
dichroite 95
dickite 29, 164
dimorphism 116, 185, 244, 255
diopside 35, **109**, 148, 227, 281
dioptase 110
diorite 111
dolerophane 56
dolomite 21, 110, **112**, 113, 166
dolomitization 113
dolostone 113, 250
doublets 237
dravite 279
duftite 91
dumortierite 114

Eilat stone 80
elaterite 48
emerald 45, 110, **115**, 212
emery 97
emulsions 175
enargite 116
enstatite 35, **117**, 227
eosphite 77
epidote 85, **118**, 143
epidote group 216, 299
epsomite 119
Epsom salts 119
erythrite 22, **120**, 165
ettringite 121
eucolite 122
eudialyte 122
evaporites 50, 51, 63, 88, 132, 282
exfoliation 226

fassaite 35
fayalite 206
feitknechtite 183
feldspar 29, 61, 106, **123**, 126
feldspathoids 61, 169, 200
ferrobrucite 58
ferro-glaucophane 133
ferrohedenbergite 148
ferrosilite 117
ferrotantalite 271
fibrolite 248
flame test 66
flint 76
fluorapatite 25

fluorite 124
fluorspar 124
forsterite 206
fossils 74, 76, 246, 252
franklinite 125, 257
freiborgite 274

gabbro 106, **126**
gabrielsonite 62, 91
gadolinite 127
gahnite 257
galena 19, 53, **128**
garnet 129, 143, 153, 212
garnierite 130
geikielite 156
gibbsite 131
glass 217
glauberite 132
Glauber's salts 132
glaucophane 133
gneiss 134
goethite 135, 165, 171
gold 90, **136**
gossan 175
granite 111, **137**, 268
granodiorite 111, **138**
granulite 139
graphite 107, **140**
greenockite 141, 297
greenstones 84
grossular 129
gypsum 7, 20, 132, **142**
gyrolite 143

hackmanite 254
halide minerals 34, 49, 63, 101, 124, 144
halite 144
harmotome 145
hausmannite 146
hauyne 147
hedenbergite 35, 109, **148**, 227
heliodor 45
heliotrope 71
helium 286
helvite group 103
hematite 149
hemimorphism 141, 150, 297
hemimorphite 116, **150**
hessonite 129
heulandite 151
hiddenite 258
hornblende 152
hörnesite 120, 165
hornfels 153
hübnerite 154, 294
humite 155
hydrothermals 52
hydrous and hydrated minerals 7, 11
hypersthene 117

Iceland spar 60
idocrase *see* vesuvianite
igneous rocks 18, 35, 41, 106, 111, 126, 137, 138, 156, 203, 204, 212, 214, 217, 222, 227, 231, 235, 268
ignimbrite 283
ilmenite 156
Inca rose 233
indialite 95
indicolite 279
inesite 157
inosilicates 28, 35, 143, 152, 201, 227
iolite 95
iridescence 98, 251
iron 21, 28, 135, 149, 158, 175, 181, 213, 247
ironstone 158
isomorphous minerals 77, 85, 183, 241, 297
isostructural minerals 2, 44, 172
isotropy 261

jade 7, 23, **159**, 220
jadeite 159, 227
jamesonite 53, **160**
jarosite 161
jasper 71, 76, 229
jet 162, 173
johannsenite 109, 148

kainite 163
kaolinite 29, 75, 81, 143, **164**
kaolinite-serpentine group 23, 164
kernite 50, 51
kidney ore 149
köttigite 120, **165**
kunzite 258
kupletskite 33
kutnohorite 21, 112, **166**
kyanite 167, 248, 259

labradorite 123
lanthanum 195
lapis lazuli 114, 147, 169
laueite 266
lazulite 168
lazurite 168, **169**
lead 19, 53, 54, 68, 105, 128, 197, 218, 219
leadhillite 170
lepidocrocite 135, **171**
leucite 15
libethenite 96, 205
libethmite 172
lignite 86, **173**
limestone 60, 74, **174**, 250
limonite 11, 36, 39, 165, **175**
linarite 176
lithage 177
lithium 258
lizardite 23
löllingite 178
ludjibaite 96, 221
ludwigite 179

magmatic segregation 156
magnesia 58, 180
magnesite 180, 247
magnesium 58, 63, 112, 113
magnetism 125, 181, 228
magnetite 156, 177, **181**, 257
malachite 34, 39, 94, 102, **182**, 186, 221
manganese 125, 146, 183, 224, 234
manganite 183
marble 23, 60, **184**
marcasite 185, 223
massicot 177
mendipite 186
mercury 82
mesolite 187, 199, 243
meta-autunite 37
metamorphic rocks 134, 139, 153, 184, 188, 191, 198, 242, 250, 252
metaquartzite 188, 230
meteorite 189
meteorites 247, 272
mica 84, **190**
migmatite 191
milarite 192
mimetite 193, 225
minette ores 135
minnesotaite 270
moldavites 272
molybdenite 194
molybdenum 194, 296
monazite 195
montebrasite 14
montmorillonite 196
monzonite 111
Moon rocks 16, 41
moonstone 123
morganite 45
mottramite 105, **197**
mudstone 246
mylonite 198

natrolite 187, **199**, 243
neodymium 195
nepheline 200
nephrite 7, 159
neptunite 201
nickel 130, 202, 213, 251
nickel bloom *see* annabergite
nickeline (niccolite) 202
niobium 89
norite 126
nosean 147, **203**

obsidian 204, 217, 222
olivenite 172, **205**
olivine 143, **206**
onyx 71, 229
opal 207
orpiment 208
orthopyroxenes 35
osumilite minerals 192

pearl 27, **209**
peat 86, **210**
pectolite 211
pegmatite 212

pentlandite 213
peridot 206
peridotite 138, **214**
pewter 24, 65
pharmacosiderite 215
phenocrysts 18, 203, 217, 231, 235, 280
phosphorus 25
phyllosilicates 190, 196, 220, 226
piemontite 216
pigments, artists' 12, 39, 82, 135, 169, 175, 182, 256, 290
pistacite 118
pitchstone 217
plattnerite 218
pleochroism 7, 17, 95, 114, 118, 167, 220, 248, 256, 279, 299
plumbogummite 219
poisons 30, 128
polymorphs 16, 27, 34, 57, 75, 117, 167, 248
porphyritic rocks 231, 280
porphyroblasts 242, 252
potash 63, 163
potash alum 12
potassium 269
prehnite 220
pseudoboleite 49
pseudocubic crystals 101, 161
pseudohexagonal crystals 27
pseudolaueite 266
pseudomalachite 96, **221**
pseudomorphism 73, 102, 132, 170, 185
pumice 222, 235
pyrite 54, 175, 185, **223**
pyrolusite 183, **224**
pyromorphite 193, **225**, 287
pyrope 129
pyrophyllite 114, **226**
pyroxenes 9, 35, 109, 126, 148, 153
pyroxenite 227
pyrrhotite 228

quartz 229
quartz group 99
quartzite 230
quartz porphyry 231

radioactive minerals 37, 64, 278
radium 286
realgar 232
refractive index 101
reichenbachite 96, 221
rhodochrosite 157, **233**, 247
rhodonite 59, 157, **234**
rhyolite 57, **235**
riebeckite 133, **236**
rock crystal 229
rock salt 144
rose quartz 229
rubellite 279
ruby 97, **237**

rutilated quartz 238
rutile 57, 109, **238**
rutile group 218, 224

safflorite 178
sandstone 188, **239**
sanidine 123, 280
sapphire 97, **240**
sard 71
sardonyx 71, 229
scheelite 241
schist 242
schorl 279
schrotterite 10
scolecite 187, 199, **243**
scorodite 244
scoria 222
seashells 27
seawater, silica in 76
sedimentary rocks 29, 55, 74, 83, 90, 113, 174, 239, 246
serpentine 81
serpentinite 32, 214, **245**
shale 83, **246**
shiller 123
siderite 180, 233, **247**
siderites 189
silica 76
silica gel 15
sillimanite 167, **248**
silver 6, 128, **249**
skarn 250
skutterudite 251
slate 252
smithsonite 253
smoky quartz 229
soapstone 270
sodalite 15, 114, 147, **254**
sodium 275
solder 128
sorosilicates 118, 150
spessartine 129
sphalerite 255
sphene 256
spinel 237, **257**
spinel group 125, 257
spodumene 227, **258**
Star of India 240
staurolite 259
steatite 270
stellerite 260
stibiconite 261
stibnite 47, 160, **262**
stichtite 23
stilbite 260, 261, **263**
stilpnomelane 264
stratification 239
stromatolites 174
strontianite 265
strontium 66, 232, 265
strunzite 266
sturmanite 121
sublimation 30, 34
sugilite 192
sulfosalts 54
sulfur 267
syenite 61, **268**
sylvine 50, 63, **269**

talc 143, 226, **270**
tantalite 89, **271**
tantalum 271

tanzanite 299
tektite 272
tektosilicates 151, 199
tellurite 273
tellurium 273
tennanite 274
tetrahedrite 274
thenardite 275
thomsonite 276
thorium 127
tin 65
titanaugite 35
titanium 16, 156, 238
topaz 212, **277**
topazolite 129
torbernite 37, **278**
tourmaline 104, 118, 150, 212, **279**
trachyte 280
tremolite 281
tridymite 99
trilling 116
troctolite 126
trona 282
troutstone 126
tuff 283
tungsten 241, 294
turquoise 67, 96, **284**
TV stone 285
twinning 14, 68, 142, 145, 185, 223
type metal 24

ulexite 285
unakite 118
uraninite 286
uranium 37, 64, 278, 286
uvarovite 129

vanadates, hydrous 105
vanadinite 287
vanadium 16, 287
vandate minerals 197
variscite 288
variscite group 244
vaterite 27
vesuvianite 220, **289**
vishnevite 61
vivianite 290
vonsenite 179

water sapphire 95
wavellite 291
weathering 19
willemite 110, **292**
witherite 293
wolframite 294
wollastonite 295
wulfenite 296
wurtzite 116, 255, **297**

xenoliths 137

yellow arsenic 208

zeolites 15, 41, 69, 145, 151, 187, 199, 243, 260, 263, 276
zinc 105, 125, 165, 255, 292
zircon 212, **298**
zirconium 122
zoisite 85, 118, **299**, 301